Pages
Dynamic Instructional Strategies	... **present clear and comprehensive coverage of middle school science.**	
	■ Each engaging chapter opener includes a *Launch Lab* and *Foldables*™.	7, 37
	■ *National Geographic Visualizing* features illustrate important concepts in middle school science.	26, 54
A Strong Reading Strand	... **encourages active reading and learning for students of all reading levels. In the** *Student Edition:*	
	■ `as you read` gives students a preview of learning objectives and vocabulary for each section;	8, 38
	■ *Reading Checks* help students check their reading comprehension; and	9, 40
	■ *Caption questions* ask students to interpret visuals.	8, 40
	■ *Reading Essentials, An Interactive Student Textbook* is designed to help struggling readers comprehend core content. It is written at a reading level of about two to three grades below the *Student Edition.*	
Meeting the Needs of All Students	... **facilitates understanding of science concepts for students of all learning levels. In the** *Teacher Wraparound Edition:*	
	■ *Differentiated Instruction* strategies help meet the needs of students with learning disabilities and physical challenges, or create opportunities to enrich and extend students' learning;	9, 46
	■ *Daily Intervention* provides intervention strategies for struggling students; and	13, 42
	■ *Identifying Misconceptions* helps uncover and address common science misconceptions.	6F
	■ The *English/Spanish Glossary*, also in the *Student Edition,* helps English-language learners comprehend science terms.	201–207
Extensive Standardized Test Practice	... **gives students the opportunity to practice for state and national exams.**	
	■ Each chapter ends with a variety of standardized test practice questions, including *Multiple Choice, Short Response/Grid In,* and *Open Ended.*	34–35
A Variety of Labs	... **gets students excited about being involved in science. The** *Student Edition* **provides:**	
	■ *MiniLABs,* traditional labs, and *Design Your Own, Model and Invent,* and *Use the Internet* labs; and	10, 50, 62
	■ *Extra Try at Home Labs* provide opportunities for students to practice their science skills at home with adult supervision using materials from the kitchen, junk drawer, or backyard.	172–174
	■ *Virtual Labs* CD-ROM contains an interactive virtual lab for each chapter.	61
	■ *Video Labs* (VHS) reinforce lab techniques and safety skills, offer troubleshooting tips, and give expected outcomes.	62
	■ The *Science Lab Manual, Probeware Lab Manual,* and *Science Inquiry Lab Manual* provide additional opportunities to practice laboratory techniques.	
Multi-Level Review	... **presents multiple opportunities for all students to review and master content.**	
	■ Each section ends with a review that contains a *Summary* of the section's major concepts and a *Self Check* that has questions to assess student learning and practice math or science skills.	13, 42
	■ The *Study Guide* at the end of each chapter can preview, review, summarize, and visualize the chapter's main ideas.	31, 65
	■ *Study Guide* and *Reinforcement* help students grasp core content.	
Teacher Resources	... **provide innovative strategies to help new and experienced teachers.**	
	■ *Chapter Resources Fast File* ™ contains important reproducible masters.	36B
	■ Section Focus, Assessment, and Teaching transparencies accompany each chapter.	70C
	■ *Performance Assessment in the Science Classroom* has assessment guidelines, strategies, sample rubrics, and more.	
Online Resources	... **enrich the learning experience with the click of a mouse.**	
	■ For prescreened Web links, standardized test practice, self-check quizzes, chapter tests, *Vocabulary PuzzleMaker,* extra math practice, science career information, current science news, and *WebQuest* interactive projects, visit **bookc.msscience.com.**	
	■ The complete interactive *Student Edition* is available at The McGraw-Hill Learning Network Web site, **mhln.com.**	
Technology	... **provides timesaving products to help teachers creatively engage their students.**	
	■ *MindJogger Videoquizzes* (VHS & DVD) provide a game-show style interactive quiz for each chapter.	
	■ Easy to edit *Interactive Chalkboard* Microsoft® PowerPoint® presentations include step-by-step lessons, an image bank, chapter and section review questions, standardized test practice, and transparencies.	
	■ *ExamView® Pro Testmaker* CD-ROM in English or Spanish allows you to customize assessments.	
	■ *TeacherWorks* CD-ROM is your all-in-one resource center that helps you plan and organize lessons.	
	■ *StudentWorks* CD-ROM solves the heavy backpack problem.	

SAFETY SYMBOLS

SAFETY SYMBOLS	HAZARD	EXAMPLES	PRECAUTION	REMEDY
DISPOSAL	Special disposal procedures need to be followed.	certain chemicals, living organisms	Do not dispose of these materials in the sink or trash can.	Dispose of wastes as directed by your teacher.
BIOLOGICAL	Organisms or other biological materials that might be harmful to humans	bacteria, fungi, blood, unpreserved tissues, plant materials	Avoid skin contact with these materials. Wear mask or gloves.	Notify your teacher if you suspect contact with material. Wash hands thoroughly.
EXTREME TEMPERATURE	Objects that can burn skin by being too cold or too hot	boiling liquids, hot plates, dry ice, liquid nitrogen	Use proper protection when handling.	Go to your teacher for first aid.
SHARP OBJECT	Use of tools or glassware that can easily puncture or slice skin	razor blades, pins, scalpels, pointed tools, dissecting probes, broken glass	Practice common-sense behavior and follow guidelines for use of the tool.	Go to your teacher for first aid.
FUME	Possible danger to respiratory tract from fumes	ammonia, acetone, nail polish remover, heated sulfur, moth balls	Make sure there is good ventilation. Never smell fumes directly. Wear a mask.	Leave foul area and notify your teacher immediately.
ELECTRICAL	Possible danger from electrical shock or burn	improper grounding, liquid spills, short circuits, exposed wires	Double-check setup with teacher. Check condition of wires and apparatus.	Do not attempt to fix electrical problems. Notify your teacher immediately.
IRRITANT	Substances that can irritate the skin or mucous membranes of the respiratory tract	pollen, moth balls, steel wool, fiberglass, potassium permanganate	Wear dust mask and gloves. Practice extra care when handling these materials.	Go to your teacher for first aid.
CHEMICAL	Chemicals can react with and destroy tissue and other materials	bleaches such as hydrogen peroxide; acids such as sulfuric acid, hydrochloric acid; bases such as ammonia, sodium hydroxide	Wear goggles, gloves, and an apron.	Immediately flush the affected area with water and notify your teacher.
TOXIC	Substance may be poisonous if touched, inhaled, or swallowed.	mercury, many metal compounds, iodine, poinsettia plant parts	Follow your teacher's instructions.	Always wash hands thoroughly after use. Go to your teacher for first aid.
FLAMMABLE	Flammable chemicals may be ignited by open flame, spark, or exposed heat.	alcohol, kerosene, potassium permanganate	Avoid open flames and heat when using flammable chemicals.	Notify your teacher immediately. Use fire safety equipment if applicable.
OPEN FLAME	Open flame in use, may cause fire.	hair, clothing, paper, synthetic materials	Tie back hair and loose clothing. Follow teacher's instruction on lighting and extinguishing flames.	Notify your teacher immediately. Use fire safety equipment if applicable.

 Eye Safety Proper eye protection should be worn at all times by anyone performing or observing science activities.

 Clothing Protection This symbol appears when substances could stain or burn clothing.

 Animal Safety This symbol appears when safety of animals and students must be ensured.

 Handwashing After the lab, wash hands with soap and water before removing goggles.

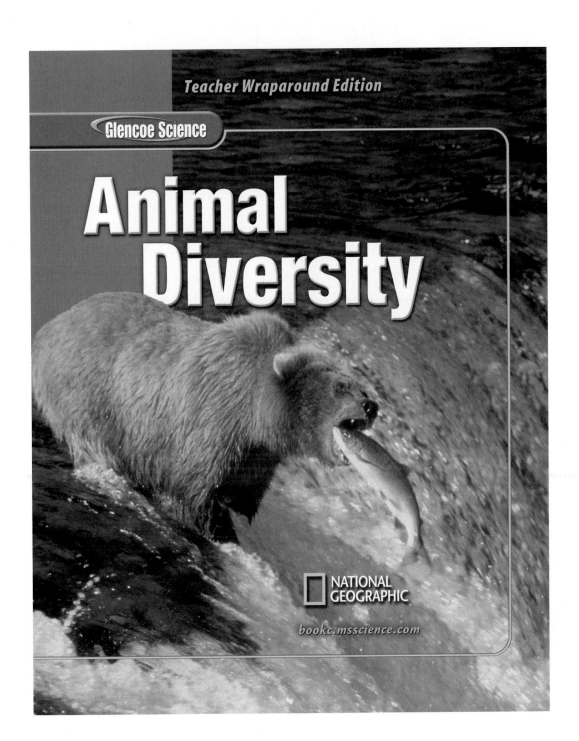

Teacher Wraparound Edition

Glencoe Science

Animal Diversity

NATIONAL GEOGRAPHIC

bookc.msscience.com

Mc Graw Hill **Glencoe**

New York, New York   Columbus, Ohio   Chicago, Illinois   Peoria, Illinois   Woodland Hills, California

Glencoe Science

Animal Diversity

This Alaskan brown bear is catching a migrating salmon. This species of bear is the largest carnivore in Alaska, growing up to nine feet tall and weighing up to 1,700 pounds. All Alaskan salmon hatch in freshwater, migrate to the sea, and then eventually return to where they hatched to reproduce.

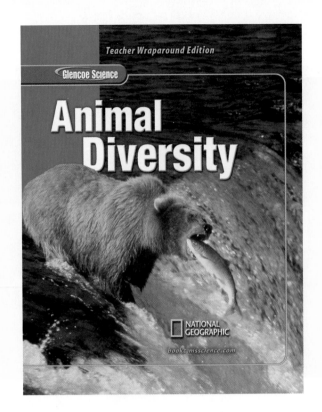

Mc Graw Hill Glencoe

The **McGraw·Hill** Companies

Send all inquiries to:
Glencoe/McGraw-Hill
8787 Orion Place
Columbus, OH 43240-4027

ISBN 0-07-861740-5 (Student Edition)
ISBN 0-07-861741-3 (Teacher Wraparound Edition)

Printed in the United States of America.

2 3 4 5 6 7 8 9 10 027/055 09 08 07 06

Authors

NATIONAL GEOGRAPHIC
Education Division
Washington, D.C.

Lucy Daniel, PhD
Teacher/Consultant
Rutherford-County High Schools
Rutherfordton, NC

Dinah Zike
Educational Consultant
Dinah-Might Activities, Inc.
San Antonio, TX

Series Consultants

CONTENT

Jerome A. Jackson, PhD
Whitaker Eminent Scholar in
Science
Program Director
Center for Science, Mathematics,
and Technology Education
Florida Gulf Coast University
Fort Meyers, FL

Dominic Salinas, PhD
Middle School Science Supervisor
Caddo Parish Schools
Shreveport, LA

MATH

Teri Willard, EdD
Mathematics Curriculum Writer
Belgrade, MT

READING

Carol A. Senf, PhD
School of Literature,
Communication, and Culture
Georgia Institute of Technology
Atlanta, GA

SAFETY

Sandra West, PhD
Department of Biology
Texas State University-San Marcos
San Marcos, TX

ACTIVITY TESTERS

Nerma Coats Henderson
Pickerington Lakeview Jr. High
School
Pickerington, OH

Mary Helen Mariscal-Cholka
William D. Slider Middle School
El Paso, TX

**Science Kit and Boreal
Laboratories**
Tonawanda, NY

Series Reviewers

Maureen Barrett
Thomas E. Harrington Middle
School
Mt. Laurel, NJ

Cory Fish
Burkholder Middle School
Henderson, NV

Amy Morgan
Berry Middle School
Hoover, AL

Dee Stout
Penn State University
University Park, PA

Darcy Vetro-Ravndal
Hillsborough High School
Tampa, FL

Glencoe Science 15-Book Series

Teach science your way!

With the 15 Life, Earth, and Physical Science titles in our modular series, you can select the science topics you want to cover and customize your science curriculum in any way you choose.

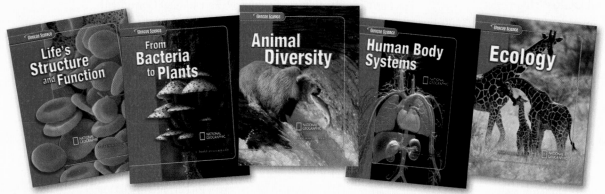

A **Life's Structure and Function**
1. Exploring and Classifying Life
2. Cells
3. Cell Processes
4. Cell Reproduction
5. Heredity
6. Adaptations over Time

B **From Bacteria to Plants**
1. Bacteria
2. Protists and Fungi
3. Plants
4. Plant Reproduction
5. Plant Processes

C **Animal Diversity**
1. Introduction to Animals
2. Mollusks, Worms, Arthropods, Echinoderms
3. Fish, Amphibians, and Reptiles
4. Birds and Mammals
5. Animal Behavior

D **Human Body Systems**
1. Structure and Movement
2. Nutrients and Digestion
3. Circulation
4. Respiration and Excretion
5. Control and Coordination
6. Regulation and Reproduction
7. Immunity and Disease

E **Ecology**
1. Interactions of Life
2. The Nonliving Environment
3. Ecosystems
4. Conserving Resources
5. Conserving Life

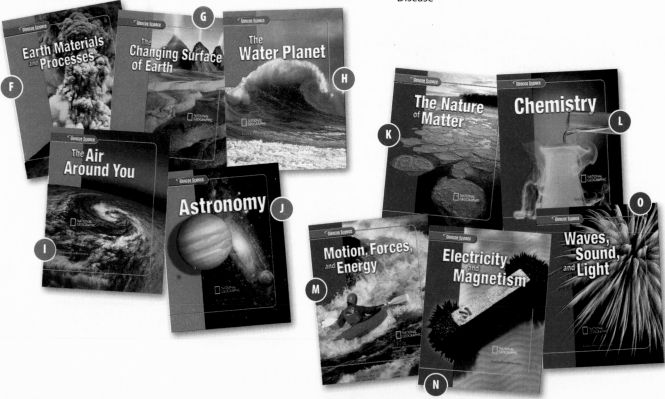

Multi-Level Review and Assessment

Each chapter provides five pages of review and testing to help you evaluate students' knowledge and ability to apply science concepts.

Section Review
- Summary pinpoints important concepts in the section.
- Skill-based questions promote critical thinking skills.

Study Guide
- Main idea summary of each section
- Concept mapping activity to help students visualize the main ideas

Chapter Review
- Using Vocabulary
- Checking Concepts
- Thinking Critically
- Performance Activities
- Applying Math

Standardized Test Practice
- Multiple Choice
- Short Response/ Grid In
- Open-Ended Questions

Dynamic Instruction

The consistent instructional strategies in each chapter strengthen students' learning—from the beginning of each chapter where students see "Chapter Preview," to the end where they have a chance to test the knowledge they have acquired and prepare for the next lesson.

Chapter Opener
- *Chapter Preview* introduces the main concepts.
- *Science Journal* promotes critical-thinking skills
- *Dinah Zike's Foldables*™ let students create interactive study guides.
- *Launch Labs* give students an opportunity to explore new ideas.

Section Opener
- *What You'll Learn* introduces main concepts.
- *Why It's Important* provides an answer to "Why do we have to learn this?"
- *Review Vocabulary* reviews a term that helps students better understand section content.
- *New Vocabulary* highlights new terms students will learn in the section.

Labs
- *Labs* allow students to design their own experiments or follow well-tested procedures, enabling them to learn and practice science processes.
- *MiniLABS* offer students quick and easy-to-do ways to clarify concepts and reinforce skills.

Assessment

Glencoe Science offers the Glencoe Assessment Advantage, a system designed to give you all the tools you need to prepare your students for success in any testing situation.

In the *Student Edition*

Section Review and **Applying Math** questions appear in every chapter.

Chapter Review questions help you evaluate students' knowledge and ability to apply science concepts.

Standardized Test Practice questions at the end of each chapter provide students with additional opportunities to practice their test-taking skills.

In the *Teacher Wraparound Edition*

Assessments located throughout the *Teacher Wraparound Edition* provide methods for assessing students' comprehension with Performance, Process, and Content exercises.

Teacher Classroom Resources

Performance Assessment in the Science Classroom
- Guidelines for assessing the performance of a task
- Reproducible activities for evaluating students
- Sample rubrics and checklists

***Fast File* Chapter Resources** provides six pages of assessement for every chapter including *Testing Concepts, Applying Concepts,* and *Writing Skills.*

Technology Support

MindJogger Videoquizzes are interactive video quizzes set in game show format. Each is designed for the full range of student learning styles.

Exam*View*® Pro Testmaker CD-ROM for Windows® and Macintosh® provides an easy way to create, edit, and customize your tests. Select your own test items by objective from two different levels of difficulty, or write and edit your own. Translate tests from English to Spanish and vice versa.

Rubrics

The following rubrics are sample scoring devices for short response and open-ended questions.

Short Response

Points	Description
2	The student demonstrates a thorough understanding of the science of the task. The response may contain minor flaws that do not detract from the demonstration of a thorough understanding.
1	The student has provided a response that is only partially correct.
0	The student has provided a completely incorrect solution or no response at all.

Open Ended

Points	Description
4	The student demonstrates a thorough understanding of the science of the task. The response may contain minor flaws that do not detract from the demonstration of a thorough understanding.
3	The student demonstrates an understanding of the science of the task. The response is essentially correct and demonstrates an essential but less than thorough understanding of the science.
2	The student demonstrates only a partial understanding of the science of the task. Although the student may have used the correct approach to a solution or may have provided a correct solution, the work lacks an essential understanding of the underlying science concepts.
1	The student demonstrates a very limited understanding of the science of the task. The response is incomplete and exhibits many flaws.
0	The student provides a completely incorrect solution or no response at all.

Time-Saving Teacher Resources

Glencoe Science provides an extensive array of support materials and resources designed to help you create and customize your science course quickly and easily.

FAST FILE Chapter Resources

For each chapter, Chapter Resources contain key reproducible masters along with additional teaching strategies, teacher support, and answer keys.

Teacher Wraparound Edition

The *Teacher Wraparound Edition* is your key to the teaching resources available. In addition to teaching strategies and suggestions, the *Teacher Wraparound Edition* provides a guide for all print and software materials available for each lesson.

Transparencies

Color Transparencies provides three types of transparencies for use while teaching each chapter. The *Section Focus Transparencies* are designed to generate interest and focus students' attention on the topic being presented in the section. The *Teaching Transparency* for each chapter addresses a major concept that will benefit from an extra visual learning aid. The *Assessment Transparency* for each chapter is set up to resemble standardized tests.

Exam*View*® Pro Testmaker CD-ROM

This CD-ROM will help you create, edit, and customize tests. In addition, it will help you create multiple versions of tests, translate tests from English to Spanish and vice versa, and build tests aligned with state standards.

Video Labs

These VHS cassettes contain step-by-step procedures for selected *Student Edition* labs. They also contain lab safety skills, teacher support, and troubleshooting advice.

Teacher Works™

This CD-ROM is your all-in-one resource center. Personalize a lesson plan, access resources from the *Teacher Wraparound Edition*, connect to the Internet, or make a to-do list. These are only a few of the many features that can assist you in the planning and organizing of your lessons.

StudentWorks™

This CD-ROM is a valuable resource for students to access content online and use online resources to continue learning chapter concepts.

Guided Reading Audio Program has been updated to StudentWorks Plus™.

 This CD-ROM brings Microsoft® PowerPoint® presentations right to your door. With the large number of graphics provided, students can use a visual approach to learning chapter content.

Virtual Labs CD-ROM Program

The Virtual Labs CD-ROM contains a collection of labs that allow students to complete labs that are too expensive, take too long to complete, or might be too dangerous in a classroom laboratory.

This website is a portal to hundreds of pre-screened Internet sites (Web links) that correlate to content in the text. Visit this link to find interactive activities that review chapter concepts and to access the *Student Edition* online.

 mhln.com is an online teaching and learning space for teachers, students, and parents.

Differentiated Instruction

Teaching Strategies

Following each suggested assessment and activity, ability levels are supplied to accommodate all students. For a key to the Teaching Strategies designations, see the C page before each chapter.

Identifying Misconceptions

These short, diagnostic, and perscriptive lessons target common science misconceptions.

Multiple Learning Styles

Look for these italicized designations under various activities to help you target your lessons to each student's preferred learning style.

- *Kinesthetic* learners learn through touch, movement, and manipulating objects.
- *Visual-Spatial* learners think in terms of images, illustrations, and models.
- *Interpersonal* learners understand and work well with other people.
- *Intrapersonal* learners can analyze their own strengths and weaknesses and may prefer to work on their own.
- *Linguistic* learners write clearly and easily understand the written word.
- *Logical-Mathematical* learners understand numbers easily and have highly-developed reasoning skills.

Daily Interventions

Found at the end of each chapter section, this feature is designed to intercept students who are struggling and prescribe a system to help them get back on track. *Reteach* provides reinforcement of the section's concepts through visual activities.

Differentiated Instruction

These activities present various teaching strategies designed to help you meet the special needs of students with learning disabilities, physical challenges, visual impairment, and hearing impairment. *Challenge* activities provide opportunities for students who excel to engage in activities and research projects that extend the chapter's concepts. English-language learners in the classroom will also find exercises that bridge the gap between language barriers and the chapter content.

Cultural Diversity

These readings provide insights into the unique ways in which people of different ethnicities and cultural heritage have approached science. The intent of these features is to build awareness and appreciation for the global community in which we live.

Inquiry-Based Science

The call for more inquiry-based science by the *National Science Education Standards* has been met by Glencoe Science.

Glencoe Science recognizes the importance of conducting inquiry-based science activities in the classroom. The process of doing inquiry models actual science practice, encouraging problem-solving strategies and developing critical thinking skills. Inquiry gets students actively involved in the learning process by allowing them to determine materials, procedures, or the topics and questions they want to investigate.

Inquiry can range from a very structured activity for those students who need more guidance to a more open-ended approach where students lead the investigations. Glencoe Science recognizes that the inquiry activities suggested will not look the same in every classroom. We encourage teachers to modify the suggested activities in a manner that best supports your students.

Glencoe also provides teachers with *Alternative Inquiry Labs,* teaching strategies or suggestions for making existing labs more inquiry-based.

Research-Based Learning Strategies

Glencoe Science incorporates the most current and applicable educational research on science learning and follows recommendations from the American Association for the Advancement of Science and the National Science Teachers Association. The following research-based strategies can be found throughout the text.

Learning Strategies

The following research-based strategies can be found throughout the text:

- **Using Prior Knowledge** Glencoe Science encourages students to use their prior knowledge to learn information because this adds relevance to the material. Students are referred back to other parts of the text or to their own real-life experiences.

- **Practicing Important Tasks** By offering students an opportunity to practice important tasks using a variety of labs and activities in the *Student Edition, Teacher Wraparound Edition,* ancillaries and technology, Glencoe Science makes learning fun and relevant for students.

- **Using Visuals to Communicate, Organize, and Reinforce Learning** High-quality art and photos throughout the text communicate concepts more efficiently and reinforce learning, while allowing students to organize information.

- **Motivating Students to Achieve** Active strategies and real-world experiences motivate students to achieve. Throughout Glencoe's programs, students are encouraged to apply their knowledge in ways that will motivate them to learn.

- **Developing Decoding and Reading Comprehension Strategies** Throughout the text, students are supplied with caption questions, reading checks, and other strategies to aid in comprehension.

- **Using Study Strategies** Through the use of highlighting, outlining, note-taking, summarizing, and other such strategies, students can monitor their own progress and organize information more effectively, thereby increasing their scientific literacy. These strategies are found throughout the text and ancillaries.

The use of these strategies within Glencoe Science will help teachers to achieve the goals set forth by the *National Science Education Standards.*

White Paper

The Glencoe Science White Paper outlines the educational strategies on which this program was based. This document provides specific examples from the *Student Edition, Teacher Wraparound Edition,* ancillary program, and technology resources, highlighting extensive use of educationally sound strategies that help students learn science.

Field Research and Testing

Feedback from students, teachers, curriculum supervisors, department chairpersons, parents, learning specialists, and science content experts was invaluable in the development of this program. The following pre-publication and post-publication research was conducted.

Prior to Publication

- Detailed classroom teacher and curriculum supervisor **surveys** were conducted by independently contracted researchers.

- A **nationwide panel** of science teachers, curriculum supervisors, and department chairpersons provided countless hours of feedback and assistance throughout program development.

- A wide range of **educator and content reviewers** provided in-depth reviews of and suggestions for manuscripts and pre-publication versions of the program.

- **Face-to-face interviews** with science teachers provided insight into teachers' day-to-day challenges.

After Publication

- Field tests were conducted in which students and teachers used a pre-publication manuscript in the classroom.

- Follow-up interviews, observations, and surveys of Glencoe Science users provide ongoing opportunities for program development and verification of program success.

Field-Test Results

- Field-test research indicates that test scores increased among students using Glencoe Science programs.

- Nine out of ten students earned higher scores after using Glencoe programs.

- Scores improved among both male and female students.

- Scores improved among both minority and non-minority students.

- Overall, the gap between the average pre-test score and a perfect score closed by 33 percent. Stated differently, on average, **scores increased 77 percent after students used the Glencoe program.**

KS Studios

National Education Standards

Correlation of *Glencoe Science* to the National Science Education Standards.

Content Standard	Chapter and Section
(UCP) Unifying Concepts and Processes	
1. Systems, order, and organization	A1-1, A1-2, A1-3, A1-4, A2-1, A2-2, A2-3, A3-1, A3-2, A3-3, A4-1, A4-2, A4-3, A5-1, A5-2, A5-3, A6-1, A6-2, A6-3, B1-1, B2-1, B2-2, B4-1, B4-2, B4-3, B5-1, B5-2, C1-1, C2-1, C2-2, C2-3, C2-4, C3-1, C3-2, C3-3, C3-4, C4-1, C4-2, C5-1, C5-2, D1-1, D1-2, D1-3, D2-1, D2-2, D3-1, D3-2, D3-3, D4-1, D4-2, D5-1, D5-2, D6-1, D6-2, D6-3, E1-1, E1-2, E1-3, E2-1, E2-2, E3-1, E3-2, E3-3
2. Evidence, models, and explanation	A1-1, A1-2, A1-3, A1-4, A2-1, A2-2, A2-3, A3-1, A3-2, A3-3, A4-1, A4-2, A4-3, A5-1, A5-2, A5-3, A6-1, A6-2, A6-3, B1-1, B2-1, B2-2, B3-2, B4-1, B4-2, B4-3, B5-1, B5-2, C1-1, C1-2, C1-3, C2-1, C2-2, C2-4, C3-1, C3-2, C3-3, C3-4, C4-1, C4-2, C5-1, C5-2, D1-1, D1-2, D1-3, D2-1, D3-1, D3-2, D3-3, D4-1, D4-2, D5-1, D5-2, D6-1, D6-2, D6-3, D7-1, D7-2, D7-3, E1-1, E1-2, E1-3, E2-1, E2-2, E3-1, E3-2, E3-3, E4-1, E4-2, E4-3, E5-1, E5-2
3. Change, constancy, and measurement	A1-1, A1-2, A1-3, A1-4, A2-1, A2-2, A3-1, A3-2, A3-3, A4-1, A4-3, A5-1, A5-2, A5-3, A6-1, A6-2, A6-3, B2-1, B2-2, B4-1, B4-2, B4-3, B5-1, B5-2, C1-1, C2-1, C2-2, C2-4, C3-1, C3-2, C3-3, C3-4, C4-1, C4-2, C5-1, C5-2, D1-1, D1-2, D1-3, D3-1, D3-2, D3-3, D4-1, D4-2, D5-1, D5-2, D6-1, D6-2, D6-3, E1-1, E1-2, E1-3, E2-1, E2-2, E3-1, E3-2, E3-3, E4-1, E4-2, E4-3, E5-1, E5-2
4. Evolution and equilibrium	A4-3, A5-2, A5-3, A6-1, A6-2, A6-3, B2-1, C3-1, C3-2, C3-3, C3-4, C4-1, C5-1, C5-2, E1-2, E1-3, E2-1, E3-1
5. Form and function	A1-1, A1-2, A1-3, A1-4, A2-1, A2-2, A2-3, A3-1, A3-2, A3-3, A4-3, A5-1, A5-2, A5-3, A6-1, A6-2, A6-3, B1-1, B1-2, B2-1, B2-2, B3-1, B3-2, B3-3, B4-1, B4-2, B4-3, B5-1, B5-2, C1-1, C1-2, C1-3, C2-1, C2-2, C2-3, C2-4, C3-2, C3-3, C3-4, C4-1, C4-2, D1-1, D1-2, D1-3, D3-1, D3-2, D3-3, D4-1, D4-2, D5-1, D5-2, D6-1, D6-2, D6-3, D7-1, D7-2, D7-3, E1-2, E1-3, E2-2, E3-1, E3-2, E3-3, E5-1, E5-2
(A) Science as Inquiry	
1. Abilities necessary to do scientific inquiry	A1-1, A1-2, A1-3, A1-4, A2-1, A2-2, A2-3, A3-1, A3-2, A3-3, A4-1, A4-2, A4-3, A5-1, A5-2, A5-3, A6-1, A6-2, A6-3, B1-1, B1-2, B2-1, B2-2, B3-1, B3-2, B3-3, B4-1, B4-2, B4-3, B5-1, B5-2, C1-1, C1-2, C1-3, C2-1, C2-2, C2-3, C2-4, C3-1, C3-2, C3-3, C3-4, C4-1, C4-2, C5-1, C5-2, D1-1, D1-2, D1-3, D2-1, D2-2, D3-1, D3-2, D3-3, D4-1, D4-2, D5-1, D5-2, D6-1, D6-2, D6-3, D7-1, D7-2, D7-3, E1-1, E1-2, E1-3, E2-1, E2-2, E3-1, E3-2, E3-3, E4-1, E4-2, E4-3, E5-1, E5-2
2. Understandings about scientific inquiry	A1-1, A1-2, A1-3, A1-4, A2-1, A2-2, A2-3, A3-1, A3-2, A3-3, A4-1, A4-3, A5-1, A5-3, A6-1, A6-2, A6-3, B1-1, B2-1, B2-2, B3-1, B4-1, B4-2, B4-3, B5-1, B5-2, C1-2, C1-3, C2-1, C2-2, C2-3, C2-4, C3-1, C3-2, C3-3, C3-4, C4-1, C4-2, C5-1, C5-2, D1-1, D1-2, D1-3, D2-1, D2-2, D3-1, D3-2, D3-3, D4-1, D4-2, D5-1, D5-2, D6-1, D6-2, D6-3, D7-1, D7-3, E5-1, E5-2, E1-1, E1-2, E1-3, E2-1, E2-2, E3-1, E3-2, E3-3, E4-1, E4-2, E4-3
(B) Physical Science	
1. Properties and changes of properties in matter	A3-1
2. Motions and forces	D1-2
3. Transfer of energy	D1-3, D2-1, D2-2, D6-3, E2-1, E2-2, E2-3
(C) Life Science	
1. Structure and function in living systems	A1-2, A1-3, A2-1, A2-2, A2-3, A3-1, A3-2, A3-3, A4-1, A4-2, A4-3, A5-1, A5-2, A5-3, A6-1, A6-3, B1-1, B2-1, B3-1, B3-2, B3-3, B4-1, B4-2, B4-3, B5-1, B5-2, C1-1, C1-2, C1-3, C2-1, C2-2, C2-3, C2-4, C3-1, C3-2, C3-3, C3-4, C4-1, D1-1, D1-2, D1-3, D2-1, D2-2, D3-1, D3-2, D3-3, D4-1, D4-2, D5-1, D5-2, D6-1, D6-2, D6-3, D7-1, D7-2, D7-3, E1-2, E1-3, E2-2, E2-3, E3-1, E3-2, E3-3, E5-1
2. Reproduction and heredity	A1-2, A2-3, A4-1, A4-2, A4-3, A5-1, A5-2, A5-3, B1-1, B2-1, B3-1, B3-2, B3-3, B4-1, B4-2, B4-3, C1-2, C2-1, C2-2, C2-3, C2-4, C3-1, C3-2, C3-3, C3-4, C4-1, C5-2, D1-1, D1-2, D1-3, D6-1, D6-2, D7-1, D7-2, D7-3, E1-1, E1-2, E1-3
3. Regulation and behavior	A1-2, A2-1, A3-2, A4-1, A4-2, A4-3, B1-1, B1-2, B2-1, B3-1, B3-2, B3-3, B5-1, B5-2, C1-1, C1-2, C1-3, C2-1, C2-2, C2-3, C2-4, C3-1, C3-2, C3-3, C3-4, C4-1, C5-1, D1-2, D1-3, D2-1, D2-2, D3-1, D3-2, D3-3, D4-1, D4-2, D5-1, D5-2, D6-1, D6-2, D6-3, D7-1, D7-2, D7-3, E1-2, E2-2, E3-1, E3-2, E3-3
4. Populations and ecosystems	A6-1, B1-1, B1-2, B2-1, B3-1, B3-2, B3-3, B4-3, C1-2, C1-3, C4-1, C5-2, E1-2, E1-3, E2-2, E3-1, E3-2, E3-3, E5-1
5. Diversity and adaptations of organisms	A1-4, A2-3, A4-2, A6-1, A6-3, B1-1, B1-2, B2-1, B3-1, B3-2, B3-3, B4-1, B4-2, B4-3, B5-2, C1-1, C1-2, C1-3, C2-2, C2-3, C2-4, C3-1, C3-2, C3-3, C3-4, C4-1, C5-1, C5-2, D1-1, D1-2, D1-3, D2-1, D2-2, D3-1, D3-2, D3-3, D5-1, D5-2, D6-3, D7-1, D7-2, D7-3, E1-2, E1-3, E2-2, E2-3, E3-3, E5-1

Content Standard	Chapter and Section
(D) Earth and Space Science	
1. Structure of the Earth system	E2-1, E2-2, E2-3
2. Earth's history	A1-3, A6-1, A6-2
3. Earth in the solar system	E2-3
(E) Science and Technology	
1. Abilities of technological design	B1-2
2. Understandings about science and technology	B1-2
(F) Science in Personal and Social Perspectives	
1. Personal health	A5-2, A6-2, B1-2, B2-2, C3-2, C4-2, D1-1, D1-2, D1-3, D2-1, D2-2, D5-1, D7-1, D7-2, D7-3
2. Populations, resources, and environments	A2-3, B4-3, E1-2, E1-3, E3-3, E4-1, E4-2, E4-3, E5-1, E5-2
3. Natural hazards	A5-3, D7-2
4. Risks and benefits	B1-2, C2-3, C3-4, D7-2, D7-3, E5-1, E5-2
5. Science and technology in society	A5-3, B1-2, C3-4, D7-2, D7-3
(G) History and Nature of Science	
1. Science as a human endeavor	A5-2, A6-1, A6-3, B3-2, D1-3, D2-2, D3-3, D7-3
2. Nature of science	A1-1, A3-3, A5-1, A6-1, A6-2, A6-3, B3-2, B4-3, C1-1, D1-3, D2-2, D3-3, D7-1, D7-3
3. History of science	A1-3, A1-4, A2-2, A2-3, A3-3, A5-1, A6-1, A6-3, B3-2, B4-3, C5-2, D4-2, D5-1

How Glencoe Science Aligns with the National Science Education Standards

The correlations at the left and above show the close alignment between Glencoe Science and the grade-appropriate standards. Glencoe Science allows students to discover concepts within each of the content standards and gives students opportunities to make connections among the science disciplines. Hands-on activities and inquiry-based lessons reinforce the science processes emphasized in the standards.

How Glencoe Science Aligns with the NCTM Standards for Grades 6–8

Throughout Glencoe Science, each Applying Math activity provides students with the opportunity to practice and apply some of the mathematical concepts and applications described in the NCTM Standards. These activities serve to reinforce mathematical skills in real-life situations, thus preparing students to meet their needs in an ever-changing world.

Correlation of *Glencoe Science* to NCTM Standards

Math Standard	Page
1. Number and Operations	A-35, A-46, A-74, A-93, A-123, A-133, A-151, A-181, B-57, B-112, B-119, B-135, B-145, C-25, C-33, C-52, C-67, C-82, C-129, C-155, D-11, D-31, D-59, D-87, D-133, D-141, D-147, D-171, D-201, E-31, E-40, E-59, E-80, E-121, E-150
2. Algebra	A-35, A-46, A-93, A-181, B-57, B-112, B-119, C-25, C-52, D-133, E-40, E-80, E-121
3. Geometry	A-46, D-11
4. Measurement	A-35, A-46, A-63, D-59, E-40, E-80
5. Data Analysis and Probability	A-35, A-93, A-133, A-151, A-181, B-27, B-57, B-89, B-119, B-135, B-145, C-67, C-101, C-129, C-155, D-31, D-59, D-87, D-113, D-141, D-171, D-201, E-40, E-59, E-89, E-121, E-150
6. Problem Solving	A-46, A-93, A-123, B-27, B-89, C-25, C-33, C-101, D-59, D-133, D-201, E-31, E-40, E-59, E-150
7. Reasoning and Proof	C-82, E-31
8. Communication	A-179, D-167
9. Connections	A-35, A-46, A-63, A-74, A-93, A-123, A-133, A-151, A-181, B-27, B-57, B-112, B-119, B-135, B-145, C-25, C-33, C-52, C-67, C-129, C-155, D-59, D-87, D-133, D-141, D-147, D-171, E-40, E-59, E-80, E-121
10. Representation	A-133, E-40

Foldables™

Foldables™ are easy-to-make, three-dimensional, interactive graphic organizers that students create out of simple sheets of paper. These unique hands-on tools for studying and reviewing were created exclusively for Glencoe by education specialist Dinah Zike.

Research Behind Foldables™

According to research (Bransford, 1979; Corno, 1994), study strategies help students understand, organize, remember and apply new information presented in science textbooks. Some study strategies include concept mapping, highlighting, outlining, note taking, summarizing, and underlining (Peverly, Brobst, Graham & Shaw, 2003). Glencoe Science offers Dinah Zike's Foldables™ Study Organizers as an organizational tool and study guide for students.

Foldables™

- Build prereading skills
- Encourage active reading and writing
- Summarize content for review

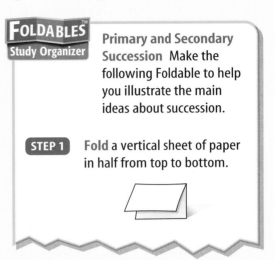

FOLDABLES™ Study Organizer

Primary and Secondary Succession Make the following Foldable to help you illustrate the main ideas about succession.

STEP 1 **Fold** a vertical sheet of paper in half from top to bottom.

For more ideas on how to incorporate Foldables™ into your lessons consult **Dinah Zike's *Teaching Science with Foldables*™**

Educational Partnerships

NATIONAL GEOGRAPHIC

Some topics in the chapter either require or benefit from a larger, more detailed visual explanation. The National Geographic Society has created *Visualizing* features that call out an important concept from the chapter and illustrate it in a way that will inform, excite, and motivate your students.

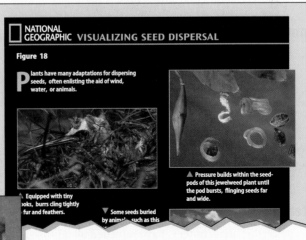

NATIONAL GEOGRAPHIC VISUALIZING SEED DISPERSAL

Figure 18

Plants have many adaptations for dispersing seeds, often enlisting the aid of wind, water, or animals.

▲ Pressure builds within the seedpods of this jewelweed plant until the pod bursts, flinging seeds far and wide.

▲ Equipped with tiny hooks, burrs cling tightly to fur and feathers.

▼ Some seeds buried by animals, such as this

TIME **SCIENCE** AND **HISTORY** SCIENCE CAN CHANGE THE COURSE OF HISTORY!

Overcoming the Odds

TIME

TIME magazine brings science topics and history together to further explain the chapter's main ideas and show how science relates to real life.

Safety in the Laboratory

All activities are designed to minimize dangers in the laboratory. Careful laboratory planning and management by both the instructor and the student are essential to a safe laboratory experience. **Local, state, and federal laboratory safety laws and regulations must be strictly followed.** The information provided here is one of the many resources to which you can refer for information about laboratory safety.

Classroom and Laboratory Preparation

1. Store equipment properly and securely and other thing.
   a. Clean and dry all equipment before storing.
   b. Protect electronic equipment and microscopes from dust, humidity, and extreme temperatures.
   c. Number, catalog, and organize equipment.
2. Ensure adequate work space for each student.
3. Ensure adequate classroom and storeroom ventilation.
4. Explain and post safety and evacuation guidelines along with expectations of conduct.
5. Ensure that all safety equipment is functioning properly and is clearly visible.
6. Provide hot plates as a heat source whenever possible. If gas burners are used, know where the central gas supply shutoff valve is located.
7. Ensure that each workstation has a GFCI-protected electrical source.
8. Provide safety goggles consistent with ANSI Standard Z87.1 for each student, including students who wear corrective lenses.

Before Each MiniLAB or Lab

1. Arrange the lab in such a way that equipment and supplies are clearly labeled and easily accessible.
2. Have available only equipment and supplies needed to complete the assigned investigation.
3. Review the procedure with students, emphasizing any caution statements or safety symbols that appear.
4. Be sure all students know the proper procedures to follow if an accident should occur.

After the MiniLAB or Lab

1. Be certain that students have returned all equipment and disposed of broken glassware and chemicals properly.
2. Be sure that all hot plates and electrical connections are off.

Storage of Chemicals

Be sure to store all chemicals properly. The following are guidelines commonly used. Your school, city, county, or state may have additional requirements for handling chemicals. It is the responsibility of each teacher to become informed of the rules or guidelines in effect in his or her area.

1. Separate chemicals by reaction type. Strong acids should be stored together. Likewise, strong bases should be stored together and should be separated from acids. Oxidants should be stored away from easily oxidized materials, and so on.
2. Be sure all chemicals are stored in labeled containers indicating contents, concentration, source, date purchased (or prepared), any precautions for handling and storage, and expiration date.
3. Hazardous chemicals require special storage containers and conditions. Be sure to know which chemicals those are and the accepted practices for your area. Some substances must be stored outside the building.

Disposal of Chemicals

Local, state, and federal laws regulate the proper disposal of chemicals. These laws should be consulted before chemical disposal is attempted. Although many substances encountered in the science classroom can be flushed down the drain with plenty of water, it is not safe to assume that this is always true.

DISCLAIMER

Glencoe Publishing Company makes no claims to the completeness of this discussion of laboratory safety and chemical storage. The material presented is not all-inclusive, nor does it address all of the hazards associated with handling, storing, and disposing of chemicals, or with laboratory management.

Preparation of Solutions

It is important to use safe laboratory techniques when handling all chemicals. Always check the MSDS (Material Safety Data Sheet) for each chemical before using it in the classroom. Many substances might appear harmless, but might be toxic, corrosive, or very reactive. Chemicals should never be ingested. Use proper techniques to smell any chemical, wear safety goggles and an apron in the laboratory, and observe the following precautions.

1. **Dilution of Acids and Bases** When diluting acids with water, always add the acids to the water. Never add water to acids. When sulfuric acid and sodium hydroxide are added to water, a large amount of thermal energy is released. Use extra care when handling these substances.

2. **Poisonous and Corrosive Liquids or Vapors** Use a fume hood if possible. Examples include hydrochloric acid, acetic acid, nitric acid, and ammonium hydroxide.

3. **Poisonous and Corrosive to Eyes, Lungs, and Skin** Examples include acids, bases, silver nitrate, iodine, and potassium permanganate.

Bromthymol blue: Add 0.5 g bromthymol blue powder to 500 mL distilled water to make a BTB stock solution. Dilute 40 mL BTB stock solution to 2 L with distilled water. Solution should be bright blue. If not, add one drop of NaOH at a time, swirling to mix. Check color.

Hydrochloric acid (HCL) solution: To make a 5% solution, add 13.6 mL concentrated HCl to 73 mL water while stirring. To make a $0.1M$ solution, add 1 mL concentrated hydrochloric acid to 100 mL water while stirring.

Iodine solution/Iodine stain: Dilute 1 part Lugol's solution with 15 parts water.

Lugol's solution: Dissolve 10 g potassium iodide in 100 mL distilled water. Then add and dissolve 5 g iodine. Store in dark bottle. Keeps indefinitely.

Phenolphthalein indicator: From a drug store, buy a package of any laxative that contains phenolphthalein. To make 1% solution, mash 4 tablets and pour the powder into 10 mL of rubbing alcohol. Let mixture soak for 15 minutes. Pour liquid into and store in a dropper bottle.

Potassium permanganate: For a $0.01M$ solution of potassium permanganate, dissolve 0.15 g $KMnO_4$ in 100 mL water.

Red cabbage concentrate: Put 5 leaves of red cabbage in a pot. Add 1 L of water, bring to a boil, and simmer until water turns a deep purple. Pour liquid through a strainer or piece of cheesecloth into a storage bottle. Keep refrigerated.

Salt solution: For a 3.5% salt (NaCl) solution that simulates the concentration of ocean water, dissolve 35 g of salt (NaCl) in 965 mL of water. For a 1% solution (weak), dissolve 1 g of salt (NaCl) in 99 mL of water. For a 6% solution, dissolve 6 g of salt (NaCl) in 94 mL of water.

Silver nitrate solution: To make a 10% solution, put 5 g of silver nitrate in 50 mL of distilled water.

Sugar solution: Add 1 tablespoon of sugar to 1 cup of warm water in a deep jar or flask. Stir to dissolve.

Sodium hydroxide (dilute): To make a 1% solution, dissolve 1 g NaOH in 99 mL of water.

Equipment and Materials List

Refer to the Chapter Organizer in front of each chapter for a list of equipment and materials used for each laboratory activity in the chapter.

Consumables

Material	Launch Lab (Chapter)	MiniLAB (Chapter-Section)	Lab (Chapter-Section)
assorted fruit peels			2-4
balloon		3-2	
banana		2-3	2-4
cheesecloth		2-3	
cloth		4-1	3-1
cracked corn	4		
fiberfill			3-1
gravel	4		
ground beef, uncooked			2-3
humus			2-4
nuts	4		
perfume or air freshener		5-2	
petroleum jelly		4-1	
plastic bag, self-sealing		4-1	
poster board			5-3
sock, old	4		
soil, potting			2-4
sunflower seeds	4		
toothpick(s)			1-2
vegetable shortening		4-1	

Nonconsumables

Material	Launch Lab (Chapter)	MiniLAB (Chapter-Section)	Lab (Chapter-Section)
aquarium with water			3-4
bowl		3-2	
compound microscope			1-3
dish, small			1-2
dropper		1-3	1-2, 1-3
fishnet, small			3-4
flashlight			5-2
footprint diagram			4-2
jar(s)		2-3, 3-3	2-4
light source			1-3
magnifying lens	2		
paintbrush, small			1-3
petri dish			1-3
photos of foods and landscapes		5-1	
rubber	3		
shoe box with lid			5-2
stereomicroscope		1-3	1-2, 1-3
stirring rod			2-3, 3-4
timer			5-2
tuning fork	3		
watch glass		1-3	

Biological

Material	Launch Lab (Chapter)	MiniLAB (Chapter-Section)	Lab (Chapter-Section)
clam shell	2		
crayfish			2-3
Daphnia or brine shrimp			1-2
earthworms			2-4, 5-2, 5-3
frog		3-3	
goldfish			3-4
hydra culture			1-2
liver, small piece			1-3
planarian(s)		1-3	1-3
tapeworm slide			1-3

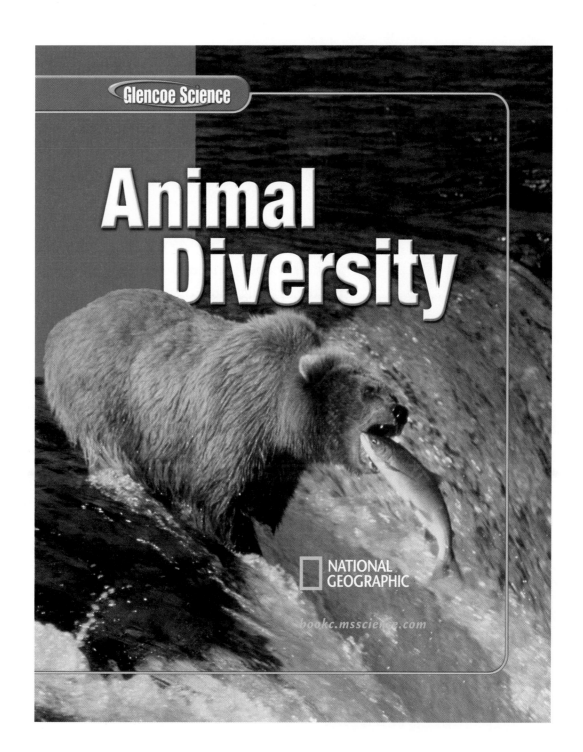

Glencoe Science

Animal Diversity

NATIONAL GEOGRAPHIC

bookc.msscience.com

Mc Graw Hill **Glencoe**

New York, New York   Columbus, Ohio   Chicago, Illinois   Peoria, Illinois   Woodland Hills, California

HOW TO...

Use Your Science Book

Before You Read

- **Chapter Opener** Science is occurring all around you, and the opening photo of each chapter will preview the science you will be learning about. The **Chapter Preview** will give you an idea of what you will be learning about, and you can try the **Launch Lab** to help get your brain headed in the right direction. The **Foldables** exercise is a fun way to keep you organized.

- **Section Opener** Chapters are divided into two to four sections. The **As You Read** in the margin of the first page of each section will let you know what is most important in the section. It is divided into four parts. **What You'll Learn** will tell you the major topics you will be covering. **Why It's Important** will remind you why you are studying this in the first place! The **Review Vocabulary** word is a word you already know, either from your science studies or your prior knowledge. The **New Vocabulary** words are words that you need to learn to understand this section. These words will be in **boldfaced** print and highlighted in the section. Make a note to yourself to recognize these words as you are reading the section.

Glencoe Science

Animal Diversity

NATIONAL GEOGRAPHIC

As You Read

- **Headings** Each section has a title in large red letters, and is further divided into blue titles and small red titles at the beginnings of some paragraphs. To help you study, make an outline of the headings and subheadings.

- **Margins** In the margins of your text, you will find many helpful resources. The **Science Online** exercises and **Integrate** activities help you explore the topics you are studying. **MiniLabs** reinforce the science concepts you have learned.

- **Building Skills** You also will find an **Applying Math** or **Applying Science** activity in each chapter. This gives you extra practice using your new knowledge, and helps prepare you for standardized tests.

- **Student Resources** At the end of the book you will find **Student Resources** to help you throughout your studies. These include **Science, Technology,** and **Math Skill Handbooks,** an **English/Spanish Glossary,** and an **Index.** Also, use your **Foldables** as a resource. It will help you organize information, and review before a test.

- **In Class** Remember, you can always ask your teacher to explain anything you don't understand.

FOLDABLES
Study Organizer

Science Vocabulary Make the following Foldable to help you understand the vocabulary terms in this chapter.

STEP 1 Fold a vertical sheet of notebook paper from side to side.

STEP 2 Cut along every third line of only the top layer to form tabs.

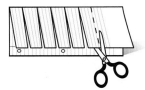

STEP 3 Label each tab with a vocabulary word from the chapter.

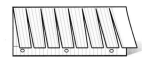

Build Vocabulary As you read the chapter, list the vocabulary words on the tabs. As you learn the definitions, write them under the tab for each vocabulary word.

Look For...

FOLDABLES

At the beginning of every section.

In Lab

Working in the laboratory is one of the best ways to understand the concepts you are studying. Your book will be your guide through your laboratory experiences, and help you begin to think like a scientist. In it, you not only will find the steps necessary to follow the investigations, but you also will find helpful tips to make the most of your time.

- Each lab provides you with a **Real-World Question** to remind you that science is something you use every day, not just in class. This may lead to many more questions about how things happen in your world.

- Remember, experiments do not always produce the result you expect. Scientists have made many discoveries based on investigations with unexpected results. You can try the experiment again to make sure your results were accurate, or perhaps form a new hypothesis to test.

- Keeping a **Science Journal** is how scientists keep accurate records of observations and data. In your journal, you also can write any questions that may arise during your investigation. This is a great method of reminding yourself to find the answers later.

Look For...
- **Launch Labs** start every chapter.
- **MiniLabs** in the margin of each chapter.
- **Two Full-Period Labs** in every chapter.
- **EXTRA Try at Home Labs** at the end of your book.
- the **Web site** with laboratory demonstrations.

Before a Test

Admit it! You don't like to take tests! However, there *are* ways to review that make them less painful. Your book will help you be more successful taking tests if you use the resources provided to you.

- Review all of the **New Vocabulary** words and be sure you understand their definitions.

- Review the notes you've taken on your **Foldables,** in class, and in lab. Write down any question that you still need answered.

- Review the **Summaries** and **Self Check questions** at the end of each section.

- Study the concepts presented in the chapter by reading the **Study Guide** and answering the questions in the **Chapter Review.**

Look For...

- **Reading Checks** and **caption questions** throughout the text.
- the **Summaries** and **Self Check questions** at the end of each section.
- the **Study Guide** and **Review** at the end of each chapter.
- the **Standardized Test Practice** after each chapter.

Let's Get Started

To help you find the information you need quickly, use the Scavenger Hunt below to learn where things are located in Chapter 1.

1. What is the title of this chapter?

2. What will you learn in Section 1?

3. Sometimes you may ask, "Why am I learning this?" State a reason why the concepts from Section 2 are important.

4. What is the main topic presented in Section 2?

5. How many reading checks are in Section 1?

6. What is the Web address where you can find extra information?

7. What is the main heading above the sixth paragraph in Section 2?

8. There is an integration with another subject mentioned in one of the margins of the chapter. What subject is it?

9. List the new vocabulary words presented in Section 2.

10. List the safety symbols presented in the first Lab.

11. Where would you find a Self Check to be sure you understand the section?

12. Suppose you're doing the Self Check and you have a question about concept mapping. Where could you find help?

13. On what pages are the Chapter Study Guide and Chapter Review?

14. Look in the Table of Contents to find out on which page Section 2 of the chapter begins.

15. You complete the Chapter Review to study for your chapter test. Where could you find another quiz for more practice?

Teacher Advisory Board

The Teacher Advisory Board gave the editorial staff and design team feedback on the content and design of the Student Edition. They provided valuable input in the development of the 2005 edition of *Glencoe Science.*

John Gonzales
Challenger Middle School
Tucson, AZ

Rachel Shively
Aptakisic Jr. High School
Buffalo Grove, IL

Roger Pratt
Manistique High School
Manistique, MI

Kirtina Hile
Northmor Jr. High/High School
Galion, OH

Marie Renner
Diley Middle School
Pickerington, OH

Nelson Farrier
Hamlin Middle School
Springfield, OR

Jeff Remington
Palmyra Middle School
Palmyra, PA

Erin Peters
Williamsburg Middle School
Arlington, VA

Rubidel Peoples
Meacham Middle School
Fort Worth, TX

Kristi Ramsey
Navasota Jr. High School
Navasota, TX

Student Advisory Board

The Student Advisory Board gave the editorial staff and design team feedback on the design of the Student Edition. We thank these students for their hard work and creative suggestions in making the 2005 edition of *Glencoe Science* student friendly.

Jack Andrews
Reynoldsburg Jr. High School
Reynoldsburg, OH

Peter Arnold
Hastings Middle School
Upper Arlington, OH

Emily Barbe
Perry Middle School
Worthington, OH

Kirsty Bateman
Hilliard Heritage Middle School
Hilliard, OH

Andre Brown
Spanish Emersion Academy
Columbus, OH

Chris Dundon
Heritage Middle School
Westerville, OH

Ryan Manafee
Monroe Middle School
Columbus, OH

Addison Owen
Davis Middle School
Dublin, OH

Teriana Patrick
Eastmoor Middle School
Columbus, OH

Ashley Ruz
Karrer Middle School
Dublin, OH

The Glencoe middle school science Student Advisory Board taking a timeout at COSI, a science museum in Columbus, Ohio.

Contents

In each chapter, look for these opportunities for review and assessment:
• Reading Checks
• Caption Questions
• Section Review
• Chapter Study Guide
• Chapter Review
• Standardized Test Practice
• Online practice at bookc.msscience.com

Student Resources

Cross-Curricular Readings/Labs

Content Details

INTEGRATE

Content Details

Monarch Migration

Introduction

This feature introduces students to scientific inquiry by capturing their interest and then guiding them through the steps scientists used to determine how monarch butterflies are able to navigate on a long distance migration. Scientists who are examining this question use the scientific method by:

1. Asking the question "How do butterflies that have never made the trip before find their way from Canada to Mexico?"
2. Gathering and using information to form hypotheses;
3. Testing hypotheses by making observations;
4. Describing and analyzing what they observe; and
5. Drawing conclusions about their data.

What are other animals that migrate? Possible answers: birds (geese, ducks, robins, terns, warblers, vultures, and hummingbirds), fish (salmon, tuna, and eels), sea turtles, humpback whales, elk **What mechanisms do these animals use to navigate?** Possible answers: Sun, stars, Earth's magnetism, visual cues such as landscape and landmarks, and genetics; aquatic organisms use cues such as water temperature and chemistry, currents, the Sun, and Earth's magnetic field.

Monarch Migration

Although the beautiful black and orange wings of the monarch butterfly are a common sight during summer in the United States, as fall and colder temperatures arrive, the butterflies disappear. Each fall they begin a seasonal migration. Scientists have had some success in unlocking the mystery of monarch migration through the use of scientific methods. Through this example, you can see how each step of this scientific method contributes to reliable results that can lead to better-informed conclusions.

The monarch population that lives west of the Rocky Mountains flies to the coast of California. The eastern population of monarchs flies to the mountains of central Mexico. Sometimes they travel up to 145 km per day. Some eastern monarchs, such as those living in southern Canada, fly more than 3,200 km to reach their winter home.

Figure 1 Eastern monarch butterflies lay their eggs on milkweed plants.

Navigation

Just as astonishing as the distance traveled by these insect voyagers is their ability to find their way. Since no butterfly completes the entire round-trip, the butterflies cannot learn the route from others. So, how do butterflies that have never made the trip before find their way from Canada and the eastern United States to Mexico? This is the question that some entomologists—scientists who study insects—set out to answer.

Figure 2 When they reach Mexico, eastern monarch butterflies gather in large groups.

2 ◆ **C** Monarch Migration

Visual Learning

Figure 2 As students examine the photo of monarchs crowded onto tree branches in Mexico, review with them what they know about butterflies. Review could include that butterflies are insects, the characteristics they have, what they eat, their life cycle, and any other facts students know.

Figure 3 Magnetite is a mineral with natural magnetic properties.

One of the first hypotheses about how eastern monarchs navigate was that they use the Sun as a guide. Researchers based this hypothesis on other research, which showed that some migrating birds rely on the Sun to guide them. However, this failed to explain how the butterflies find their way on cloudy days.

Magnetism

Scientists later discovered that the bodies of eastern monarchs contain tiny grains of a naturally occurring, magnetic substance called magnetite. Magnetite was used to make the first directional compasses. From this discovery, scientists developed a hypothesis that butterflies use an internal magnetic compass to help them plot their route.

University scientists tested this hypothesis by performing an experiment. They caught some eastern monarchs during the fall migration. They divided the monarchs into three groups and exposed each group to different magnetic fields. The group exposed to Earth's normal magnetic field flew to the southwest, which is the correct direction for eastern monarchs to migrate. Those exposed to the opposite of Earth's normal magnetic field flew to the northeast. Finally, those exposed to no magnetic field fluttered about randomly.

Final Conclusions

After analyzing the results, the researchers concluded that eastern monarchs use an internal magnetic compass to navigate from Canada and the eastern United States to Mexico. However, most researchers also believe the butterflies also use the Sun and landmarks, such as mountains and rivers, to make their incredible journey.

Figure 4 A magnet has oppositely charged poles.

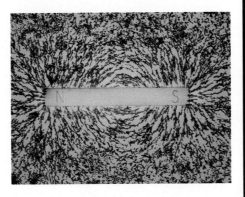

Curriculum Connection

Geography Have students plot on a map of North America a course of eastern monarch migration that begins in Montreal, Quebec. From there students can be creative, indicating stops between Maine and Texas as the butterflies move in a southwesterly direction. From Texas, have them continue the migration south until the butterflies reach areas in the mountains between 70 km and 170 km west of Mexico City, Mexico. Point out that the overwintering sites of the eastern monarchs are in the states of Mexico and Michoacan.

Content Background

In the 1970s the first question of where the ultimate destination of eastern monarch migration was located was finally answered. After nearly forty years of tagging and subsequent reporting and searching, it was discovered that the butterflies overwinter in the mountains west of Mexico City, Mexico. The butterflies migrate by the millions to ten sites where oyamel forests, which are composed of fir, pine, and cypress tress, are found at elevations of approximately 3,300 m.

The conditions in the oyamel forests vary slightly from the surrounding clearings in the mountains. At high elevations, the temperatures in clearings are frequently below freezing and snow falls. Within the oyamel forests, daytime temperatures range between 5°C and 15°C. Thus, the forests offer protection from freezing temperatures and winter storms.

The butterflies occupy the lower branches of the trees and are protected from the strong winds that pass over the higher branches, as well as being off the snow-covered ground. The forests also offer enough moisture to enable the butterflies to survive the winter. The butterflies are in a state of semi-dormancy during this time, conserving energy, stored in the form of fat, for the spring journey to breeding grounds in the southern United States.

Discussion

List reasons why animals migrate. Possible answers: Seasonal migration helps to ensure that animals have mild weather year round. It also ensures that resources such as food and space are plentiful. Some organisms migrate to a specific breeding place such as salmon, American eels, and sea turtles.

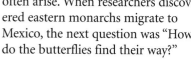
Activity

Have students review the terms *independent variable*, *dependent variable*, *experimental group*, and *control group* as they are used in the context of performing a scientific experiment. In the experiment concerning the butterflies and magnetism, have students label these components and present the results in a data table. **Why is it important to have a control group in an experiment?** A control group does not have any variables manipulated—all variables remain constant. The control group is used as a baseline for comparison to other experimental groups where the variable being tested has been manipulated. In this experiment the independent variable is the type of magnetic field to which the butterflies are exposed. The dependent variable is the direction in which the butterflies flew after being exposed. The two experimental groups consist of the butterflies exposed to the reverse magnetic field and those not exposed to any magnetic field. The control group consists of the butterflies exposed to Earth's normal magnetic field.

Extension

Have students make a list of other variables that could affect the results of the experiment described in the feature. Possible answers: Not all of the butterflies began the migration at the same time, started from the same location, are the age or possibly even of the same generation, or of the same health. There may be an interaction between using the Sun and Earth's magnetic field that the butterflies use to navigate.

Science

Scientists learned about the migration of eastern monarch butterflies by starting with questions such as "Where do monarchs go each fall? How do they find their way there?" Scientists use experiments and careful observations to answer questions about how the world works. When you test an idea, you are doing science.

Life science is the study of living things. In this book, you will learn about the diversity of animals and their adaptations and behaviors, such as migration, that enable them to survive.

Scientific Methods

Researchers used scientific methods to learn about how eastern monarchs navigate. Scientific methods are a series of procedures used to investigate a question scientifically.

Identifying a Question

Figure 5 Sometimes, a scientist must collect data outside of the laboratory.

Sometimes, scientific methods begin with identifying a question, such as "Where do eastern monarch butterflies go every autumn?" After one question has been answered, others often arise. When researchers discovered eastern monarchs migrate to Mexico, the next question was "How do the butterflies find their way?"

Forming a Hypothesis

Once a question is identified, scientists collect information and develop a hypothesis or possible explanation.

They might read the information available on how birds migrate and use it as a basis for the hypothesis that eastern monarchs use the Sun to navigate. This idea, however, failed to explain how the butterflies find their way on cloudy days. As a result, scientists developed another hypothesis—eastern monarchs use an internal magnetic compass that enables them to maintain a course in a specific direction.

Science Journal

Writing About Migration Have students write a chronicle of monarch butterfly migration. The account could be written as a poem, or a song. Encourage students to be creative and incorporate facts into their writing such as what cues the butterflies use to begin the journey, what the butterflies eat along the way, what happens at night, or during a storm.

Fun Fact

At one of the sites where the eastern monarchs overwinter, scientists found up to 14 million butterflies in an area of only 1.5 hectares. Although the weight of each butterfly is small, at times, the butterflies are so thickly packed onto the branches that their collective weight causes the trees to bend and branches to break sometimes.

Testing the Hypothesis

Scientists test hypotheses to determine if they are true or false. Such tests often involve experiments, such as one where eastern monarchs were exposed to different kinds of magnetic fields.

Analyzing Results

During experiments, scientists gather information, or data. Data about the butterfly experiment included the direction that the butterflies were flying when captured, what type of magnetic field they were exposed to in the experiment, and how they reacted to that magnetic field.

Drawing a Conclusion

After data have been collected and carefully analyzed, scientists draw conclusions. Sometimes the original hypothesis is not supported by the data and scientists must start the entire process over. In the case of the eastern monarchs, researchers observed how the butterflies reacted to the magnetic fields and concluded they use an internal magnetic compass to navigate. Just how the butterflies use Earth's magnetic field to find their way is another question for scientists to answer using scientific methods.

Figure 6 Data from observations are important in science investigations.

Figure 7 Scientists hypothesize that monarchs also navigate by landmarks.

You Do It

When eastern monarch butterflies reach Mexico's mountains, the insects abruptly change direction. Scientists hypothesize that the butterflies then switch to steering by landmarks, such as mountains. Describe one way scientists could test this hypothesis.

You Do It

Lead students through this exercise as a class to reinforce the steps in the scientific method. Emphasize that there are no right or wrong answers. Scientists may test a hypothesis in several different ways. Scientists may also interpret the data differently. One way to begin would be to make detailed observations of exactly where the butterflies change course. Do they all change direction upon reaching the same location? Is there something specific about the topography, such as a mountain peak, that stands out in this location?

Section/Objectives	Standards		Labs/Features
Chapter Opener	**National**	**State/Local**	**Launch Lab:** Animal Symmetry, p. 7 **Foldables,** p. 7 A data-collection lab using Probeware technology can be found in **Probeware Labs,** pp. 17–20
	See pp. 16T–17T for a Key to Standards.		
Section 1 Is it an animal? 🕐 2 sessions 📦 1 block 1. **Identify** the characteristics common to most animals. 2. **Determine** how animals meet their needs. 3. **Distinguish** between invertebrates and vertebrates.	National Content Standards: UCP.1–UCP.3, UCP.5, A.1, C.1, C.3, C.5, G.2		**Integrate Language Arts,** p. 9 **MiniLAB:** Modeling Animal Camouflage, p. 10 **Science Online,** p. 12
Section 2 Sponges and Cnidarians 🕐 2 sessions 📦 1 block 4. **Describe** the characteristics of sponges and cnidarians. 5. **Explain** how sponges and cnidarians obtain food and oxygen. 6. **Determine** the importance of living coral reefs.	National Content Standards: UCP.2, UCP.5, A.1, A.2, C.1–C.5		**Integrate Chemistry,** p. 16 **Science Online,** p. 17 **Lab:** Observing a Cnidarian, p. 21
Section 3 Flatworms and Roundworms 🕐 3 sessions 📦 1.5 blocks 7. **List** characteristics of flatworms and roundworms. 8. **Distinguish** between free-living and parasitic organisms. 9. **Identify** disease-causing flatworms and roundworms.	National Content Standards: UCP.2, UCP.5, A.1, A.2, C.1, C.3–C.5		**MiniLAB:** Observing Planarian Movement, p. 24 **Applying Math:** p. 25 **Visualizing Parasitic Worms,** p. 26 **Lab:** Comparing Free-Living and Parasitic Flatworms, pp. 28–29 **Science and History:** Sponges, p. 30

Lab Materials	Reproducible Resources	Section Assessment	Technology
Launch Lab: sheet of paper, scissors	**Chapter FAST FILE Resources** Foldables Worksheet, p. 15 Directed Reading Overview, p. 17 Note-taking Worksheets, pp. 31–33	GLENCOE'S ASSESSMENT ADVANTAGE	**Teacher Works** includes: • Interactive Teacher Edition • Lesson Planner with calendar • Access to all program blacklines • Correlations to standards • Web links
MiniLAB: assorted materials such as paper, buttons, fabric scraps, and glitter; scissors; glue *Need materials?* Contact Science Kit at 1-800-828-7777 or www.sciencekit.com on the Internet.	**Chapter FAST FILE Resources** Transparency Activity, p. 42 MiniLAB, p. 3 Lab Activity, pp. 9–12 Enrichment, p. 28 Reinforcement, p. 25 Transparency Activity, pp. 45–46 Directed Reading, p. 18 **Cultural Diversity,** p. 21 **Science Inquiry Labs,** pp. XX	Portfolio Check for Understanding, p. 13 Performance MiniLab, p. 10 Applying Skills, p. 13 Content Section Review, p. 13	Section Focus Transparency Teaching Transparency Virtual Lab CD-ROM Guided Reading Audio Program Interactive Chalkboard CD-ROM
Lab: dropper, hydra culture, small dish, toothpick, *Daphnia* or brine shrimp, stereomicroscope	**Chapter FAST FILE Resources** Transparency Activity, p. 43 Enrichment, p. 29 Reinforcement, p. 26 Directed Reading, p. 19 Lab Worksheet, pp. 5–6 **Home and Community Involvement,** p. 38	Portfolio Curriculum Connection, p. 15 Performance Applying Math, p. 20 Content Section Review, p. 20	Section Focus Transparency Virtual Lab CD-ROM Guided Reading Audio Program Interactive Chalkboard CD-ROM Video Lab
MiniLAB: dropper, planarian culture, watch glass, water, stereomicroscope **Lab:** petri dish with planarian, compound microscope, prepared slide of a tapeworm, stereomicroscope, light source, small paintbrush, small piece of liver, dropper, water	**Chapter FAST FILE Resources** Transparency Activity, p. 44 MiniLAB, p. 4 Lab Activity, pp. 13–14 Enrichment, p. 30 Reinforcement, p. 27 Directed Reading, pp. 19, 20 Lab Worksheet, pp. 7–8 **Lab Management and Safety,** p. 43	Portfolio Science Journal, p. 24 Performance MiniLab, p. 24 Applying Math, p. 25 Applying Skills, p. 27 Content Section Review, p. 27	Section Focus Transparency Virtual Lab CD-ROM Guided Reading Audio Program Interactive Chalkboard CD-ROM Probeware Lab

End of Chapter Assessment

GLENCOE'S ASSESSMENT ADVANTAGE

Blackline Masters	Technology	Professional Series
Chapter FAST FILE Resources Chapter Review, pp. 35–36 Chapter Tests, pp. 37–40 **Standardized Test Practice,** pp. 7–10	MindJogger Videoquiz Virtual Labs CD-ROM ExamView® Pro Testmaker TeacherWorks CD-ROM Interactive Chalkboard CD-ROM	**Performance Assessment in the Science Classroom (PASC)**

chapter 1 — Introduction to Animals

Transparencies

Section Focus

Section 1 Focus Transparency — Mite Get a Bit Ugly

At the broadest level, scientists divide all living things into six kingdoms. For example, there are different kingdoms for plants, animals, and bacteria. At first, assigning a living thing to a kingdom may seem pretty easy, but sometimes it gets a little tricky. Where do you think this microscopic living thing belongs?

1. Describe the creature in the photo.
2. What are some characteristics that all animals share? Do you think the creature in the photo has these characteristics?
3. Where do you think this creature lives?

L2

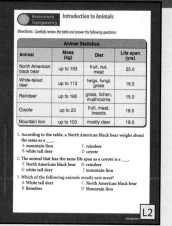

Section 2 Focus Transparency — Sea-Floor Scrubbers

What you see here is the remains of a sponge called a Venus' flower basket. It is a member of a group of sponges that live in very deep water; as a consequence, relatively little is known about them. One interesting fact, though, is that the Venus' flower basket contains two shrimp in its inner chambers. The trapped shrimp and the sponge help each other survive.

1. What are some uses of sponges?
2. Do you think a sponge is a plant or an animal? Explain.
3. How do you think the sponge and shrimp help each other?

L2

Section 3 Focus Transparency — Round and Round Underground

This is a microscopic roundworm. It lives in the soil. Some worms can be very destructive to crops, and scientists are finding ways to limit crop damage caused by these harmful roundworms.

1. Some species of roundworms are parasites. What is a parasite?
2. What part of the plant do you think this worm damages?
3. How are some roundworms beneficial?

L2

This is a representation of key blackline masters available in the Teacher Classroom Resources. See Resource Manager boxes within the chapter for additional information.

Key to Teaching Strategies

The following designations will help you decide which activities are appropriate for your students.

L1 Level 1 activities should be appropriate for students with learning difficulties.

L2 Level 2 activities should be within the ability range of all students.

L3 Level 3 activities are designed for above-average students.

ELL ELL activities should be within the ability range of English-Language Learners.

COOP LEARN Cooperative Learning activities are designed for small group work.

LS Multiple Learning Styles logos, as described on page 12T, are used throughout to indicate strategies that address different learning styles.

P These strategies represent student products that can be placed into a best-work portfolio.

PBL Problem-Based Learning activities apply real-world situations to learning.

Assessment

Assessment Transparency — Introduction to Animals

Directions: *Carefully review the table and answer the following questions.*

Animal Statistics

Animal	Mass (kg)	Diet	Life span (yrs)
North American black bear	up to 193	fruit, nut, meat	25.0
White-tailed deer	up to 113	twigs, fungi, grass	16.5
Reindeer	up to 180	grass, lichen, mushrooms	15.0
Coyote	up to 23	fruit, meat, insects	18.0
Mountain lion	up to 103	mostly deer	18.0

1. According to the table, a North American black bear weighs about the same as a ___.
   A mountain lion   C reindeer
   B white tail deer   D coyote
2. The animal that has the same life span as a coyote is a ___.
   F North American black bear   H reindeer
   G white tail deer   J mountain lion
3. Which of the following animals mostly eats meat?
   A White tail deer   C North American black bear
   B Reindeer   D Mountain lion

L2

Teaching

Section 1 Teaching Transparency — Animal Classification

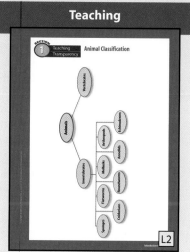

L2

Hands-on Activities

Student Text Lab Worksheet

Activity — Observing a Cnidarian

Lab Preview
Directions: *Answer these questions before you begin the Activity.*
1. What safety symbols are associated with this activity?

2. What structures do hydra have for capturing food?

The hydra has a body cavity that is a simple, hollow sac. It is one of the few freshwater cnidarians. Try this activity to see how the tubelike body of the hydra reacts to food and other stimuli.

What You'll Investigate
How does a hydra react to food and other stimuli?

Materials
dropper
hydra culture
small dish
toothpick
Daphnia or brine shrimp
stereomicroscope

Goals
• **Predict** how a hydra will respond to various stimuli.
• **Observe** a hydra's response to various stimuli.

Safety Precautions
CAUTION: *Be careful with living animals.*

Procedure
1. Record your observations in the Table 1.
2. Use a dropper to place a hydra and some of the water in which it is living into a dish.
3. Place the dish on the stage of a stereomicroscope. Bring the hydra into focus. Record the hydra's color.

4. **Identify** and count the number of tentacles. Locate the mouth.
5. Study the basal disk by which the hydra attaches itself to a slide.
6. **Predict** what will happen if the hydra is touched with a toothpick. Carefully touch the tentacles with a toothpick. Describe the reaction in the data table.
7. Drop a *Daphnia* or a small amount of brine shrimp into the dish. Observe how the hydra takes to food. Record your observations.
8. Return the hydra to the culture.

Tentacle
Mouth
Basal disk

L2

Lab Activities

Lab 1 Laboratory Activity — Regeneration

If you lost your arm, could you grow a new one? Some animals can do this. If part of its body is lost, this kind of animal will grow a new part. One animal that can do this is a flatworm called a planarian. If a planarian is cut into several pieces, each piece will develop into a complete animal. This regrowth is called regeneration.

Strategy
You will cut three planaria into two pieces.
You will observe the pieces for 10 days.
You will record any changes you are taking place in the planaria pieces.

Materials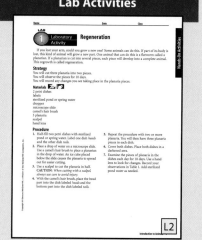
2 petri dishes
labels
sterilized pond or spring water
dropper
microscope slide
camel's hair brush
3 planaria
scalpel
hand lens

Procedure
1. Half-fill two petri dishes with sterilized pond or spring water. Label one dish heads and the other dish tails.
2. Place a drop of water on a microscope slide. Use a camel's hair brush to place a planarian in the drop of water. An ice cube placed below the slide causes the planaria to spread out for easier cutting.
3. Use a scalpel to cut the planaria in half. CAUTION: *When cutting with a scalpel, always use care to avoid injury.*
4. With the camel's hair brush, place the head part into the dish labeled heads and the bottom part into the dish labeled tails.

5. Repeat the procedure with two or more planaria. You will then have three planaria pieces in each dish.
6. Cover both dishes. Place both dishes in a darkened area.
7. Examine the pieces of planaria in the dishes each day for 10 days. Use a hand lens to look for changes. Record your observations in Table 1. Add sterilized pond water as needed.

L2

Meeting Different Ability Levels

Content Outline

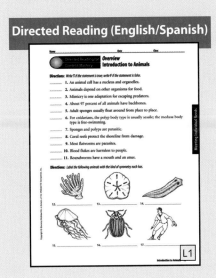

Reinforcement

Enrichment

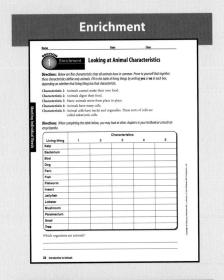

Directed Reading (English/Spanish)

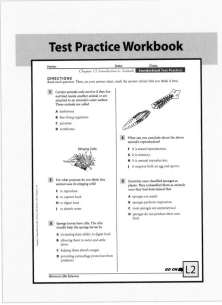

L1

Study Guide

Study Guide

Features
• Contains a study guide page for each section of the chapter
• Reviews key concepts
• Includes answer pages

L2

Reading Essentials

Reading Essentials for Glencoe Science
An Interactive Student Workbook

Features
• Condensed core content
• Actively involves students in reading
• Reinforces key vocabulary

L1

Assessment

Test Practice Workbook

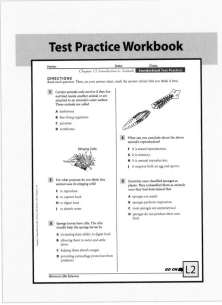

GO ON ▶
Glencoe Life Science
L2

Chapter Review

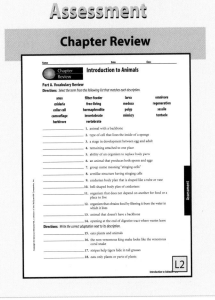

L2

Chapter Tests

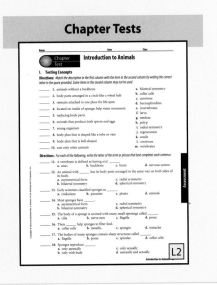

L2

Science Content Background

section 1 — Is it an animal?

Animal Characteristics

From sponges to monkeys there is considerable diversity in the animal kingdom. Yet there are characteristics that all animals share. Animals are heterotrophic—they consume parts of other organisms for their nutritional needs. Animals are composed of eukaryotic cells, which have nuclei and cell membranes.

Ken Lucas/Visuals Unlimited

Teacher to Teacher

Jeff Remington
Palmyra Middle School
Palmyra, PA

"Before I have students participate in a dissection I show a video that I have made myself demonstrating proper safety techniques and procedures for each dissection that I do. It saves me time, specimens, and the students get a good view of the dissection prior to doing it themselves."

Jeff Remington

How Animals Meet Their Needs

Animals have adaptions that make them either carnivores, herbivores, or omnivores. Consider the length of the alimentary canal. Many students are surprised to learn that herbivores have a much longer alimentary canal than do carnivores. The extra length is an adaption that helps with breaking down cellulose, the hard-to-digest plant material. The length of the human alimentary canal is between the lengths of herbivores and carnivores.

Another area where adaptations can be seen is with dentition. Herbivores have hard, flat molars that are used for grinding plant material. The sharp back teeth of a carnivore is for cutting and shredding meat.

Many land herbivores have eyes far apart on both sides of their head, which helps them spot predators. Land carnivores often have eyes in the front of their heads. This arrangement gives binocular vision, which better helps the predator estimate distance.

Sponges and Cnidarians

Sponges

Sponges belong to the phylum Porifera, which comes from the Latin words *porus*, which means "hole," and *ferre*, which means "to carry." They have this name because sponges carry materials in through their holes. The sponges your students typically encounter are artificial sponges. As a defense against bacteria, fungi, and predators, real sponges have chemical defenses. Scientists are studying these compounds to see if they can be used to combat human diseases.

Cnidarians

These animals belong to the aquatic invertebrate phylum called Cnidaria and are also called coelenterate animals. Sea anemones are carnivores, but they have symbiotic relationships with photosynthetic organisms that produce nutrients and oxygen for the anemone. For this reason, sea anemones will not survive for long in marine aquariums unless they contain proper lighting systems.

Flatworms and Roundworms

Flatworms

Flatworms belong to the phylum Platyhelminthes. The name comes from the Greek word *platys*, meaning "flat" and *helminthos*, meaning "worm." There are 3,500 species of tapeworms that live in different animals. The size of the worm usually varies with the organism in which it lives. For example, a tapeworm in a sperm whale may be 30 meters long.

Roundworms

Members of the phylum Nematoda are the simplest organisms that have tubelike digestive systems starting with a mouth and ending with an anus. These are abundant animals that live in large quantities in places as diverse as soils, plants, animals, freshwater, salt water, and even vinegar.

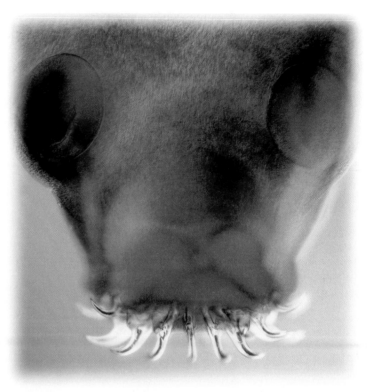

Alferd Pasieka/Science Library/Photo Researchers, Inc.

chapter content resources

Internet Resources

For additional content background, visit **bookc.msscience.com** to:

- access your book online
- find references to related articles in popular science magazines
- access Web links with related content background
- access current events with science journal topics

Print Resources

Coral Reefs: Ecology, Threats, and Conservation by Charles Sheppard, Voyageur Press, 2002

Parasitic Worms by Jim Flegg, Shire Publications, 1999

Invertebrate Zoology by Ellen Doris, Len Rubenstein, Thames & Hudson, 1993

Jellyfish to Insects: Projects With Biology (Hands on Science) by William Hemsley, Richard Hull, Gloucester Pr, 1991

Chapter Vocabulary

herbivore, p. 9
carnivore, p. 9
omnivore, p. 9
vertebrate, p. 12
invertebrate, p. 12
radial symmetry, p. 13
bilateral symmetry, p. 13
sessile, p. 15
hermaphrodite, p. 16
polyp, p. 17
medusa, p. 17
tentacle, p. 18
stinging cell, p. 18
free-living organism, p. 22
anus, p. 25

Science Journal In this picture, students will find various corals, fishes, and sea aneome.

INTERACTIVE CHALKBOARD with Image Bank

PowerPoint® Presentations

This CD-ROM is an editable Microsoft® PowerPoint® presentation that includes:
- a pre-made presentation for every chapter
- interactive graphics
- animations
- audio clips
- image bank
- all new section and chapter questions
- Standardized Test Practice
- transparencies
- pre-lab questions for all labs
- Foldables directions
- links to bookc.msscience.com

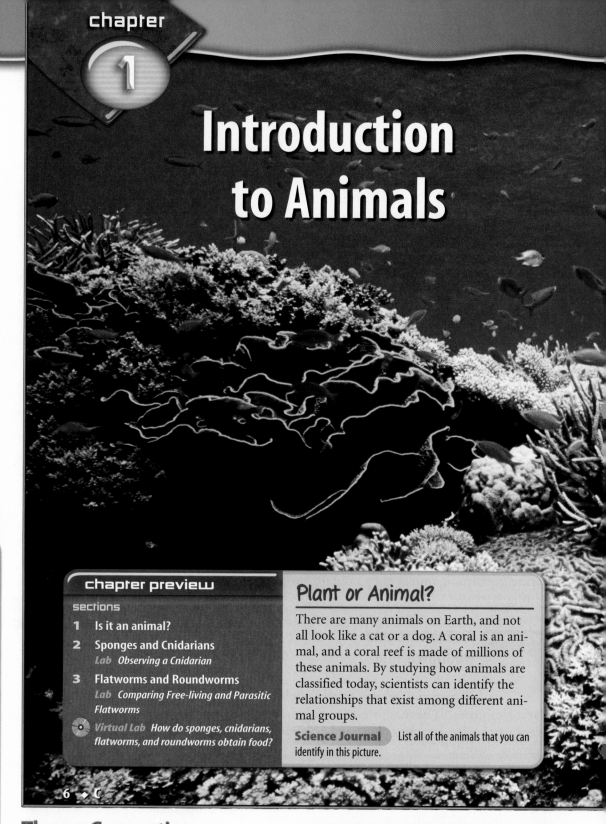

Introduction to Animals

chapter preview

sections

1 Is it an animal?

2 Sponges and Cnidarians
Lab Observing a Cnidarian

3 Flatworms and Roundworms
Lab Comparing Free-living and Parasitic Flatworms

Virtual Lab How do sponges, cnidarians, flatworms, and roundworms obtain food?

6 ◆ C

Plant or Animal?

There are many animals on Earth, and not all look like a cat or a dog. A coral is an animal, and a coral reef is made of millions of these animals. By studying how animals are classified today, scientists can identify the relationships that exist among different animal groups.

Science Journal List all of the animals that you can identify in this picture.

Theme Connection

Stability and Change Changing environments lead to changes in the complexity of animals inhabiting these environments. The groups of animals from invertebrates to vertebrates show a trend toward increasing complexity.

About the Photo

Disappearing Reefs Coral reefs are often called the rain forests of the ocean because of the abundance of life there. Many animals in the ocean depend on the reef for food and protection, and coral polyps feed on plant and animal plankton. Unfortunately, coral reefs are disappearing at an alarming rate due to warmer waters and human activities.

Start-Up Activities

Animal Symmetry

The words *left* and *right* have meaning to you because your body has a left and a right side. But what is left or right to a jellyfish or sea star? How an animal's body parts are arranged is called symmetry. In the following lab, you will compare three types of symmetry found in animals.

1. On a piece of paper, draw three shapes—a circle, a triangle with two equal sides, and a free-form shape—then cut them out.

2. See how many different ways you can fold each shape through the center to make similar halves with each fold.

3. **Think Critically** Record which shapes can be folded into equal halves and which shapes cannot. Can any of the shapes be folded into equal halves more than one way? Which shape would be similar to a human? A sea star? A sponge?

 **Study Organizer**

Animal Classification Make the following Foldable to help you classify the main characteristics of different animals.

STEP 1 Fold a piece of paper in half from top to bottom and then fold it in half again to divide it into fourths.

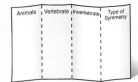

STEP 2 Turn the paper vertically, **unfold and label** the four columns as shown.

Read for Main Ideas As you read this chapter, list the characteristics of different animals in the appropriate column.

Science Online Preview this chapter's content and activities at bookc.msscience.com

 Dinah Zike Study Fold

Student preparation materials for this Foldable are available in the **Chapter FAST FILE Resources.**

Purpose Use this lab to introduce students to symmetry. Explain that in this chapter they will be learning about different types of symmetry and invertebrates L2

Preparation Cut out shapes that represent different animals with radial or bilateral symmetry. Show students the cutouts after they have finished the activity. Ask them to identify the type of symmetry of each.

Materials scissors, sheet of paper or colored construction paper

Teaching Strategy Have students compare the shapes they made with the shapes of animals from different phyla. Ask them to classify their "animals" into a phylum or to devise their own phyla for classifying organisms.

Safety Precaution Caution students to use scissors safely.

Think Critically

Answers will vary, but many of the shapes will have either radial or bilateral symmetry. triangle—human; circle—sea star; free-form shape—sponge.

Assessment

Performance Organize the class into groups and have each group make a poster display of their shapes. Similar shapes should be grouped together and classified. Use **Performance Assessment in the Science Classroom,** p. 145. L2

Probeware Labs

This chapter's data-collection lab using Probeware technology is included on the *Video Labs CD-ROM.* See the *Probeware Lab Manual* pages 17–20 for student worksheets.

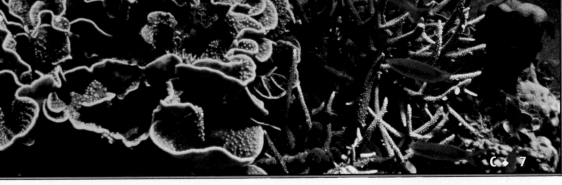

Is it an animal?

Tie to Prior Knowledge

Animal Characteristics Ask what characteristics animals have that distinguish them from other living things. They cannot make their own food and most are capable of movement. Discuss the characteristics they have in common with all living things. They are made of cells, reproduce, grow, develop, respond, and have basic needs such as energy and water.

Caption Answer

Figure 1 These organisms are hydroids. They catch tiny plankton with their tentacles.

as you read

What You'll Learn

- **Identify** the characteristics common to most animals.
- **Determine** how animals meet their needs.
- **Distinguish** between invertebrates and vertebrates.

Why It's Important

Animals provide food, medicines, and companionship in your daily life.

Review Vocabulary

adapation: any variation that makes an organism better suited to its environment

New Vocabulary

- herbivore
- carnivore
- omnivore
- vertebrate
- invertebrate
- radial symmetry
- bilateral symmetry

Figure 1 These organisms look like plants, but they're one of the many plantlike animals that can be found growing on shipwrecks and other underwater surfaces.
Infer *how these animals obtain food.*

Animal Characteristics

From microscopic worms to giant whales, the animal kingdom includes an amazing variety of living things, but all of them have certain characteristics in common. What makes the animals in **Figure 1** different from plants? Is it because animals eat other living things? Is this enough information to identify them as animals? What characteristics do animals have?

1. Animals are made of many cells. Different kinds of cells carry out different functions such as sensing the environment, getting rid of wastes, and reproducing.

2. Animal cells have a nucleus and specialized structures inside the cells called organelles.

3. Animals depend on other living things in the environment for food. Some eat plants, some eat other animals, and some eat plants and animals.

4. Animals digest their food. The proteins, carbohydrates, and fats in foods are broken down into simpler molecules that can move into the animal's cells.

5. Many animals move from place to place. They can escape from their enemies and find food, mates, and places to live. Animals that move slowly or not at all have adaptations that make it possible for them to take care of these needs in other ways.

6. All animals are capable of reproducing sexually. Some animals also can reproduce asexually.

Section 1 Resource Manager

Chapter *FAST FILE* Resources

Transparency Activity, pp. 42, 45–46

Directed Reading for Content Mastery, pp. 17, 18

Note-taking Worksheets, pp. 31–33

MiniLAB, p. 3

Lab Activity, pp. 9–12

Enrichment, p. 28

Reinforcement, p. 25

Figure 2 Animals eat a variety of foods.

Chitons eat algae from rocks.

A red-tailed hawk uses its sharp beak to tear the flesh.

Cardinal fish eat small invertebrates and some plant material.

How Animals Meet Their Needs

Any structure, process, or behavior that helps an organism survive in its environment is an adaptation. Adaptations are inherited from previous generations. In a changing environment, adaptations determine which individuals are more likely to survive and reproduce.

Adaptations for Obtaining Energy One of the most basic needs of animals is the need for food. All animals have adaptations that allow them to obtain, eat, and digest different foods. The chiton, shown in **Figure 2,** deer, some fish, and many insects are examples of herbivores. **Herbivores** eat only plants or parts of plants. In general, herbivores eat more often and in greater amounts than other animals because plants don't supply as much energy as other types of food.

✔ **Reading Check** *Why are butterflies considered to be herbivores?*

Animals that eat only other animals, like the red-tailed hawk in **Figure 2,** are **carnivores.** Most carnivores capture and kill other animals for food. But some carnivores, called scavengers, eat only the remains of other animals. Animal flesh supplies more energy than plants do, so carnivores don't need to eat as much or as often as herbivores.

Animals that eat plants and animals or animal flesh are called **omnivores.** Bears, raccoons, robins, humans, and the cardinal fish in **Figure 2** are examples of omnivores.

Many beetles and other animals such as millipedes feed on tiny bits of decaying matter called detritus (dih TRI tus). They are called detritivores (dih TRI tih vorz).

INTEGRATE
Language Arts

Carnivore Lore
Carnivores have always been written about as having great power and strength. Find a poem or short story about a carnivore and interpret what the author is trying to convey about the animal.

Quick Demo

Fish v. Plants

Materials classroom aquarium with both fish and live plants inside

Estimated Time 10 minutes

Procedure Have students observe the fish and plants in the classroom aquarium. Ask them to compare and contrast the two. Both are many-celled, reproduce sexually, and move. Green plants make their own food, but fish cannot. Animals can move from place to place. Plant movement is a result of growth and environmental stimulus. L1 IS **Visual-Spatial**

Activity

Energy Sources Display pictures of herbivores, carnivores, and omnivores on the bulletin board. Have students group them according to their source of obtaining energy. L1 COOP LEARN IS **Visual-Spatial**

✔ **Reading Check**

Answer They feed on plant products.

INTEGRATE
Language Arts

Carnivore Lore Answers will vary depending on literary work chosen.

Differentiated Instruction

Challenge Have students research the characteristics of extinct animals, such as dinosaurs, and explain why they were classified as animals. L3

Teacher FYI

Animal Classification The branch of biology that deals with the study of animals is zoology. Early zoologists classified animals according to physical structure, where they lived, or economic use. Modern zoologists use cell structure and function, embryology, physiology, and genetics to classify animals.

Mini LAB

Purpose to model camouflage

L1 LS **Logical-Mathematical**

Materials assorted materials such as paper, buttons, and fabric scraps; scissors; glue

Safety Precautions

Teaching Strategy Encourage students to use the materials provided to make animals from various links in a food chain, and infer how camouflage assists both predator and prey in their survival.

Analysis

1. Generally, an animal will be well camouflaged in one environment and only partially camouflaged in other environments.
2. Answers will vary depending on students' designs.

Assessment

Process Have students place their animals in various locations in the room. How does changing an animal's environment affect it chances for survival? Most of the "animals" will no longer be camouflaged and have difficulty pursuing prey or fleeing from predators. Use **Performance Activities in the Science Classroom,** p. 89. L1

Try at Home

Reading Check

Answer An animal can be mistaken for another type of animal. Sometimes this may save the animal's life, sometimes this may get the animal killed.

Caption Answer

Figure 4 The scarlet king snake's bands are nearly uniform in width and black alternates with red and yellow. The coral snake has wide and narrow bands and yellow alternates with red and black. The coral snake is venomous, while the king snake is not.

Figure 3 The pill bug's outer covering protects it and reduces moisture loss from its body.

Mini LAB

Modeling Animal Camouflage

Procedure

1. Pretend that a room in your home is the world of some fictitious animal. From **materials you can find around your home,** build a fictitious animal that would be camouflaged in this world.
2. Put your animal into its world and ask someone to find it.

Analysis

1. In how many places was your animal camouflaged?
2. What changes would increase its chances of surviving in its world?

Try at Home

Figure 4 Mimicry helps some animals survive.
Describe the difference between the two snakes.

Physical Adaptations Some prey species have physical features that enable them to avoid predators. Outer coverings protect some animals. Pill bugs, as seen in **Figure 3,** have protective plates. Porcupines have sharp quills that prevent most predators from eating them. Turtles and many animals that live in water have hard shells that protect them from predators.

Size is also a type of defense. Large animals are usually safer than small animals. Few predators will attack animals such as moose or bison simply because they are so large.

Mimicry is an adaptation in which one animal closely resembles another animal in appearance or behavior. If predators cannot distinguish between the two, they usually will not eat either animal. The venomous coral snake and the non-venomous scarlet king snake, shown in **Figure 4,** look alike. In some cases, this is a disadvantage for scarlet king snakes because people mistake them for coral snakes and kill them.

Reading Check
How might mimicry be an advantage and a disadvantage for an animal?

Many animals, like the flounder in **Figure 5,** blend into their surrounding environment, enabling them to hide from their predators. English peppered moths are brown and speckled like the lichens (LI kunz) on trees, making it difficult for their predators to see them. Many freshwater fish, like the trout also in **Figure 5,** have light bellies and dark, speckled backs that blend in with the gravelly bottoms of their habitats when they are viewed from above. Any marking or coloring that helps an animal hide from other animals is called camouflage. Some animals, like the cuttlefish in **Figure 5,** have the ability to change their color depending on their surroundings.

Coral snake

Scarlet king snake

Active Reading

Jigsaw In this collaborative learning technique, individuals become experts on a portion of a text and share their expertise with a small group, called their home group. Everyone shares responsibility for learning the assigned reading. Assign each person in each home group an expert number (1 through 5, for example). Have students gather into the expert groups that correspond to the number they were assigned. Have them read, discuss, and master chapter concepts and determine how best to teach them to their home groups. Have students return to their home groups and share the content they learned in their expert groups. Have students use the Jigsaw strategy as they study animal characteristics. L2

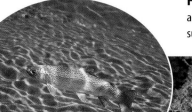

Figure 5 Many types of animals blend with their surroundings.

Bottom fish like this flounder, blend with the ocean floor.

A trout blends with the bottom of a stream.

Cuttlefish can be especially difficult to find because they can change color to blend with their surroundings.

Predator Adaptations Camouflage is an adaptation for many predators so they can sneak up on their prey. Tigers have stripes that hide them in tall grasses. Killer whales are black on their upper surface and white underneath. When seen from above, the whale blends into the darkness of the deep ocean. The killer whale's white underside appears to be nearly the same color as the bright sky overhead when viewed from below. Adaptations such as these enable predators to hunt prey more successfully.

Behavioral Adaptations In addition to physical adaptations, animals have behavioral adaptations that enable them to capture prey or to avoid predators. Chemicals are used by some animals to escape predators. Skunks spray attacking animals with a bad-smelling liquid. Some ants and beetles also use this method of defense. When squid and octopuses are threatened, they release a cloud of ink so they can escape, as shown in **Figure 6.**

Some animals are able to run faster than most of their predators. The Thomson's gazelle can run at speeds up to 80 km/h. A lion can run only about 36 km/h, so speed is a factor in the Thomson's gazelle's survival.

Traveling in groups is a behavior that is demonstrated by predators and prey. Herring swim in groups called schools that resemble an organism too large for a predator fish to attack. On the other hand, when wolves travel in packs, they can successfully hunt large prey that one predator alone could not capture.

Figure 6 An octopus's cloud of ink confuses a predator long enough for the octopus to escape.

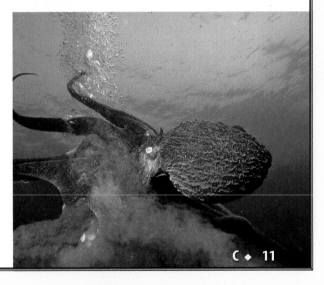

C ◆ 11

Figure 7 Animals can be classified into two large groups. These groups can be broken down further based on different animal characteristics.

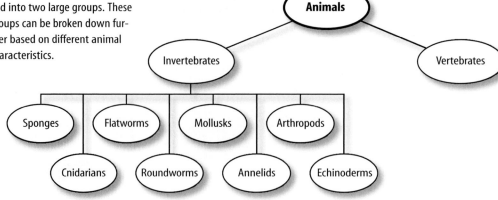

Animal Classification

Scientists have identified and named more than 1.8 million species of animals. It is estimated that there are another 3 million to 30 million more to identify and name. Animals can be classified into two major groups, as shown in **Figure 7.** All animals have common characteristics, but those in one group have more, similar characteristics because all the members of a group probably descended from a common ancestor. When a scientist finds a new animal, how does he or she begin to classify it?

Check for a Backbone To classify an animal, a scientist first looks to see whether or not the animal has a backbone. Animals with backbones are called **vertebrates.** Their backbones are made up of a stack of structures called vertebrae that support the animal. The backbone also protects and covers the spinal cord—a bundle of nerves that is connected to the brain. The spinal cord carries messages to all other parts of the body. It also carries messages from other parts of the body to the brain. Examples of vertebrates include fish, frogs, snakes, birds, and humans.

An animal without a backbone is classified as an **invertebrate.** About 97 percent of all animal species are invertebrates. Sponges, jellyfish, worms, insects, and clams are examples of invertebrates. Many invertebrates are well protected by their outer coverings. Some have shells, some have a skeleton on the outside of their body, and others have a spiny outer covering.

Symmetry After determining whether or not a backbone is present, a scientist might look at an animal's symmetry (SIH muh tree). Symmetry is how the body parts of an animal are arranged. Organisms that have no definite shape are called asymmetrical. Most sponges are asymmetrical animals.

Fun Fact

Animals with radial symmetry are common in the ocean, but all land animals have bilateral symmetry.

Figure 8 Symmetry is a characteristic of all animals.
Sea urchins can sense things from all directions.

Animals that have body parts arranged in a circle around a center point, the way spokes of a bicycle wheel are arranged, have **radial symmetry.** Hydras, jellyfish, sea urchins, like the one in **Figure 8,** and some sponges have radial symmetry.

Most animals have bilateral symmetry. In Latin, the word *bilateral* means "two sides." An animal with **bilateral symmetry,** like the crayfish shown in **Figure 8,** can be divided into right and left halves that are nearly mirror images of each other.

After an animal is classified as an invertebrate or a vertebrate and its symmetry is determined, other characteristics are identified that place it in one of the groups of animals with which it has the most characteristics in common. Sometimes a newly discovered animal is different from any existing group, and a new classification group is formed for that animal.

Most animals have bilateral symmetry like this crayfish.
Name *the type of symmetry you have.*

Discussion
Sense Organs Where are the nerves and sense organs of animals with bilateral symmetry located? Why? In the front end; this arrangement allows animals to sense the environment as they move forward.

Caption Answer
Figure 8 bilateral

3 Assess

DAILY INTERVENTION

Check for Understanding
Visual-Spatial Have students make diagrams of a sea star, a butterfly, and a sponge, and label each diagram with the type of symmetry it represents. L1 LS P

Reteach
Animal Symmetry Have students look through magazines to find pictures of animals. Then have them work in groups to identify each animal's symmetry. L1
COOP LEARN LS **Visual-Spatial**

Assessment

Content Place a number of pictures of animals on the bulletin board. Ask students to choose one and use the section on classification to explain how they would classify that organism. Use **Performance Assessment in the Science Classroom,** p. 121. L2

---

section 1 review

Summary

Animal Characteristics
- Animals are made of many eukaryotic cells.
- Animals obtain and digest food, reproduce and most move from place to place.

How Animals Meet Their Needs
- Animals have many different physical, predatory, and behavioral adaptations.
- Animals can be herbivores, carnivores, omnivores, or detritivores depending on what they eat.

Animal Classification
- Scientists classify animals in two large groups: vertebrates and invertebrates.
- An animal's symmetry plays a role in its classification.

Self Check

1. **Explain** different adaptations for obtaining food.
2. **Compare and contrast** invertebrates and vertebrates.
3. **List** the three types of symmetry. Give an example for each type.
4. **Think Critically** Radial symmetry is found among species that live in water. Why might radial symmetry be an uncommon adaptation of animals that live on land?

Applying Skills

5. **Concept Map** Make an events-chain concept map showing the steps used to classify a new animal.
6. **Communicate** Choose an animal you are familiar with. Describe the adaptations it has for getting food and avoiding predators.

 bookc.msscience.com/self_check_quiz

SECTION 1 Is it an animal? **C ◆ 13**

---

section 1 review

1. physical—teeth; behavioral—traveling in groups; predator—camouflage
2. Invertebrates do not have backbones; vertebrates do.
3. radial symmetry—sea star; bilateral symmetry—dog; asymmetry—sponge

4. An animal that lives in water may be stationary, move with water, or move up and down. Radial symmetry allows for all of these movements, but such an adaptation would be less useful on land. Radial symmetry enables animals to sense their environment from all directions.

5. Determine whether the animal has a backbone; determine the animal's symmetry; compare the organism's characteristics with those of other organisms.
6. Allow students to research their chosen animal, if necessary.

Sponges and Cnidarians

Bellringer

INTERACTIVE CHALKBOARD
PowerPoint® Presentations

Section Focus Transparencies also are available on the Interactive Chalkboard CD-ROM.

L2 ELL

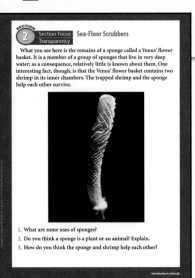

SECTION 2 | Section Focus Transparency | Sea-Floor Scrubbers

What you see here is the remains of a sponge called a Venus' flower basket. It is a member of a group of sponges that live in very deep water; as a consequence, relatively little is known about them. One interesting fact, though, is that the Venus' flower basket contains two shrimp in its inner chambers. The trapped shrimp and the sponge help each other survive.

1. What are some uses of sponges?
2. Do you think a sponge is a plant or an animal? Explain.
3. How do you think the sponge and shrimp help each other?

Introduction to Animals

Tie to Prior Knowledge

Many-celled Organization Review how cells are organized into tissues, organs, systems, and organisms to help students understand the differences in the body structures of sponges and cnidarians.

---

as you read

What You'll Learn

- **Describe** the characteristics of sponges and cnidarians.
- **Explain** how sponges and cnidarians obtain food and oxygen.
- **Determine** the importance of living coral reefs.

Why It's Important

Sponges and cnidarians are important to medical research because they are sources of chemicals that fight disease.

Review Vocabulary
flagella: long, thin whiplike structures that grow from a cell

New Vocabulary
- sessile
- hermaphrodite
- polyp
- medusa
- tentacle
- stinging cell

Sponges

In their watery environments, sponges play many roles. They interact with many other animals such as worms, shrimp, snails, and sea stars. These animals live on, in, and under sponges. Sponges also are important as a food source for some snails, sea stars, and fish. Certain sponges contain photosynthetic bacteria and protists that provide oxygen and remove wastes for the sponge.

Only about 17 species of sponges are commercially important. Humans have long used the dried and cleaned bodies of some sponges for bathing and cleaning. Most sponges you see today are synthetic sponges or vegetable loofah sponges, but natural sea sponges like those in **Figure 9** still are available.

Today scientists are finding other uses for sponges. Chemicals made by sponges are being tested and used to make drugs that fight disease-causing bacteria, fungi, and viruses. These chemicals also might be used to treat certain forms of arthritis.

Origin of Sponges Fossil evidence shows that sponges appeared on Earth about 600 million years ago. Because sponges have little in common with other animals, many scientists have concluded that sponges probably evolved separately from all other animals. Sponges living today have many of the same characteristics as their fossilized ancestors.

Figure 9 Sponges can be found in a variety of habitats.

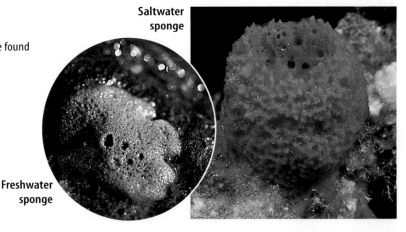

Saltwater sponge

Freshwater sponge

Section 2 Resource Manager

Chapter FAST FILE Resources
Transparency Activity, p. 43
Directed Reading for Content Mastery, p. 19
Enrichment, p. 29
Reinforcement, p. 26
Lab Worksheet, pp. 5–6

Life Science Critical Thinking/Problem Solving, p. 10
Earth Science Critical Thinking/Problem Solving, p. 1
Cultural Diversity, p. 7

Characteristics of Sponges

Most of the 5,000 species of sponges are found in warm, shallow salt water near coastlines, although some are found at ocean depths of 8,500 m or more. A few species, like the one in **Figure 9,** live in freshwater rivers, lakes, and streams. The colors, shapes, and sizes of sponges vary. Saltwater sponges are brilliant red, orange, yellow, or blue, while freshwater sponges are usually a dull brown or green. Some sponges have radial symmetry, but most are asymmetrical. Sponges can be smaller than a marble or larger than a compact car.

Adult sponges live attached to one place unless they are washed away by strong waves or currents. Organisms that remain attached to one place during their lifetimes are called **sessile** (SE sile). They often are found with other sponges in permanent groups called colonies. Early scientists classified sponges as plants because they didn't move. As microscopes were improved, scientists observed that sponges couldn't make their own food, so sponges were reclassified as animals.

Body Structure A sponge's body, like the one in **Figure 10,** is a hollow tube that is closed at the bottom and open at the top. The sponge has many small openings in its body. These openings are called pores.

Sponges have less complex body organization than other groups of animals. They have no tissues, organs, or organ systems. The body wall has two cell layers made up of several different types of cells. Those that line the inside of the sponge are called collar cells. The beating motion of the collar cells' flagella moves water through the sponge.

Many sponge bodies contain sharp, pointed structures called spicules (SPIH kyewlz). The soft-bodied, natural sponges that some people use for bathing or washing their cars have skeletons of a fibrous material called spongin. Other sponges contain spicules and spongin. Spicules and spongin provide support for a sponge and protection from predators.

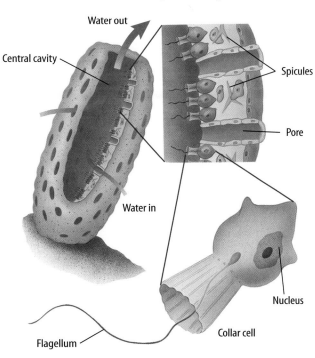

Figure 10 Specialized cells, called collar cells, have flagella that move water through the pores in a sponge. Other cells filter microscopic food from the water as it passes through.

Water out

Central cavity

Spicules

Pore

Water in

Nucleus

Collar cell

Flagellum

SECTION 2 Sponges and Cnidarians **C ◆ 15**

Differentiated Instruction

Visually Impaired Have students pass around different sponges, both natural and synthetic. Ask if they can feel any differences between the two types of sponges. L2

Curriculum Connection

Art Artists use sponges to create unique effects in their paintings. Painters use sponges for walls. Unlike brushes, which leave evidence of strokes, sponges provide a more natural texture. Have students use sponges to create a work of art for display in the classroom. L2 ELL IS **Kinesthetic and Visual-Spatial** P

Discussion

Sessile Animals Why are there no sessile animals on land? Sessile animals get their energy from food that passes by them. Food that swims or is suspended in water often cannot avoid sessile animals because of ocean currents.

Fun Fact

Of the thousands of sponge species, only about 100 species live in freshwater.

Inquiry Lab

Water-holding Capacity of Sponges

Purpose To explore and observe the ability of a sponge to hold water, have students design a method for testing which types of sponges hold more water.

Possible Materials water, various sponges, writing materials, a balance, a stopwatch or clock with a second hand

Estimated Time 1 class section

Teaching Strategies

• Students can compare the masses of wet and dry, and synthetic and natural sponges.

• Students can calculate the amount of water a sponge can hold.

• Students can also test absorption time to find what type of sponge absorbs more quickly.

• As part of the school's consumer awareness committee, students could test various consumer sponge products for their effectiveness and share their results with the school's custodian for purchase consideration.

• Allow students to explore questions as they arise. L2 PBL
IS **Logical-Mathematical**

For additional inquiry activities, see *Science Inquiry Labs.*

Figure 11 Have students make an events chain concept map in which they sequence the events in sponge reproduction. L2 LS
Visual-Spatial

Quick Demo

Filtration

Materials soil, plant material, water, beaker, coffee filter, container

Estimated Time 15 minutes

Procedure Mix soil and plant material in a beaker of water. Pour the water mixture through a coffee filter into a container. Let students examine the filter contents and the container to see how sponge cells might filter food particles from water. L2
Visual-Spatial

Reading Check

Answer from water pulled in through their pores

Spicule Composition The makeup of spicules reflects the composition of the water in which they live.

Research Look for possible uses for the substances that make up spicules.

Spicule Composition
Spicules of glass sponges are composed of silica. Other sponges have spicules of calcium carbonate. Relate the composition of spicules to the composition of the water in which the sponge lives. Write your answer in your Science Journal.

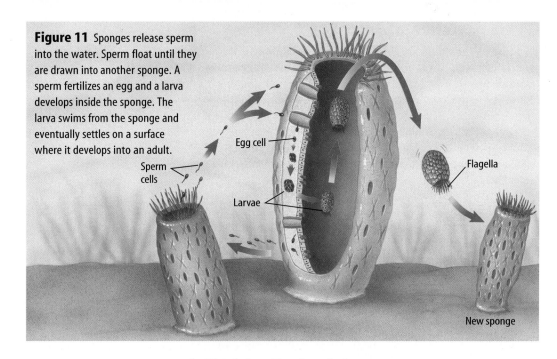

Figure 11 Sponges release sperm into the water. Sperm float until they are drawn into another sponge. A sperm fertilizes an egg and a larva develops inside the sponge. The larva swims from the sponge and eventually settles on a surface where it develops into an adult.

Egg cell

Sperm cells

Flagella

Larvae

New sponge

Obtaining Food and Oxygen Sponges filter microscopic food particles such as bacteria, algae, protists, and other materials from the water as it is pulled in through their pores. Oxygen also is removed from the water. The filtered water carries away wastes through an opening in the top of the sponge.

Reading Check *How do sponges get oxygen?*

Reproduction Sponges can reproduce sexually, as shown in **Figure 11.** Some species of sponges have separate sexes, but most sponge species are **hermaphrodites** (hur MA fruh dites)—animals that produce sperm and eggs in the same body. However, a sponge's sperm cannot fertilize its own eggs. After an egg is released, it might be fertilized and then develop into a larva (plural, *larvae*). The larva usually looks different from the adult form. Sponge larvae have cilia that allow them to swim. After a short time, the larvae settle down on objects where they will remain and grow into adult sponges.

Asexual reproduction occurs by budding or regeneration. A bud forms on a sponge, then drops from the parent sponge to grow on its own. New sponges also can grow by regeneration from small pieces of a sponge. Regeneration occurs when an organism grows new body parts to replace lost or damaged ones. Sponge growers cut sponges into pieces, attach weights to them, and put them back into the ocean to regenerate.

16 ◆ **C CHAPTER 1** Introduction to Animals

Curriculum Connection

Language Arts Have students research and report on *Xestospongi muta*, a barrel sponge that grows like a giant vase off the Cayman Islands. Sponges of this type are being tested for potential medicinal usage. L3

Cnidarians

Another group of invertebrates includes colorful corals, flowerlike sea anemones, tiny hydras, delicate jellyfish, and the iridescent Portuguese man-of-war, shown in **Figure 12.** These animals are classified as cnidarians (ni DAR ee uhnz).

Cnidarian Environments Most cnidarians live in salt water, although many types of hydras live in freshwater. Sea anemones and most jellyfish, also called jellies, live as individual organisms. Hydras and corals tend to form colonies.

Two Body Forms Cnidarians have two different body forms. The **polyp** (PAH lup) form, shown in **Figure 13** on the left, is shaped like a vase and usually is sessile. Sea anemones, corals, and hydras are cnidarians that live most of their lives as polyps. The **medusa** (mih DEW suh) form, shown in **Figure 13** on the right, is bell-shaped and free-swimming. A jelly spends most of its life as a medusa floating on ocean currents. Some species of jellies have tentacles that grow to 30 m and trail behind the animal.

✔ Reading Check *What are some possible benefits of having a medusa and a polyp form?*

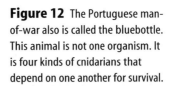

Figure 12 The Portuguese man-of-war also is called the bluebottle. This animal is not one organism. It is four kinds of cnidarians that depend on one another for survival.

Figure 13 Cnidarians have medusa and polyp body forms.

Adult sea anemones are polyps that grow attached to the ocean bottom, a rock, coral, or any surface. They depend on the movement of water to bring them food.

Jellies can perform upward movements but must float to move downward.

Fun Fact

The lion's mane jelly (*Cyanea capillata*) is the largest true jelly. It can grow to 2.5m in diameter and have tentacles more than 30m long.

IDENTIFYING Misconceptions

Colonial Cnidarian Students may think that the Portuguese man-of-war (PMOW) is a single organism. It is actually a colony of four different highly-developed polyps. Each polyp has a job within the colony—reproduction, digestion, stinging cells, or as the float. Each organism can survive on its own if separated. When the colony beaches itself, three of the polyps die very quickly, except for the one that acts as stinging cells. That is why a beached PMOW is still dangerous and should not be touched.

Make a Model

Stinging Cells Have students use lengths of string to make models of stinging cells for capturing prey. They can attach washers, adhesive tape, and toothpicks to the end of the string to model stinging cells that wrap around, stick to, or impale prey. Have them make models of small invertebrates from plastic foam to show how these types of stinging cells can be used to capture prey. L2 ELL LS **Kinesthetic**

Science Online

Topic: Cnidarian Ecology
Visit bookc.msscience.com for Web links to information about cnidarian ecology.

Activity Describe a cnidarian that is endangered, and the reasons why it is endangered.

Figure 14 Tentacles surround the mouth of a sea anemone.

A Clown fish are protected from the sea anemone's sting by a special mucous covering. The anemone eats scraps that the fish drop, and the fish are protected from predators by the anemone's sting.

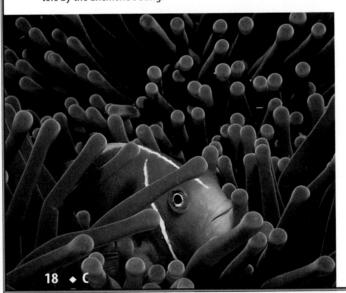

18 ◆ C

Body Structure All cnidarians have one body opening and radial symmetry. They have more complex bodies than sponges do. They have two cell layers that are arranged into tissues and a digestive cavity where food is broken down. In the two-cell-layer body plan of cnidarians, no cell is ever far from the water. In each cell, oxygen from the water is exchanged for carbon dioxide and other cell wastes.

Cnidarians have a system of nerve cells called a nerve net. The nerve net carries impulses and connects all parts of the organism. This makes cnidarians capable of some simple responses and movements. Hydras can somersault away from a threatening situation.

Armlike structures called **tentacles** (TEN tih kulz) surround the mouths of most cnidarians. Certain fish, shrimp, and other small animals live unharmed among the tentacles of large sea anemones, as shown in **Figure 14A.** The tentacles have stinging cells. A **stinging cell,** as shown in **Figure 14B,** has a capsule with a coiled, threadlike structure that helps the cnidarian capture food. Animals that live among an anemone's tentacles are not affected by the stinging cells. The animals are thought to help clean the sea anemone and protect it from certain predators.

Obtaining Food Cnidarians are predators. Some can stun their prey with nerve toxins produced by stinging cells. The threadlike structure in the stinging cell is sticky or barbed. When a cnidarian is touched or senses certain chemicals in its environment, the threadlike structures discharge and capture the prey. The tentacles bring the prey to the mouth, and the cnidarian ingests the food. Because cnidarians have only one body opening, undigested food goes back out through the mouth.

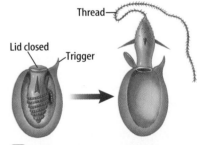

Thread
Lid closed
Trigger

B A sea anemone's stinging cells have triggerlike structures. When prey brushes against the trigger, the thread is released into the prey. A toxin in the stinging cell stuns the prey.
Identify the type of adaptation this is: physical, behavior, or predatory. Explain your answer.

Fun Fact

A Portuguese man-of-war's float is filled with argon gas. No one knows why.

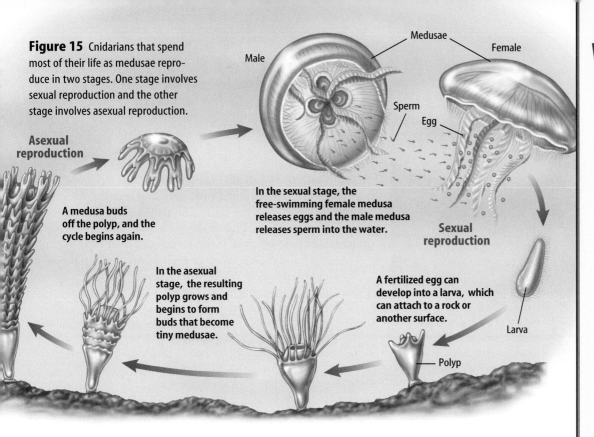

Figure 15 Cnidarians that spend most of their life as medusae reproduce in two stages. One stage involves sexual reproduction and the other stage involves asexual reproduction.

Medusae

Male

Female

Sperm

Egg

Asexual reproduction

A medusa buds off the polyp, and the cycle begins again.

In the sexual stage, the free-swimming female medusa releases eggs and the male medusa releases sperm into the water.

Sexual reproduction

In the asexual stage, the resulting polyp grows and begins to form buds that become tiny medusae.

A fertilized egg can develop into a larva, which can attach to a rock or another surface.

Larva

Polyp

Activity

Jelly Life Cycle Have students make cards of all the stages in the life cycle of a jelly and write the name of each stage on the card. Then have them scramble the cards and place them back in the correct sequence. L2 LS **Logical-Mathematical**

Activity

Coral Reefs Have students work in groups to find out how fringing reefs, barrier reefs, and atolls differ from one another. Suggest that they make models, labeled drawings, or picture collages illustrating the differences among the three types of coral reefs. L2 COOP LEARN LS **Kinesthetic**

Reproduction Cnidarians reproduce asexually and sexually, as shown in **Figure 15.** Polyp forms reproduce asexually by producing buds that eventually fall off the cnidarian and develop into new polyps. Polyps also reproduce sexually by producing eggs or sperm. Sperm are released into the water and fertilize the eggs, which also are released into the water.

Medusa (plural, *medusae*) forms of cnidarians have two stages of reproduction—a sexual stage and an asexual stage. Free-swimming medusae produce eggs or sperm and release them into the water. The eggs are fertilized by sperm from another medusa of the same species and develop into larvae. The larvae eventually settle down and grow into polyps. When young medusae bud off the polyp, the cycle begins again.

Origin of Cnidarians

The first cnidarians might have been on Earth more than 600 million years ago. Scientists hypothesize that the medusa body was the first form of cnidarian. Polyps could have formed from larvae of medusae that became permanently attached to a surface. Most of the cnidarian fossils are corals.

Differentiated Instruction

Challenge Have students investigate the relationship between some species of anemones and certain types of fish, such as the clownfish and the damselfish. Students should find that these animals have symbiotic relationships. L3

Teacher FYI

Coral Reef Types There are three types of coral reefs. Fringing reefs are submerged platforms of living coral that extend from the shore into the sea. Barrier reefs follow the shoreline but are separated from it by water. An atoll is a ring-shaped coral island in the open sea.

Discussion

Tentacle Differences How do the tentacles of a jellyfish and a sea anemone differ? How is this difference an advantage to each animal? The tentacles of the jellyfish, which is free-swimming, point downward and the tentacles of the sea anemone, which is sessile, point upward. Each animal has tentacles adapted to its way of life. L2

Caption Answer

Figure 16 protection

DAILY INTERVENTION

Check for Understanding

Kinesthetic Have students make drawings in their Science Journals to describe how a stinging cell is used to capture food. L1 LS

Reteach

Skeletal Support Bring pieces of hard coral and sponges to class for students to observe and feel. Explain that the skeletons, like the bones and shells of other animals, provide protection and support for these organisms.

✔ Assessment

Performance Have students make clay models of medusas and polyps and discuss how the two body forms are similar. Use **Performance Activities in the Science Classroom**, p. 123. L2
P

Figure 16 Coral reefs are colonies made up of many individual corals.
Infer *the benefit of living in a colony for the corals.*

Corals

INTEGRATE Earth Science

The large coral reef formations found in shallow tropical seas are built as one generation of corals secretes their hard external skeletons on those of earlier generations. It takes millions of years for large reefs, such as those found in the waters of the Indian Ocean, the south Pacific Ocean, and the Caribbean Sea, to form.

Importance of Corals Coral reefs, shown in **Figure 16,** are productive ecosystems and extremely important in the ecology of tropical waters. They have a diversity of life comparable to tropical rain forests. Some of the most beautiful and fascinating animals of the world live in the formations of coral reefs.

Beaches and shorelines are protected from much of the action of waves by coral reefs. When coral reefs are destroyed or severely damaged, large amounts of shoreline can be washed away.

If you go scuba diving or snorkeling, you might explore a coral reef. Coral reefs are home for organisms that provide valuable shells and pearls. Fossil reefs can give geologists clues about the location of oil deposits.

Like sponges, corals produce chemicals to protect themselves from diseases or to prevent other organisms from settling on them. Medical researchers are learning that some of these chemicals might provide humans with drugs to fight cancer. Some coral is even used as a permanent replacement for missing sections of bone in humans.

section 2 review

Summary

Sponges

- Most sponges live in salt water, are sessile, and vary in size, color, and shape.
- A sponge has no tissues, organs, or organ systems.
- Sponges filter food from the water, and reproduce sexually and asexually.

Cnidarians

- Cnidarians live mostly in salt water and have two body forms: polyp and medusa.
- Cnidarians have nerve cells, tissues, and a digestive cavity.
- Corals are cnidarians that make up a diverse ecosystem called a coral reef.

Self Check

1. **Compare and contrast** how sponges and cnidarians get their food.
2. **Describe** the two body forms of cnidarians and tell how each reproduces.
3. **Infer** why most fossils of cnidarians are coral fossils. Would you expect to find a fossil sponge? Explain.
4. **Think Critically** What effect might the destruction of a large coral reef have on other ocean life?

Applying Math

5. **Solve One-Step Equations** A sponge 1 cm in diameter and 10 cm tall can move 22.5 L of water through its body each day. What volume of water will it pump through its body in 1 h? In 1 min?

 Science Online bookc.msscience.com/self_check_quiz

section 2 review

1. Sponges: filter food out of the water; cnidarians: stinging cells on the tentacles paralyze an organism, tentacles pull the organism into the mouth.
2. polyps: vase-shaped, sessile, reproduce asexually by budding;

medusae: bell-shaped, free-swimming, reproduce sexually by egg and sperm
3. Corals secrete a hard skeleton around themselves, which fossilizes easily. Fossil sponges would be rare, except for fossilized spicules.

4. There would be no homes for the animals that lived on the coral reef. Food supply would decrease.
5. The sponge will move about 0.94 L of water in one hour, and about 0.02 L of water per minute.

 **LAB**

 **BENCH TESTED**

⊙bserving a Cnidarian

The hydra has a body cavity that is a simple, hollow sac. It is one of the few freshwater cnidarians.

◉ Real-World Question

How does a hydra react to food and other stimuli?

Goals
- **Predict** how a hydra will respond to various stimuli.
- **Observe** how a hydra responds to stimuli.

Materials

dropper	toothpick
hydra culture	*Daphnia* or brine shrimp
small dish	stereomicroscope

Safety Precautions

◉ Procedure

1. Copy the data table and use it to record your observations.

Hydra Observations	
Features	**Observations**
Color	Answers will vary.
Number of tentacles	
Reaction to touch	
Reaction to food	

2. Use a dropper to place a hydra and some of the water in which it is living into a dish.

3. Place the dish on the stage of a stereomicroscope. Bring the hydra into focus. Record the hydra's color.

4. **Identify** and count the number of tentacles. Locate the mouth.

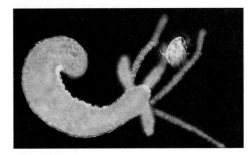

5. Study the basal disk by which the hydra attaches itself to a surface.

6. **Predict** what will happen if the hydra is touched with a toothpick. Carefully touch the tentacles with a toothpick. Describe the reaction in the data table.

7. Drop a *Daphnia* or a small amount of brine shrimp into the dish. Observe how the hydra takes in food. Record your observations.

8. Return the hydra to the culture.

◉ Conclude and Apply

1. **Analyze** what happened when the hydra was touched. What happened to other areas of the animal?

2. **Describe** the advantages tentacles provide for hydra.

 **Communicating** **Your Data**

Compare your results with those of other students. Discuss whether all of the hydras studied had the same responses, and how the responses aid hydras in survival.

◉ Real-World Question

Purpose to observe the structure and feeding method of a cnidarian L1 ELL IS **Interpersonal**

Process Skills observe and infer, identify, predict, make and use tables

Time Required 40 minutes

Safety Precautions Caution students to use extreme care when working with live animals.

◉ Procedure

Teaching Strategy Assign one person to place the hydra in the dish under the stereoscopic microscope and another to record the data.

Troubleshooting Place several coverslips into the jar the day before the hydra are needed. The hydra will probably cling to the coverslips. When you need hydra, remove the coverslips with forceps and place the coverslips directly into the dish that contains aquarium water.

◉ Conclude and Apply

1. When certain parts were touched, other parts may have responded by stretching or contracting.
2. The tentacles wrap around food and bring it into the mouth. Stinging cells stun the prey.

✓ Assessment

Performance To further assess students' abilities to observe the structure and method of feeding in a cnidarian, have them view a short video on cnidarians and describe the cnidarians' activities. Use **Performance Assessment in the Science Classroom**, p. 89. L2

Communicating **Your Data**

Have students discuss their results in small groups. Then, copy the data table onto the board and fill it in as a class. L2

Bellringer

Section Focus Transparencies also are available on the Interactive Chalkboard CD-ROM.

L2 ELL

Tie to Prior Knowledge

Worm Review Students will be familiar with worms. Ask them to describe the appearance and shape of earthworms they have seen. Review bilateral symmetry and discuss the presence or absence of tissues in organisms in this chapter. L2

Flatworms and Roundworms

as you read

What You'll Learn

- **List** the characteristics of flatworms and roundworms.
- **Distinguish** between free-living and parasitic organisms.
- **Identify** disease-causing flatworms and roundworms.

Why It's Important

Many species of flatworms and roundworms cause disease in plants and animals.

🔎 Review Vocabulary

cilia: short, threadlike structures that aid in locomotion

New Vocabulary

- free-living organism
- anus

What is a worm?

Worms are invertebrates with soft bodies and bilateral symmetry. They have three tissue layers, as shown in **Figure 17,** which are organized into organs and organ systems.

Flatworms

As their name implies, flatworms have flattened bodies. Members of this group include planarians, flukes, and tapeworms. Some flatworms are free-living, but most are parasites, which means that they depend on another organism for food and a place to live. Unlike a parasite, a **free-living organism** doesn't depend on another organism for food or a place to live.

Planarians An example of a free-living flatworm is the planarian, as shown in **Figure 18.** It has a triangle-shaped head with two eyespots. Its one body opening—a mouth—is on the underside of the body. A muscular tube called the pharynx connects the mouth and the digestive tract. A planarian feeds on small organisms and dead bodies of larger organisms. Most planarians live under rocks, on plant material, or in freshwater. They vary in length from 3 mm to 30 cm. Their bodies are covered with fine, hairlike structures called cilia. As the cilia move, the worm is moved along in a slimy mucous track that is secreted from the underside of the planarian.

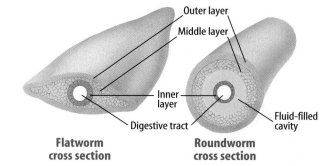

Figure 17 Worms have cells that are arranged into three specialized tissue layers and organs.

Outer layer
Middle layer
Inner layer
Digestive tract
Fluid-filled cavity

Flatworm cross section

Roundworm cross section

Section 3 Resource Manager

Chapter *FAST FILE* Resources

Transparency Activity, p. 44

Directed Reading for Content Mastery, pp. 19, 20

MiniLAB, p. 4

Enrichment, p. 30

Reinforcement, p. 27

Lab Worksheet, pp. 7–8

Lab Activity, pp. 13–14

Lab Management and Safety, p. 43

Figure 18 The planarian is a common freshwater flatworm.

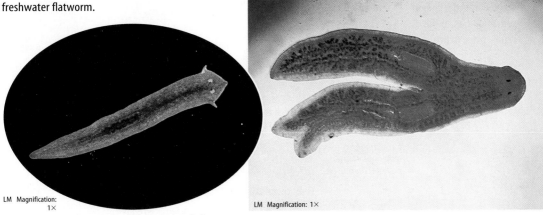

LM Magnification: 1×

The planarian's eyespots sense light.

LM Magnification: 1×

Planarians can reproduce asexually by splitting, then regenerating the other half.

Planarians reproduce asexually by dividing in two, as shown in **Figure 18.** A planarian can be cut in two, and each piece will grow into a new worm. They also have the ability to regenerate. Planarians reproduce sexually by producing eggs and sperm. Most are hermaphrodites and exchange sperm with one another. They lay fertilized eggs that hatch in a few weeks.

Flukes All flukes are parasites with complex life cycles that require more than one host. Most flukes reproduce sexually. The male worm deposits sperm in the female worm. She lays the fertilized eggs inside the host. The eggs leave the host in its urine or feces. If the eggs end up in water, they usually infect snails. After they leave the snail, the young worms can burrow into the skin of a new host, such as a human, while he or she is standing or swimming in the water.

Of the many diseases caused by flukes, the most widespread one affecting humans is schistosomiasis (shis tuh soh MI uh sus). It is caused by blood flukes—flatworms that live in the blood, as shown in **Figure 19.** More than 200 million people, mostly in developing countries, are infected with blood flukes. It is estimated that 1 million people die each year because of them. Other types of flukes can infect the lungs, liver, eyes, and other organs of their host.

Reading Check *What is the most common disease that is caused by flukes?*

Figure 19 Female blood flukes deposit their eggs in the blood of their host. The eggs travel through the host and eventually end up in the host's digestive system.

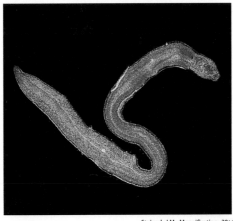

Stained LM Magnification: 20×

SECTION 3 Flatworms and Roundworms **C** ◆ **23**

Purpose to observe planarian

movement L1 ELL IS **Kines-thetic and Visual-Spatial**

Materials planarian culture, dropper, watch glass, stereomicroscope, water

Teaching Strategy Planarians may be placed in water from the classroom aquarium.

Troubleshooting If planarians don't move, students may have to gently prod them with a small brush.

Analysis

1. Planarians ripple and flex their muscles in successive waves to propel themselves over surfaces.
2. Students may infer that movement is by means of muscular undulations on the underside of the planarian's body.
3. Planarians can move freely and are not confined within the body of another organism.

Assessment

Performance Have students feed the planarians pinhead-sized pieces of liver and describe their behavior. Use **Performance Activities in the Science Classroom,** p. 89. L1

Quick Demo

Tapeworm Characteristics

Materials preserved tapeworm specimens, stereomicroscope

Estimated Time 15 minutes

Procedure Obtain preserved tapeworm specimens from a local veterinarian or a biological supply company. Have students observe and list the characteristics of each. L2 IS **Visual-Spatial**

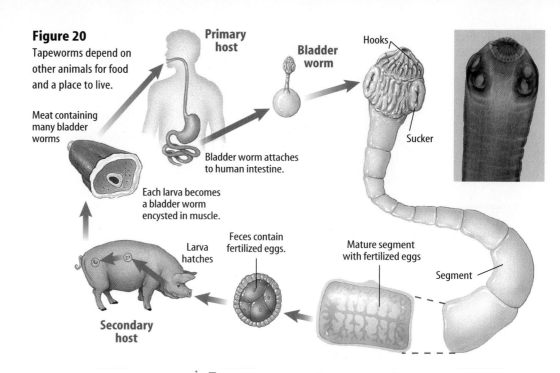

Figure 20
Tapeworms depend on other animals for food and a place to live.

Primary host

Meat containing many bladder worms

Bladder worm

Hooks

Sucker

Bladder worm attaches to human intestine.

Each larva becomes a bladder worm encysted in muscle.

Feces contain fertilized eggs.

Mature segment with fertilized eggs

Segment

Larva hatches

Secondary host

Observing Planarian Movement

Procedure
1. Use a **dropper** to transfer a **planarian** to a **watch glass.**
2. Add enough **water** so the planarian can move freely.
3. Place the glass under a **stereomicroscope** and observe the planarian.

Analysis
1. Describe how a planarian moves in the water.
2. What body parts appear to be used in movement?
3. Explain why a planarian is a free-living flatworm.

Tapeworms Another type of flatworm is the tapeworm. These worms are parasites. The adult form uses hooks and suckers to attach itself to the intestine of a host organism, as illustrated in **Figure 20.** Dogs, cats, humans, and other animals are hosts for tapeworms. A tapeworm doesn't have a mouth or a digestive system. Instead, the tapeworm absorbs food that is digested by the host from its host's intestine.

A tapeworm grows by producing new body segments immediately behind its head. Its ribbonlike body can grow to be 12 m long. Each body segment has both male and female reproductive organs. The eggs are fertilized by sperm in the same segment. After a segment is filled with fertilized eggs, it breaks off and passes out of the host's body with the host's wastes. If another host eats a fertilized egg, the egg hatches and develops into an immature tapeworm called a bladder worm.

Origin of Flatworms

Because of the limited fossil evidence, the evolution of flatworms is uncertain. Evidence suggests that they were the first group of animals to evolve bilateral symmetry with senses and nerves in the head region. They also were probably the first group of animals to have a third tissue layer that develops into organs and systems. Some scientists hypothesize that flatworms and cnidarians might have had a common ancestor.

24 ◆ C CHAPTER 1 Introduction to Animals

Science Journal

Controlling Flukes Have students research actions taken by the Department of Agriculture to control fluke infection in this country. Ask them to write the data as an article to be published in a consumer health magazine and include the article in their Science Journals. L2 IS **Linguistic** P

Differentiated Instruction

Challenge Health problems associated with infections by parasitic worms are often compounded by poverty, improper sanitation, and lack of governmental services to help infected people. Have students research some of the countries that are most affected by these parasites and report on what is being done to alleviate the health and social problems. L3

Roundworms

If you own a dog, you've probably had to get medicine from your veterinarian to protect it from heartworms—a type of roundworm. Roundworms also are called nematodes and more nematodes live on Earth than any other type of many-celled organism. It is estimated that more than a half million species of roundworms exist. They are found in soil, animals, plants, freshwater, and salt water. Some are parasitic, but most are free-living.

Roundworms are slender and tapered at both ends like the one in **Figure 21.** The body is a tube within a tube, with fluid in between. Most nematode species have male and female worms and reproduce sexually. Nematodes have two body openings, a mouth, and an anus. The **anus** is an opening at the end of the digestive tract through which wastes leave the body.

✓ **Reading Check** *What characteristics of roundworms might contribute to the success of the group?*

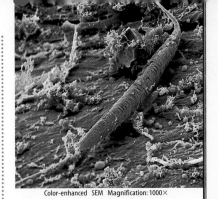
Color-enhanced SEM Magnification: 1000×

Figure 21 Some roundworms infect humans and other animals. Others infect plants, and some are free-living in the soil.

Applying Math Use Percentages

SPECIES COUNTS In a forest ecosystem, about four percent of the 400 different animal species are roundworm species. How many roundworm species are in this ecosystem?

Solution

1 *This is what you know:*
- total animal species = 400
- roundworms species = 4% of total animal species

2 *This is what you must find out:*

How many roundworm species are in the ecosystem?

3 *This is the procedure you need to use:*
- Change 4% to a decimal. $\frac{4}{100} = 0.04$
- Use following equation: (roundworm-species percent as a decimal) × (total animal species) = number of roundworm species
- Substitute in known values: $0.04 \times 400 = 16$ roundworm species

4 *Check your answer:*

Divide 16 by 0.04 and you should get 400.

Practice Problems

1. Flatworms make up 1.5 percent of all animal species in the forest ecosystem. How many flatworms species probably are present?

2. If there are 16 bird species present, what percent of the animal species are the bird species?

 For more practice, visit bookc.msscience.com/math_practice

SECTION 3 Flatworms and Roundworms **C** ◆ **25**

Visualizing Parasitic Worms

Have students examine the pictures and read the captions. Then ask the following questions.

Why do parasitic worms often cause weight loss in the host organism? Students should note that many of these types of worms infest the intestines, interfering with absorption of nutrients from food.

Identify one way you could reduce your chances of being infected with hookworms if you lived in a tropical climate. Hookworms usually enter through the skin of bare feet, so wearing shoes while outdoors is an effective way to reduce the risk of contracting hookworms.

Activity

Parasitic Worm Infestations Divide students into teams. Each team should research and compare the prevalence of human infestation with a specific species of parasitic worm in different parts of the world. Students should use a map when they present their findings to the class. Students should also identify any socioeconomic factors (i.e. limited access to health care) that cause certain areas to have a greater incidence of parasitic worm infestations. L2

Figure 22

Many diseases are caused by parasitic roundworms and flatworms that take up residence in the human body. Some of these diseases result in diarrhea, weight loss, and fatigue; others, if left untreated, can be fatal. Micrographs of several species of roundworms and flatworms and their magnifications are shown here.

▶ **78×** BLOOD FLUKE These parasites live as larvae in lakes and rivers and penetrate the skin of people wading in the water. After maturing in the liver, the flukes settle in veins in the intestine and bladder, causing schistosomiasis (shis tuh soh MI uh sus), which damages the liver and spleen.

▼ **125×** PINWORMS Typically inhabiting the large intestine, the female pinworm lays her eggs near the host's anus, causing discomfort. The micrograph below shows pinworm eggs on a piece of clear tape.

▲ **6×** LIVER FLUKE Humans and other mammals ingest the larvae of these parasites by eating contaminated plant material. Immature flukes penetrate the intestinal wall and pass via the liver into the bile ducts. There they mature into adults that feed on blood and tissue.

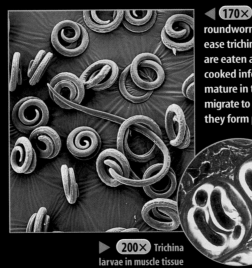

◀ **170×** ROUNDWORMS The roundworms that cause the disease trichinosis (trih kuh NOH sus) are eaten as larvae in undercooked infected meat. They mature in the intestine, then migrate to muscle tissue, where they form painful cysts.

Hookworm head 25×

▶ **4×** HOOKWORM These parasites enter their human hosts as larvae by penetrating the skin of bare feet. From there, they migrate to the lungs and eventually to the intestine, where they mature.

▶ **200×** Trichina larvae in muscle tissue

Differentiated Instruction

Challenge Have students research and diagram the complete life cycle of one of the parasitic worms shown in this feature. Students should present their diagrams to the class. L3 LS **Visual-Spatial**

Visual Learning

Figure 22 Have students create a table in which they list each of the diseases mentioned in this figure and what organism causes the disease. Students may do research to find methods of disease prevention for each listed disease. Any relevant information should be added to their table. L2 LS **Visual-Spatial**

Origin of Roundworms More than 550 million years ago, roundworms appeared early in animal evolution. They were the first group of animals to have a digestive system with a mouth and an anus. Scientists hypothesize that roundworms are more closely related to arthropods than to vertebrates. However, it is still unclear how roundworms fit into the evolution of animals.

Importance of Roundworms Some roundworms, shown in **Figure 22,** cause diseases in humans. Others are parasites of plants or of other animals, such as the fish shown in **Figure 23.** Some nematodes cause damage to fiber, agricultural products, and food. It is estimated that the worldwide annual amount of nematode damage is in the millions of dollars.

Not all roundworms are a problem for humans, however. In fact, many species are beneficial. Some species of roundworms feed on termites, fleas, ants, beetles, and many other types of insects that cause damage to crops and human property. Some species of beneficial nematodes kill other pests. Research is being done with nematodes that kill deer ticks that cause Lyme disease.

Roundworms also are important because they are essential to the health of soil. They provide nutrients to the soil as they break down organic material. They also help in cycling nutrients such as nitrogen.

Figure 23 This fish's fin is infected with parasitic roundworms. These roundworms damage the fin, which makes it difficult for the fish to swim and escape from predators.

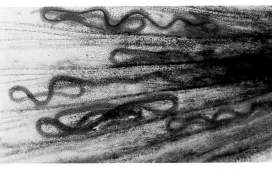

---

section 3 review

Summary

Common Characteristics
- Both flatworms and roundworms are invertebrates with soft bodies, bilateral symmetry, and three tissue layers that are organized into organs and organ systems.

Flatworms
- Flatworms have flattened bodies, and can be free-living or parasitic. They generally have one body opening.

Roundworms
- Also called nematodes, roundworms have a tube within a tube body plan. They have two openings: a mouth and an anus.

Self Check

1. **Compare and contrast** the body plan of a flatworm to the body plan of a roundworm.
2. **Distinguish** between a free-living flatworm and a parasitic flatworm.
3. **Explain** how tapeworms get energy.
4. **Identify** three roundworms that cause diseases in humans. How can humans prevent infection from each?
5. **Think Critically** Why is a flatworm considered to be more complex than a hydra?

Applying Skills

6. **Concept Map** Make an events-chain concept map for tapeworm reproduction.

Science Online booke.msscience.com/self_check_quiz SECTION 3 Flatworms and Roundworms **C ◆ 27**

Check for Understanding

Linguistic Have each student write one short-answer question relating to flatworms and roundworms. Read the questions aloud. Ask students to respond as a group. L1 LS

Reteach

Flatworms and Roundworms Have students compare and contrast specimens of flatworms and roundworms by observing them with a magnifying lens, microscopes, and the naked eye. What characteristics do they observe in both? Are there differences between the free-living specimens and the parasites? L2

☑ Assessment

Performance Assess students' abilities to sequence by having them sequence information on reproduction of each animal group in the chapter. Use **Performance Assessment in the Science Classroom,** p. 163. L2

Virtual Labs

Obtaining Food *How do sponges, cnidarians, flatworms, and roundworms obtain food?*

---

section 3 review

1. Flatworms have flattened bodies with one body opening, the mouth. Roundworms' bodies have a tube within a tube and fluid in between, and two body openings—a mouth and an anus.
2. Free-living flatworms find food in their environment; parasitic flatworms attach to a host and absorb food from the host.
3. They absorb food from the host's intestine.
4. Hookworm—wear shoes; *Trichinella*—cook meat thoroughly; Pinworm—wash hands
5. A hydra has two cell layers. A flatworm has three tissue layers, which are organized into organs and organ systems.
6. Student concept maps should be consistent with the information in this section.

Design Your Own

◉ Real-World Question

Purpose Students compare and contrast free-living and parasitic worms. L2 COOP LEARN LS
Logical-Mathematical

Process Skills form a hypothesis, compare and contrast, observe and infer, communicate, classify, describe

Time Required 50 minutes

Materials

- Use prepared whole mount slides of tapeworms with heads and proglottids.
- Use a small brush to transfer planaria to culture dishes.
- Make sure the fed planaria are returned to a labeled dish so they will not be used again the same day.

Safety Precautions Caution students to use extreme care when working with live animals. Soft-bodied animals are easily injured.

◉ Form a Hypothesis

Possible Hypothesis Most students will hypothesize that planarians have body parts for the environment in which they live and tapeworms have body parts for attaching to a host.

Comparing Free-Living and Parasitic Flatworms

◉ Real-World Question

How are the body parts of flatworms adapted to the environment in which they live? Are the adaptations of free-living flatworms and parasitic flatworms the same?

◉ Form a Hypothesis

Form a hypothesis about what adaptations you think free-living and parasitic worms might have. What would be the benefits of these adaptations?

Goals
- **Compare and contrast** the body parts and functions of free-living and parasitic flatworms.
- **Observe** how flatworms are adapted to their environments.

Possible Materials
petri dish with a planarian
compound microscope
prepared slide of a
    tapeworm
stereomicroscope
light source, such as a lamp
small paintbrush
small piece of liver
dropper
water

Safety Precautions

Alternative Inquiry Lab

Authentic Questions To make this Lab an Inquiry Lab, build on your students' experiences. Encourage them to use what they have learned to brainstorm questions about free-living and parasitic flatworms. Have each student choose one question to explore. Unsafe or impractical questions should be eliminated. Ask students to choose the materials they need to explore their questions. Students should have their plan approved before continuing. Conduct the experiments after all of the necessary materials have been gathered.

Test Your Hypothesis

Make a Plan

1. As a group, make a list of possible ways you might design a procedure to compare and contrast types of flatworms. Your teacher will provide you with information on handling live flatworms.

2. Choose one of the methods you described in step 1. List the steps you will need to take to follow the procedure. Be sure to describe exactly what you will do at each step of the activity.

3. **List** the materials that you will need to complete your experiment.

4. If you need a data table, design one in your Science Journal so it is ready to use when your group begins to collect data.

Follow Your Plan

1. Make sure your teacher approves your plan before you start.

2. Carry out the experiment according to the approved plan.

3. While the experiment is going on, record any observations that you make and complete the data table in your Science Journal.

Analyze Your Data

1. **Explain** how parasitic and free-living flatworms are similar.

2. **Describe** the differences between parasitic and free-living worms.

Conclude and Apply

1. **Identify** which body systems are more developed in free-living flatworms.

2. **Identify** which body system is more complex in parasitic flatworms.

3. **Infer** which adaptations allow some flatworms to live as free-living organisms.

Communicating Your Data

Compare and discuss your experiment design and conclusions with other students. **For more help, refer to the** Science Skill Handbook.

LAB C ◆ 29

Communicating Your Data

Have students sketch the body designs of both types of worms, labeling the similarities and differences. L2

✔ Assessment

Performance To further assess students' understanding of the differences between free-living and parasitic worms, assign them to different groups and have them use their drawings and observations to explain the differences. Assess explanations for accuracy. Use **Performance Assessment in the Science Classroom,** p. 99. L2

Test Your Hypothesis

Possible Procedures One possible procedure is to observe the body structures of both free-living and parasitic worms using a hand lens or a stereomicroscope and prepared slides.

Expected Outcome

- Students' observations of planaria may include those already listed: planaria move with a gliding motion; the most sensitive body parts are those near the head; the tube-like structure (pharynx) pulls food into the body. Planarians have flat bodies. The mouth is on the bottom of the body. L2

- Students' observations of the tapeworm will include body parts adapted for attaching to a host and a well-developed reproductive system. L2

Analyze Your Data

Answers to Questions

1. Both are invertebrates, have flattened bodies, and have three tissue layers organized into organs and organ systems.

2. Parasitic worms have body parts adapted for attaching to a host. Free-living flatworms have no such parts.

Error Analysis Have students compare their results and their hypotheses and explain why differences may have occurred. L2

Conclude and Apply

1. The digestive and reproductive systems are better developed in free-living flatworms.

2. The reproductive system is more complex in parasitic worms.

3. cilia, feeding organs, light-sensitive behavior

TIME

TIME

SCIENCE AND HISTORY

A natural sponge

SPONGES

A common household item contains a lot of history

Sponges and baths. They go together like a hammer and nails. But sponges weren't always used just to scrub people and countertops. Some Greek artists dipped sponges into paint to dab on their artwork and crafts. Greek and Roman soldiers padded their helmets with soft sponges similar to modern padded bicycle helmets to soften enemies' blows. The Roman soldiers also used sponges like a canteen to soak up water from a nearby stream and squeeze it into their mouths. Sponges have appeared in artwork from prehistoric times and the Middle Ages, and are mentioned in Shakespeare's play Hamlet.

Natural sponges have been gathered over time from the Mediterranean, Caribbean Sea, and off the coast of Florida. Divers used to carry up the sponges from deep water, but today sponges are harvested in shallower water. Synthetic sponges, made of rubber or cellulose, are used more today than natural ones. Natural sponges absorb more water and last longer, but synthetic sponges are less expensive. Natural sponges may also cure diseases. Medical researchers hypothesize that an enzyme produced by sponges might help cure cancer. Who says natural sponges are washed up?

Brainstorm Work with your classmates to come up with as many sayings and phrases as you can using the word *sponge*. Use some of them in a story about sponges. Share your stories with the class.

Science Online

For more information, visit bookc.msscience.com/time

Content Background

Members of the phylum Porifera are commonly called sponges. There are approximately 5,000 living sponge species. Sponges were long thought to be plants until scientists closely observed the way in which water was "ingested" by sponges. An enormous amount of water can pass through a sponge, sometimes 20,000 times its volume in a 24-hour period.

There are many different types of sponges. In the world's oceans, they can be quite colorful and beautiful. Sponges come in two basic types: encrusting and freestanding. Encrusting sponges typically cover hard surfaces in the same manner that mosses cover objects on land. Freestanding sponges sometimes grow into strange shapes, often reaching gigantic proportions.

Discussion

Sponge History Compare and contrast uses for sponges through history and their uses today. Possible answer: Sponges were used in more utilitarian ways, such as by the Greeks, who padded their helmets with them. They were also used to apply paint, to wipe surfaces, and to absorb liquids, just as they are today. L2

Historical Significance

Ask the students to compare natural to synthetic sponges. They can do this as a homework assignment or in class as a group activity. You might suggest that some students investigate the origin of the "loofah sponge," which is actually a member of the gourd family, Cucurbitaceae. Tell students to include a visual representation of sponges in their presentations. These can include photographs, drawings, models, or real-life sponges. L2

Brainstorm While brainstorming for the activity make use of the board to write down some of the students' suggestions. If possible use a theme related to the entire unit. Perhaps the setting of the story could be a coral reef, a salt-water aquarium, or a natural sponge retail store. Encourage students to use their imaginations for this exercise. L2

Resources for Teachers and Students

Sponges: Science Under the Sea, by Lynn M. Stone, The Rourke Book Company, 2002

Sponges: Filters of the Sea (Secrets Animal World), by Andreeu Llamas, Gabriel Casadevall and Ali Garousi (Ill.'s), Gareth Stevens, 1997

Reviewing Main Ideas

Section 1 Is it an animal?

1. Animals are many-celled organisms that must find and digest their food.

2. Herbivores eat plants, carnivores eat animals or animal flesh, omnivores eat plants and animals, and detritivores feed on decaying plants and animals.

3. Animals have many ways to escape from predators such as speed, mimicry, protective outer coverings, and camouflage.

4. Invertebrates are animals without backbones. Animals that have backbones are called vertebrates.

5. When body parts are arranged the same way on both sides of the body, it is called bilateral symmetry. If body parts are arranged in a circle around a central point, it is known as radial symmetry. Animals without a specific central point are asymmetrical.

Section 2 Sponges and Cnidarians

1. Adult sponges are sessile and obtain food by filtering water through their pores. Sponges can reproduce sexually and asexually.

2. Cnidarians are hollow-bodied animals with radial symmetry. Most have tentacles with stinging cells to obtain food.

3. Coral reefs have been deposited by reef-building corals over millions of years.

Section 3 Flatworms and Roundworms

1. Flatworms have bilateral symmetry. Free-living and parasitic forms exist.

2. Roundworms have a tube-within-a-tube body plan and bilateral symmetry.

3. Flatworm and roundworm species can cause disease in humans.

Visualizing Main Ideas

Copy and complete the following concept map.

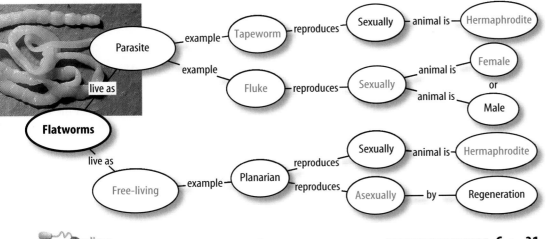

 bookc.msscience.com/interactive_tutor

CHAPTER STUDY GUIDE C ◆ 31

Reviewing Main Ideas

Summary statements can be used by students to review the major concepts of the chapter.

Visualizing Main Ideas

See student page.

Science Online

Visit bookc.msscience.com
/self_check_quiz
/interactive_tutor
/vocabulary_puzzlemaker
/chapter_review
/standardized_test

Assessment Transparency

For additional assessment questions, use the *Assessment Transparency* located in the transparency book.

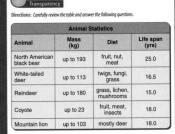

Using Vocabulary

1. invertebrate
2. radial symmetry
3. carnivore
4. herbivore
5. hermaphrodite
6. vertebrate
7. bilateral symmetry
8. polyp
9. sessile
10. medusa

Checking Concepts

11. D	16. C
12. A	17. C
13. A	18. A
14. A	19. B
15. A	20. B

Using Vocabulary

anus p. 25	omnivore p. 9
bilateral symmetry p. 13	polyp p. 17
carnivore p. 9	radial symmetry p. 13
free-living organism p. 22	sessile p. 15
herbivore p. 9	stinging cell p. 18
hermaphrodite p. 16	tentacle p. 18
invertebrate p. 12	vertebrate p. 12
medusa p. 17	

Find the correct vocabulary word(s).

1. animal without backbones

2. body parts arranged around a central point

3. animal that eat only other animals

4. animal that eat just plants

5. animal that produce sperm and eggs in one body

6. animal with backbones

7. body parts arranged similarly on both sides of the body

8. cnidarian body that is vase shaped

9. attached to one place

10. cnidarian body that is bell shaped

Checking Concepts

Choose the word or phrase that best answers the question.

11. Which of the following animals is sessile?
    A) jellyfish   C) planarian
    B) roundworm   D) sponge

12. What characteristic do all animals have?
    A) digest their food
    B) radial symmetry
    C) free-living
    D) polyp and medusa forms

13. Which term best describes a hydra?
    A) carnivore   C) herbivore
    B) filter feeder   D) parasite

14. Which animal has a mouth and an anus?
    A) roundworm   C) planarian
    B) jellyfish   D) tapeworm

15. What characteristic do scientists use to classify sponges?
    A) material that makes up their skeletons
    B) method of obtaining food
    C) reproduction
    D) symmetry

16. Which animal is a cnidarian?
    A) fluke   C) jellyfish
    B) heartworm   D) sponge

Use the photo below to answer question 17.

17. The photo above shows which hermaphroditic invertebrate organism?
    A) fluke   C) tapeworm
    B) coral   D) roundworm

18. How do sponges reproduce asexually?
    A) budding   C) medusae
    B) polyps   D) eggs and sperm

19. What is the young organism that the fertilized egg of a sponge develops into?
    A) bud   C) medusa
    B) larva   D) polyp

20. Which group do roundworms belong to?
    A) cnidarians   C) planarians
    B) nematodes   D) sponges

Science nline bookc.msscience.com/vocabulary_puzzlemaker

Use the Exam*View*® Pro Testmaker CD-ROM to:
- create multiple versions of tests
- create modified tests with one mouse click for inclusion students
- edit existing questions and add your own questions
- build tests aligned with state standards using built-in State Curriculum Tags
- change English tests to Spanish with one mouse click and vice versa

Thinking Critically

21. Compare and contrast the body organization of a sponge to that of a flatworm.

22. Infer the advantages of being able to reproduce sexually and asexually for animals like sponges, cnidarians, and flatworms.

23. List the types of food that sponges, hydras, and planarians eat. Explain why each organism eats a different size of particle.

24. Compare and contrast the medusa and polyp body forms of cnidarians.

25. Infer why scientists think the medusa stage was the first stage of the cnidarians.

26. Form a hypothesis about why cooking pork at high temperatures prevents harmful roundworms from developing, if they are present in the uncooked meat.

27. Predict what you can about the life of an organism that has no mouth or digestive system but has suckers and hooks on its head.

28. Interpret Scientific Illustrations Look at the photograph below. This animal escapes from predators by mimicry. Where in nature might you find the animal in this photo?

Performance Activities

29. Report Research tapeworms and other parasitic worms that live in humans. Find out how they are able to live in the intestines without being digested by the human host. Report your findings to the class.

 Science Online bookc.msscience.com/chapter_review

30. Video Presentation Create a video presentation using computer software or slides to illustrate the variety of sponges and cnidarians found on a coral reef.

Applying Math

31. Reef Ecology Coral reefs are considered the "rain forests of the ocean" due to the number of different species that depend on them. If scientists estimate that out of 4,000 species, 1,000 are from the coral reef ecosystem, what percentage of life is dependent on the reef?

Use the table below to answer questions 32 and 33.

Reef Area Data	
Country/Geographical Location	**Reef Area [km²]**
Indonesia	51,000
Australia	49,000
Philippines	25,100
France	14,300
Papua, New Guinea	13,800
Fiji	10,000
Maledives	8,900
Saudi Arabia	6,700
Marshall Islands	6,100
India	5,800
United States	3,800
Other	89,800

32. Reef Disappearance Coral reefs are disappearing for many reasons, such as increased temperatures, physical damage, and pollution. In 2003, scientists predict that at the current rate of disappearance, in 2100 coral reefs will be gone. Use the table above to calculate the current rate of coral reef disappearance.

33. Reef Locations What percentage of coral reefs are off of the Australian coast?

Thinking Critically

21. Sponges have two cell layers, little cell organization, and are asymmetrical; flatworms have three cell layers—organized into tissues, organs, and organ systems—and are bilaterally symmetrical.

22. Being able to reproduce sexually and asexually enables them to respond to changing conditions, survive poor conditions, and take advantage of favorable conditions.

23. Sponges eat bacteria, algae, and protozoans. Hydra eat small animals they capture with their tentacles. Planarians eat smaller animals or the remains of organisms. The size of a particle is determined by the size of the opening the organism has for ingesting food.

24. The medusa stage is bell-shaped and free-swimming. The polyp stage is vase-shaped and sessile.

25. The polyp stage develops from the medusa, a free-moving form. More polyp fossils exist, possibly indicating later existence on Earth.

26. Cysts are destroyed by heat; the worm has no protection and is killed.

27. It is a parasite.

28. on a plant

Performance Activities

29. Some parasites are protected by a thick mucus. The hosts may not have the enzymes to break down the mucus. Use **PASC**, p. 159.

30. Students should be able to identify each organism in their video presentation or slide show. Use **PASC**, p. 149.

Applying Math

National Math Standards
1, 6, 9

31. 25%

32. 2,931 km² per year.

33. 17%

FAST FILE

Answer Sheet A practice answer sheet can be found at bookc.m.science.com/answer_sheet.

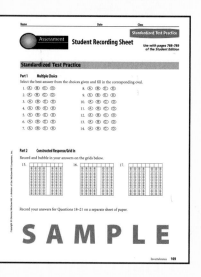

S A M P L E

Part 1 | Multiple Choice

1. C	6. D
2. B	7. C
3. D	8. B
4. A	9. B
5. A	10. D

Part 2 | Short Response

11. physical, like protective coverings, predator, such as camouflage, and behavioral, for example traveling in groups

12. invertebrate, because no backbone and radial symmetry; The parts are arranged around a central point.

13. Humans are vertebrates and have bilateral symmetry.

14. They filter food and oxygen from the water through pores.

Part 1 | Multiple Choice

Record your answers on the answer sheet provided by your teacher or on a sheet of paper.

1. An animal that kills and then only eats other animals is an
   A) omnivore.   C) carnivore.
   B) herbivore.   D) scavenger.

2. An animal that does not have a backbone is called
   A) a vertebrate.   C) a hermaphrodite.
   B) an invertebrate. D) a medusa.

Use the illustration below to answer questions 3 and 4.

3. This animal escapes from predators by using
   A) behavioral adaptation.
   B) predator adaptation.
   C) mimicry.
   D) physical adaptation.

4. Markings that help an animal hide from its predators are called
   A) camouflage.   C) behaviour.
   B) sessile.   D) mimicry.

5. Which of the following is not a cnidarian?
   A) coral   C) sea anemone
   B) hydra   D) sponge

---

6. Animals that have body parts arranged around a center point
   A) exhibit radial symmetry.
   B) exhibit bilateral symmetry.
   C) exhibit asymmetry.
   D) exhibit no symmetry.

Use the photo below to answer questions 7 and 8.

7. This organism would typically be found in which environment?
   A) lake   C) ocean
   B) river   D) pond

8. It would likely spend most of its life
   A) floating on water currents.
   B) attached to rock or coral.
   C) grouped in a colony.
   D) dependent on three other cnidarians.

9. Worms have which type of symmetry?
   A) asymmetry
   B) bilateral symmetry
   C) radial symmetry
   D) no symmetry

10. Which animal's body has the least complex body organization?
    A) cnidarians   C) worms
    B) nematodes   D) sponges

---

15. asexually—budding or regeneration; sexually—some species are hermaphroditic, others have separate sexes

16. Cnidarians can be a sessile polyp or a free-swimming medusa.

17. It is a capsulelike cell with a trigger and lid and contains a toxin that stuns prey. When the trigger is

touched by a prey, a coiled, threadlike structure is released and captures the prey.

18. Flatworms have flattened bodies, while roundworms have a tube-within-a-tube-body plan.

19. two digestive openings, a mouth, and an anus

Part 3 | Open Ended

20. obtain and digest their food from living things, move, capable of reproducing sexually

21. herbivores, deer, eat plants; carnivores, lions, eat other animals; omnivores, humans, eat both plants and animals; detritivores, vultures, eat remains of organisms.

Part 2 | Short Response/Grid In

Record your answers on the answer sheet provided by your teacher or on a sheet of paper.

11. Name three adaptations, and give an example for each.

Use the photo below to answer questions 12 and 13.

12. What types of classification and symmetry does this animal have and why?

13. Compare and contrast this with the type of classification and symmetry you have as a human.

14. How do sponges get food and oxygen?

15. Explain how sponges reproduce. Do they have more than one method of reproduction?

16. Explain the two forms of cnidarians.

17. Describe structure of the stinging cells unique to cnidarians. What are the purposes of these cells?

18. Explain the primary difference between a roundworm and a flatworm.

19. Roundworms and flatworms are the simplest organism to have what feature?

Part 3 | Open Ended

Record your answers on a sheet of paper.

20. What are the characteristics that animals have in common and causes them to be included in their own kingdom?

21. Animals need energy. They get this from food. Explain the differences between herbivores, carnivores, omnivores and detritivores. Be sure to include examples of all categories.

22. Compare and contrast mimicry and camouflage. Give an example of both mimicry and camouflage.

Use the photo below to answer question 23.

23. How is this animal useful to humans?

24. Why is coral so important to us?

25. Explain how two types of animals may interact in a host and parasitic relationship. Include humans in this discussion.

26. Compare and contrast flatworms and roundworms. In your opinion, which are more developed? Defend your answer by providing examples.

Rubrics

The following rubrics are sample scoring devices for short response and open-ended questions.

Short Response

Points	Description
2	The student demonstrates a thorough understanding of the science of the task. The response may contain minor flaws that do not detract from the demonstration of a thorough understanding.
1	The student has provided a response that is only partially correct.
0	The student has provided a completely incorrect solution or no response at all.

Open Ended

Points	Description
4	The student demonstrates a thorough understanding of the science of the task. The response may contain minor flaws that do not detract from the demonstration of a thorough understanding.
3	The student demonstrates an understanding of the science of the task. The response is essentially correct and demonstrates an essential but less than thorough understanding of the science.
2	The student demonstrates only a partial understanding of the science of the task. Although the student may have used the correct approach to a solution or may have provided a correct solution, the work lacks an essential understanding of the underlying science concepts.
1	The student demonstrates a very limited understanding of the science of the task. The response is incomplete and exhibits many flaws.
0	The student provides a completely incorrect solution or no response at all.

22. Camouflage allows an animal to blend into the environment—flounder. Mimicry is when one organism looks or behaves like another—a viceroy butterfly looks like the poisonous monarch butterfly.

23. Sponges are a food source for other animals, have symbiotic relationships, used in bathing and cleaning, and are being studied for their medicinal value.

24. support a large diversity of life, break waves that would wash away large amounts of the coastlines, and chemicals secreted by coral polyps may be used medicinally

25. A blood fluke burrows into the skin of its host, a human.

26. Both—invertebrates, bilateral symmetry, soft bodies with three tissue layers; free living and parasitic forms, sexual reproduction; flatworms—flat bodies, one body opening, can regenerate; roundworms—cylindrical bodies with a fluid-filled cavity between its middle and inner layers, a mouth and an anus, cannot regenerate.

Section/Objectives	Standards		Labs/Features
Chapter Opener	**National**	**State/Local**	**Launch Lab:** Mollusk Protection, p. 37 **Foldables,** p. 37
	See pp. 16T–17T for a Key to Standards.		
Section 1 Mollusks 🕐 2 sessions 📦 1 block 1. **Identify** the characteristics of mollusks. 2. **Describe** gastropods, bivalves, and cephalopods. 3. **Explain** the environmental importance of mollusks.	National Content Standards: UCP.1–UCP.3, UCP.5, A.1, A.2, C.1–C.3		**Integrate Earth Science,** p. 41
Section 2 Segmented Worms 🕐 2 sessions 📦 1 block 4. **Identify** the characteristics of segmented worms. 5. **Describe** the structures of an earthworm and how it takes in and digests food. 6. **Explain** the importance of segmented worms.	National Content Standards: UCP.1–UCP.3, UCP.5, A.1, A.2, C.1–C.3, C.5		**Science Online,** p. 46
Section 3 Arthropods 🕐 2 sessions 📦 1 block 7. **Determine** the characteristics that are used to classify arthropods. 8. **Explain** how the structure of the exoskeleton relates to its function. 9. **Distinguish** between complete and incomplete metamorphosis.	National Content Standards: UCP.1, UCP.5, A.1, A.2, C.1–C.3, C.5, F.4		**MiniLAB:** Observing Metamorphosis, p. 50 **Integrate Social Studies,** p. 51 **Applying Math:** Use Percentages, p. 52 **Visualizing Arthropod Diversity,** p. 54 **Lab:** Observing a Crayfish, p. 57
Section 4 Echinoderms 🕐 3 sessions 📦 1.5 blocks 10. **List** the characteristics of echinoderms. 11. **Explain** how sea stars obtain and digest food. 12. **Discuss** the importance of echinoderms.	National Content Standards: UCP.1–UCP.3, UCP.5, A.1, A.2, C.1–C.3, C.5		**MiniLAB:** Modeling the Strength of Tube Feet, p. 59 **Science Online,** p. 60 **Lab:** What do worms eat?, p. 62 **Science and Language Arts:** from "The Creatures on My Mind," p. 64

Lab Materials	Reproducible Resources	Section Assessment	Technology
Launch Lab: magnifying lens, clam shell	**Chapter** *FAST FILE* **Resources** Foldables Worksheet, p. 15 Directed Reading Overview, p. 17 Note-taking Worksheets, pp. 33–36	*GLENCOE'S* **ASSESSMENT** *ADVANTAGE*	**Teacher**Works includes: • Interactive Teacher Edition • Lesson Planner with calendar • Access to all program blacklines • Correlations to standards • Web links
	Chapter *FAST FILE* **Resources** Transparency Activity, p. 46 Enrichment, p. 29 Reinforcement, p. 25 Directed Reading, p. 18	**Portfolio** Visual Learning, p. 41 **Performance** Applying Skills, p. 42 **Content** Section Review, p. 42	👆 Section Focus Transparency 💿 Virtual Labs CD-ROM 🎧 Guided Reading Audio Program 💿 Interactive Chalkboard CD-ROM
	Chapter *FAST FILE* **Resources** Transparency Activity, p. 47 Lab Activity, pp. 9–12 Enrichment, p. 30 Reinforcement, p. 26 Transparency Activity, pp. 51–52 Directed Reading, p. 18	**Portfolio** Reteach, p. 47 **Performance** Applying Math, p. 47 **Content** Section Review, p. 47	👆 Section Focus Transparency 👆 Teaching Transparency 💿 Virtual Labs CD-ROM 🎧 Guided Reading Audio Program 💿 Interactive Chalkboard CD-ROM
MiniLAB: ripe banana, jar, cheesecloth, rubber band, magnifying lens **Lab:** crayfish in a small aquarium, uncooked ground beef, stirrer	**Chapter** *FAST FILE* **Resources** Transparency Activity, p. 48 MiniLAB, p. 3 Lab Activity, pp. 13–14 Enrichment, p. 31 Reinforcement, p. 27 Directed Reading, p. 19 Lab Worksheet, pp. 5–6	**Portfolio** Activity, p. 51 **Performance** MiniLAB, p. 50 Applying Math, p. 52 Applying Math, p. 56 **Content** Section Review, p. 56	👆 Section Focus Transparency 💿 Virtual Labs CD-ROM 🎧 Guided Reading Audio Program 💿 Interactive Chalkboard CD-ROM
MiniLAB: heavy book, clock or watch with second hand **Lab:** skins of 5 different fruits, wide-mouth jars, potting soil, humus, earthworms, black paper, masking tape, marker, rubber bands, peat moss, water	**Chapter** *FAST FILE* **Resources** Transparency Activity, p. 49 MiniLAB, p. 4 Enrichment, p. 32 Reinforcement, p. 28 Directed Reading, pp. 19, 20 Lab Worksheet, pp. 7–8	**Portfolio** Visual Learning, p. 59 **Performance** MiniLAB, p. 59 Applying Skills, p. 61 **Content** Section Review, p. 61	👆 Section Focus Transparency 💿 Virtual Labs CD-ROM 🎧 Guided Reading Audio Program 💿 Interactive Chalkboard CD-ROM 📼 Video Lab

Need materials? Contact Science Kit at 1-800-828-7777 or www.sciencekit.com on the Internet.

End of Chapter Assessment

GLENCOE'S **ASSESSMENT** *ADVANTAGE*

Blackline Masters	Technology	Professional Series
Chapter *FAST FILE* **Resources** Chapter Review, pp. 39–40 Chapter Tests, pp. 41–44 **Standardized Test Practice,** pp. 11–14	📼 MindJogger Videoquiz 💿 Virtual Labs CD-ROM 💿 Exam*View*® Pro Testmaker 💿 TeacherWorks CD-ROM 💿 Interactive Chalkboard CD-ROM	**Performance Assessment in the Science Classroom (PASC)**

Transparencies

Section Focus

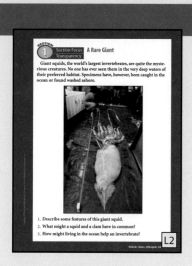

Section Focus Transparency 1 — A Rare Giant

Giant squids, the world's largest invertebrates, are quite the mysterious creatures. No one has ever seen them in the very deep waters of their preferred habitat. Specimens have, however, been caught in the ocean or found washed ashore.

1. Describe some features of this giant squid.
2. What might a squid and a clam have in common?
3. How might living in the ocean help an invertebrate?

L2

Section Focus Transparency 2 — A Monster from the Deep?

Below is a close-up of an ice worm, a segmented worm that lives on underwater methane ice mounds, shown on the right. These worms are part of a recently discovered ecosystem 700 meters below the surface of the Gulf of Mexico.

1. How is this animal's body divided?
2. How is this animal similar to an earthworm?
3. What is unusual about worms living in mounds of ice 700 meters below the surface of the ocean?

L2

Section Focus Transparency 3 — Natural Pest Control

The name ladybird beetle is commonly used for several different species of beetles. While a few ladybird beetles are harmful to crops, most of these beetles actually eat the pests that damage plants. This means they sometimes can be used instead of chemicals to protect crops.

1. What advantages do ladybird beetles have over chemicals for pest control?
2. Describe the appearance of this beetle. Does it look hard or soft on the outside?

L2

This is a representation of key blackline masters available in the Teacher Classroom Resources. See Resource Manager boxes within the chapter for additional information.

Assessment

Assessment Transparency — Mollusks, Worms, Arthropods, Echinoderms

Directions: Carefully review the graph and answer the following questions.

Southern Pine Beetle Infestations

1. According to the graph, which year had half the number of infestations that occurred in 1976?
   A 1993   C 1984
   B 1977   D 1991
2. According to the graph, the year that probably had the highest population of southern pine beetles was ___.
   F 1992   H 1982
   G 1976   J 1985
3. According to the graph, which year had twice as many infestations as 1977?
   A 1986   C 1996
   B 1991   D 1987

L2

Teaching

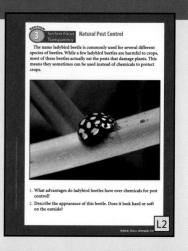

Teaching Transparency 2 — Earthworm Anatomy

L2

Key to Teaching Strategies

The following designations will help you decide which activities are appropriate for your students.

L1 — Level 1 activities should be appropriate for students with learning difficulties.

L2 — Level 2 activities should be within the ability range of all students.

L3 — Level 3 activities are designed for above-average students.

ELL — ELL activities should be within the ability range of English-Language Learners.

COOP LEARN — Cooperative Learning activities are designed for small group work.

LS — Multiple Learning Styles logos, as described on page 12T, are used throughout to indicate strategies that address different learning styles.

P — These strategies represent student products that can be placed into a best-work portfolio.

PBL — Problem-Based Learning activities apply real-world situations to learning.

Hands-on Activities

Student Text Lab Worksheet

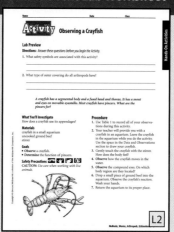

Activity — Observing a Crayfish

Lab Preview

Directions: Answer these questions before you begin the Activity.

1. What safety symbols are associated with this activity?

2. What type of outer covering do all arthropods have?

A crayfish has a segmented body and a fused head and thorax. It has a mouth and eyes on movable eyestalks. Most crayfish have pincers. What are the pincers for?

What You'll Investigate
How does a crayfish use its appendages?

Materials
crayfish in a small aquarium
uncooked ground beef
stirrer

Goals
• Observe a crayfish.
• Determine the function of pincers.

Safety Precautions
CAUTION: Use care when working with live animals.

Procedure
1. Use Table 1 to record all of your observations during this activity.
2. Your teacher will provide you with a crayfish in an aquarium while you do the activity. Use the space in the Data and Observations section to draw your crayfish.
3. Gently touch the crayfish with the stirrer. How does the body feel?
4. Observe how the crayfish moves in the water.
5. Observe the compound eyes. On which body region are they located?
6. Drop a small piece of ground beef into the aquarium. Observe the crayfish's reaction. Wash your hands.
7. Return the aquarium to its proper place.

L2

Laboratory Activities

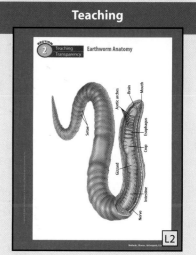

Laboratory Activity 1 — Earthworm Anatomy

The earthworm is an invertebrate that has a segmented body and specialized body parts. Oxygen from the air moves into its body through its moist skin. Carbon dioxide moves out of its body through the skin. The earthworm has a series of enlarged tubes that act as hearts. The tubes pump blood through the blood vessels of an earthworm's body. The segmented body plan makes an earthworm's anatomy easy to study.

Strategy
You will observe the external parts of an earthworm.
You will dissect an earthworm.
You will identify the internal organs and organ systems of an earthworm.

Materials
earthworm (preserved)
paper towel
dissecting pan
hand lens
dissecting pins
dissecting scissors
dissecting needle

Visit the Glencoe Science Web site at science.glencoe.com for an alternate activity about earthworm anatomy.

Procedure

Part A—External Structure
1. Place a preserved earthworm lengthwise on a paper towel in the dissecting pan with the darker side up. This is the dorsal or top side.
2. Examine the external structure and identify the parts shown in Figure 1.
3. Run your fingers lightly along the top, bottom, and sides of the earthworm. The bristles that you feel are setae. Examine the setae with a hand lens. Estimate the number of setae on each segment.
4. Locate the mouth. The part that hangs over the mouth is called the prostomium.
5. Find the thickened band circling the body. This is the clitellum. It forms a cocoon for depositing the eggs during reproduction.
6. Locate the anus. See Figure 1.

Figure 1

L2

Meeting Different Ability Levels

Content Outline

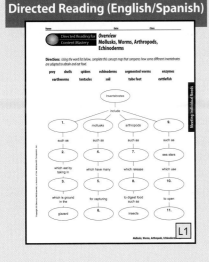

L2

Reinforcement

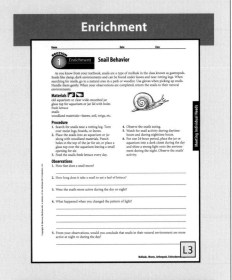

L2

Enrichment

L3

Directed Reading (English/Spanish)

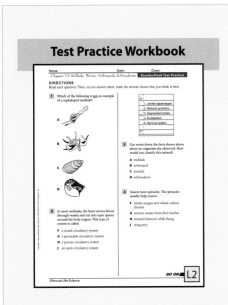

L1

Study Guide

Study Guide

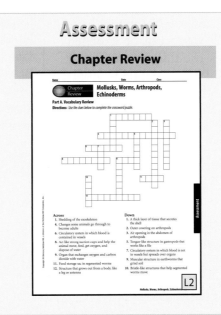

Features
- Contains a study guide page for each section of the chapter
- Reviews key concepts
- Includes answer pages

L2

Reading Essentials

Reading Essentials for Glencoe Science
An Interactive Student Workbook

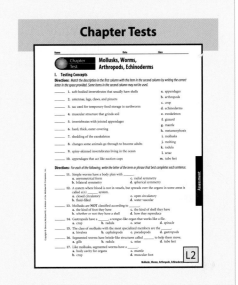

Features
- Condensed core content
- Actively involves students in reading
- Reinforces key vocabulary

L1

Assessment

Test Practice Workbook

L2

Chapter Review

L2

Chapter Tests

L2

Science Content Background

section 1 Mollusks

Characteristics of Mollusks

Mollusca is the second-largest phylum of animals. Mollusks can be found in freshwater and salt water and on land. A mollusk is an invertebrate that has a soft-body enclosed by a mantle and a muscular organ called the foot that is generally used for locomotion. In some mollusks, the mantle secretes a hard outer shell. As the animal grows, material is added to the shell that increases its size. In the cavity between the mantle and the body are the gills. A mollusk's gills are an adaptation that increases the surface area for the absorption of oxygen and the release of carbon dioxide. Mollusks that are filter feeders also use the gills to capture food.

Classification of Mollusks

Gastropoda, Bivalvia, and Cephalopoda are three familiar classes of mollusks. The class Gastropoda includes snails and slugs and is so named because the muscular foot is below the stomach. Gastropods have distinct heads and most have a shell. Bivalves do not have distinctive heads and have a two-part shell that is hinged together. They vary in size from tiny coquinas that are several millimeters long to giant clams that can be 1.5 m wide and weigh up to 270 kg. Bivalves and cephalopods have siphons through which water can be expelled forcefully. Cephalopods use this as a means of locomotion. The foot of a cephalopod is modified into several tentacles. Each tentacle has structures—usually suction cups—that can be used for capturing prey and locomotion.

section 2 Segmented Worms

Segmented Worm Characteristics

Segmented worms belong to the phylum Annelida. Although the most familiar annelid—the earthworm—is terrestrial, most annelids are marine animals. An annelid's body is made of segments that appear similar on the outside. Internally, each segment contains circulatory, excretory, and neural structures.

Earthworm Body Systems

Earthworms do not have eyes, but special sensors in their skin allow them to differentiate light and dark areas. They are negatively phototaxic, which means they move away from lighted areas.

The first segment of an earthworm contains the mouth and the last segment contains the anus. Soil enters the mouth and then a structure called the pharynx. The pharynx acts like a pump to push soil from the mouth through the esophagus into the crop. Annelids show variety in the forms of the pharynx, which often can be pushed out through their mouths. Some pharynxes contain sharp jaws for capturing prey or for eating plant materials.

Teacher to Teacher

Jeff Remington

Palmyra Middle School

Palmyra, Pennsylvania

"I have my students 'pick-an-insect-parasite' and then research it. Students can share their findings with the class."

Jeff Remington

Jeff Hunter/Image Bank

section 3

Arthropods
Characteristics of Arthropods

The first arthropods are thought to have existed in the oceans over 600 million years ago. They have evolved into countless forms and varieties— all based on the same general body plan. In addition to segmented bodies with exoskeletons and jointed appendages, arthropods have open circulatory systems, a brain, and a ventral nerve cord.

Insects

Class Insecta is the largest group of organisms on Earth and includes the only invertebrates capable of flight. Insects have evolved adaptations that allow them to live in nearly every environment.

The body of an insect is segmented. The head usually has compound eyes, antennae, and a mouth. Feeding adaptations include structures that allow insects to be carnivores, herbivores, omnivores, scavengers, or parasites. The thorax usually has legs and, if present, wings. The abdomen contains reproductive, digestive, excretory, and respiratory structures. Respiratory exchange in insects occurs in tubes called tracheae. These are connected to the outside by openings called spiracles.

While insects are commonly called bugs, entomologists, scientists who study insects, have a more restricted use of the term. The term bug is used to describe insects in the order Hemiptera. For entomologists, a cicada and a bed bug are bugs, but a fly and an ant are not.

Crustaceans

Most crustaceans are aquatic organisms. Unlike an insect, a crustacean has appendages on its abdomen as well as its thorax. Crustaceans are the only arthropods with two pair of antennae. They generally are classified into three groups. Decapods include lobsters, shrimp, crabs, and crawfish. The second group—the terrestrial and freshwater forms—includes sowbugs, sand fleas, and copepods. Barnacles make up the third group. They are free-swimming as larvae but sessile as adults.

section 4

Echinoderms
Echinoderm Characteristics

Sea stars, sea urchins, and sand dollars are examples of echinoderms. These invertebrates are not found on land or in freshwater, they are strictly saltwater organisms. Echinoderm larvae have bilateral symmetry but adult forms have radial symmetry. They have endoskeletons and a water vascular system that is not found in any other phyla.

chapter content resources

Internet Resources
For additional content background, visit **bookc.msscience.com** to:
- access your book online
- find references to related articles in popular science magazines
- access Web links with related content background
- access current events with science journal topics

Print Resources
Earthworms, Leeches, and Sea Worms: Annelids by Beth Blexland, Chelsea House Publishing, 2002
Sorting Out Worms and Other Invertebrates: Everything You Want to Know About Insects, Corals, Mollusks, Sponges and More by Samuel G. Woods, Blackbirch Marketing, 1999
Butterflies, Bugs, and Worms (Young Discoverers: Biology Facts and Experiments Series) by Sally Morgan, Kingfisher Books, 1996

chapter 2

Chapter Vocabulary

mantle, p. 38
gill, p. 38
open circulatory system, p. 38
radula, p. 39
closed circulatory system, p.40
setae, p. 43
crop, p. 44
gizzard, p. 44
appendage, p. 48
exoskeleton, p. 48
molting, p. 48
spiracle, p. 49
metamorphosis, p. 50
water-vascular system, p. 58
tube feet, p. 58

Science Journal Student
answers will vary. Possible
answers: mollusk—snail, slug,
squid; worms—earthworm,
leech, marine worm; arthropods—butterfly, bees, flies;
echinoderms—sea star, sand
dollar, sea cucumber

INTERACTIVE CHALKBOARD
with Image Bank

PowerPoint® Presentations

This CD-ROM is an editable
Microsoft® PowerPoint®
presentation that includes:

* a pre-made presentation for
  every chapter
* interactive graphics
* animations
* audio clips
* image bank
* all new section and chapter
  questions
* Standardized Test Practice
* transparencies
* pre-lab questions for all labs
* Foldables directions
* links to bookc.msscience.com

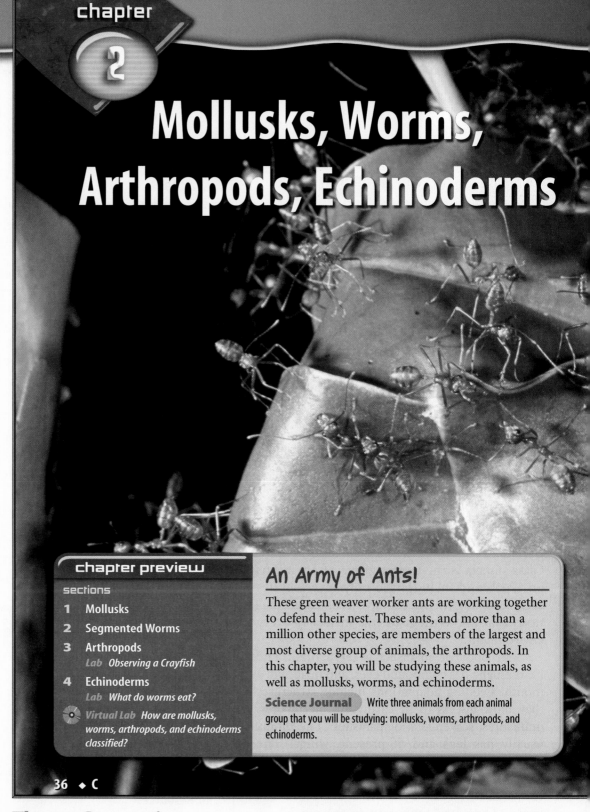

chapter

2

Mollusks, Worms, Arthropods, Echinoderms

chapter preview

sections

1. **Mollusks**
2. **Segmented Worms**
3. **Arthropods**
   Lab Observing a Crayfish
4. **Echinoderms**
   Lab What do worms eat?
   Virtual Lab How are mollusks, worms, arthropods, and echinoderms classified?

An Army of Ants!

These green weaver worker ants are working together to defend their nest. These ants, and more than a million other species, are members of the largest and most diverse group of animals, the arthropods. In this chapter, you will be studying these animals, as well as mollusks, worms, and echinoderms.

Science Journal Write three animals from each animal group that you will be studying: mollusks, worms, arthropods, and echinoderms.

36 ◆ C

Theme Connection

Stability and Change and **Scale and Structure**
Comparisons of the adaptations that have evolved in mollusks, segmented worms, arthropods, and echinoderms are explored.

About the Photo

Weaver Ants Green weaver ants build nests in trees or shrubs by binding leaves together with silk produced by their larvae. Individual colonies can be very large, with several nests spread over separate trees. They are aggressive and defend their nests, but their bites do not sting terribly. These ants sometimes are used in biological pest control because of their large population sizes and predatory habits.

Start-Up Activities

Mollusk Protection

If you've ever walked along a beach, especially after a storm, you've probably seen many seashells. They come in different colors, shapes, and sizes. If you look closely, you will see that some shells have many rings or bands. In the following lab, find out what the bands tell you about the shell and the organism that made it.

1. Use a magnifying lens to examine a clam's shell.
2. Count the number of rings or bands on the shell. Count as number one the large, top point called the crown.
3. Compare the distances between the bands of the shell.
4. **Think Critically** Do other students' shells have the same number of bands? Are all of the bands on your shell the same width? What do you think the bands represent, and why are some wider than others? Record your answers in your Science Journal.

 **Preview this chapter's content and activities at** bookc.msscience.com

---

 Invertebrates Make the following Foldable to help you organize the main characteristics of the four groups of complex invertebrates.

STEP 1 Draw a mark at the midpoint of a sheet of paper along the side edge. Then **fold** the top and bottom edges in to touch the midpoint.

STEP 2 **Fold** in half from side to side.

STEP 3 **Turn** the paper vertically. **Open and cut** along the inside fold lines to form four tabs.

STEP 4 **Label** the tabs *Mollusks, Worms, Arthropods,* and *Echinoderms.*

Classify As you read the chapter, list the characteristics of the four groups of invertebrates under the appropriate tab.

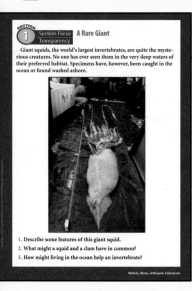
section 1
Mollusks

as you read

What You'll Learn

- **Identify** the characteristics of mollusks.
- **Describe** gastropods, bivalves, and cephalopods.
- **Explain** the environmental importance of mollusks.

Why It's Important

Mollusks are a food source for many animals. They also filter impurities from the water.

◉ Review Vocabulary
visceral mass: contains the stomach and other organs

New Vocabulary
- mantle
- gill
- open circulatory system
- radula
- closed circulatory system

Characteristics of Mollusks

Mollusks (MAH lusks) are soft-bodied invertebrates with bilateral symmetry and usually one or two shells. Their organs are in a fluid-filled cavity. The word *mollusk* comes from the Latin word meaning "soft." Most mollusks live in water, but some live on land. Snails, clams, and squid are examples of mollusks. More than 110,000 species of mollusks have been identified.

Body Plan All mollusks, like the one in **Figure 1,** have a thin layer of tissue called a mantle. The **mantle** covers the body organs, which are located in the visceral (VIH suh rul) mass. Between the soft body and the mantle is a space called the mantle cavity. It contains **gills**—the organs in which carbon dioxide from the mollusk is exchanged for oxygen in the water.

The mantle also secretes the shell or protects the body if the mollusk does not have a shell. The shell is made up of several layers. The inside layer is the smoothest. It is usually the thickest layer because it's added to throughout the life of the mollusk. The inside layer also protects the soft body.

The circulatory system of most mollusks is an open system. In an **open circulatory system,** the heart moves blood out into the open spaces around the body organs. The blood, which contains nutrients and oxygen, completely surrounds and nourishes the body organs.

Most mollusks have a well-developed head with a mouth and some sensory organs. Some mollusks, such as squid, have tentacles. On the underside of a mollusk is the muscular foot, which is used for movement.

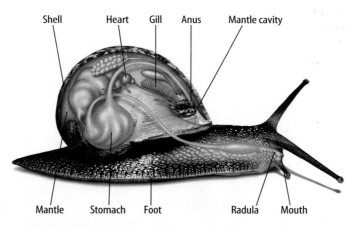

Shell   Heart   Gill   Anus   Mantle cavity

Mantle   Stomach   Foot   Radula   Mouth

Figure 1 The general mollusk body plan is shown by this snail. Most mollusks have a head, foot, and visceral mass.

38 ◆ C CHAPTER 2 Mollusks, Worms, Arthropods, Echinoderms

Conch

Garden slugs

Figure 2 Conchs, sometimes called marine snails, have a single shell covering their internal organs. Garden slugs are mollusks without a shell.

Identify the mollusk group that both conchs and garden slugs belong to.

Classification of Mollusks

The first thing scientists look at when they classify mollusks is whether or not the animal has a shell. Mollusks that have shells are then classified by the kind of shell and kind of foot that they have. The three most common groups of mollusks are gastropods, bivalves, and cephalopods.

Gastropods The largest group of mollusks, the gastropods, includes snails, conchs like the one in **Figure 2,** abalones, whelks, sea slugs, and garden slugs, also shown in **Figure 2.** Conchs are sometimes called univalves. Except for slugs, which have no shell, gastropods have a single shell. Many have a pair of tentacles with eyes at the tips. Gastropods use a **radula** (RA juh luh)— a tonguelike organ with rows of teeth—to obtain food. The radula works like a file to scrape and tear food materials. That's why snails are helpful to have in an aquarium—they scrape the algae off the walls and keep the tank clean.

☑ **Reading Check** *How do gastropods get food?*

Slugs and many snails are adapted to life on land. They move by rhythmic contractions of the muscular foot. Glands in the foot secrete a layer of mucus on which they slide. Slugs and snails are most active at night or on cloudy days when they can avoid the hot Sun. Slugs do not have shells but are protected by a layer of mucus instead, so they must live in moist places. Slugs and land snails damage plants as they eat leaves and stems.

Use Science Words

Word Meaning Have students look up the words *mantle* and *radula* in a dictionary. Mantle comes from a Latin word meaning "cloak" and radula is Latin for "scraper." How is a mantle like a cloak? It covers and helps provide protection for the mollusk's body. How does having a scraper help a mollusk? It allows the mollusk to scrape food. L2 ⟨IS⟩ **Linguistic**

Caption Answer

Figure 2 gastropods

Use an Analogy

File Analogy Show students a steel file, and let them touch its surface. Use the file on a piece of scrap wood. Explain that a radula works in much the same way as the file as it scrapes algae from surfaces. L2

☑ **Reading Check**

Answer They use a tonguelike organ called a radula with rows of teeth for scraping and tearing algae from rocks.

Activity

Snail Observations Collect snails from a local pond or purchase them from a pet shop. Have students observe how the snails move. Have them examine the snails' eyes with a hand lens. Feed lettuce to the snails so students can observe their feeding method with a hand lens. L1 **ELL** ⟨IS⟩ **Visual-Spatial**

Differentiated Instruction

Challenge Why is an open circulatory system able to meet the needs of a gastropod? Gastropods move slowly and use energy at a low rate, so their needs for food and gas exchange are low. L3 ⟨IS⟩ **Logical-Mathematical**

English-Language Learners Make flashcards for this section, with English vocabulary words and definitions on one side, and the equivalent in the appropriate language of your student on the other side. You can pair your students up, or have your students work with the flashcards on their own. L2

<table><tr><td></td></tr></table>

Teacher FYI

Royal Purple Romans extracted a purple dye from the Mediterranean rock whelk, *Murex brandaris*. Each whelk yielded only a small amount of dye, so it was very expensive. Only wealthy people could afford to have purple clothing. As a result, the color purple became associated with royalty.

Fun Fact

The giant clam has been known to grow up to 1.5 m (4.8 ft.) long and weigh up to 250 kg (550 lbs.).

Quick Demo

Beak Sharpening

Materials piece of cuttlebone used in bird cages

Estimated Time 5 minutes

Procedure Show students a cuttlebone—the internal skeleton of the cuttlefish. Caged birds use the cuttlebone to sharpen their beaks.
L2 | **Visual-Spatial**

✔ Reading Check

Answer a closed circulatory system; a foot divided into tentacles; a well-developed nervous system, and eyes; predators

Caption Answer

Figure 4 An internal shell provides support and buoyancy. It is reduced in most cephalopods, and some, like octopuses, have no shell. This allows them to squeeze into tight spaces.

Figure 3 Scallops force water between their valves to move away from sea stars and other predators. They can move up to 1 m with each muscular contraction.

Figure 4 Most cephalopods, like this cuttlefish, have an internal shell.
Infer why an internal shell would be a helpful adaptation.

Bivalves Mollusks that have a hinged, two-part shell joined by strong muscles are called bivalves. Clams, oysters, and scallops are bivalve mollusks and are a familiar source of seafood. These animals pull their shells closed by contracting powerful muscles near the hinge. To open their shells, they relax these muscles.

Bivalves are well adapted for living in water. For protection, clams burrow deep into the sand by contracting and relaxing their muscular foot. Mussels and oysters attach themselves with a strong thread or cement to a solid surface. This keeps waves and currents from washing them away. Scallops, shown in **Figure 3,** escape predators by rapidly opening and closing their shells. As water is forced out, the scallop moves rapidly in the opposite direction.

Cephalopods The most specialized and complex mollusks are the cephalopods (SE fuh luh pawdz). Squid, octopuses, cuttlefish, and chambered nautiluses belong to this group. The word *cephalopod* means "head-footed" and describes the body structure of these invertebrates. Cephalopods, like the cuttlefish in **Figure 4,** have a large, well-developed head. Their foot is divided into many tentacles with strong suction cups or hooks for capturing prey. All cephalopods are predators. They feed on fish, crustaceans, worms, and other mollusks.

Squid and octopuses have a well-developed nervous system and large eyes similar to human eyes. Unlike other mollusks, cephalopods have closed circulatory systems. In a **closed circulatory system,** blood containing food and oxygen moves through the body in a series of closed vessels, just as your blood moves through your blood vessels.

✔ Reading Check
What makes a cephalopod different from other mollusks?

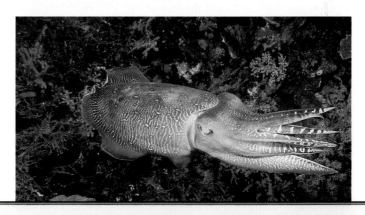

LAB DEMONSTRATION

Purpose to observe mollusk traits

Materials squid, plastic tray, forceps, magnifying lens, goggles

Procedure As you demonstrate have students draw and label the body, head, eyes, tentacles, mouth, fins, beak, mantle and suction cups. Find the hard point at one end of the squid's fin (pen) and use forceps to pull it out.

Preparation Purchase squid from the supermarket. Wash the squid thoroughly before the demonstration.

Expected Outcome Students should observe mollusk traits in a squid.

Assessment

What are the suction cups used for? to capture and hold prey What mollusk traits were observed? soft body, head with eyes, foot divided into tentacles, internal shell (pen), beak used to tear food L2

Water in

Direction
of squid

Water out

Figure 5 Squid and other cephalopods use jet propulsion to move quickly away from predators.

Cephalopod Propulsion All cephalopods live in oceans and are adapted for swimming. Squid and other cephalopods have a water-filled cavity between an outer muscular covering and its internal organs. When the cephalopod tightens its muscular covering, water is forced out through an opening near the head, as shown in **Figure 5.** The jet of water propels the cephalopod backwards, and it moves away quickly. According to Newton's third law of motion, when one object exerts a force on a second object, the second object exerts a force on the first that is equal and opposite in direction. The movement of cephalopods is an example of this law. Muscles exert force on water under the mantle. Water being forced out exerts a force that results in movement backwards.

A squid can propel itself at speeds of more than 6 m/s using this jet propulsion and can briefly outdistance all but whales, dolphins, and the fastest fish. A squid even can jump out of the water and reach heights of almost 5 m above the ocean's surface. It then can travel through the air as far as 15 m. However, squid can maintain their top speed for just a few pulses. Octopuses also can swim by jet propulsion, but they usually use their tentacles to creep more slowly over the ocean floor.

Origin of Mollusks Some species of mollusks, such as the chambered nautilus, have changed little from their ancestors. Mollusk fossils date back more than 500 million years. Many species of mollusks became extinct about 65 million years ago. Today's mollusks are descendants of ancient mollusks.

INTEGRATE
Earth Science

Mollusk Extinction By about 65 million years ago, many mollusks had become extinct. What were the major physical events of the time that could have contributed to changing the environment? Write your answers in your Science Journal.

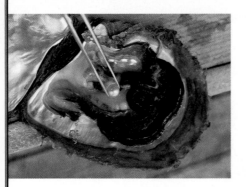

Figure 6 A pearl starts as an irritant—a grain of sand or a parasite—to an oyster. The oyster coats the irritant with a material that forms smooth, hard layers. It can take years for a pearl to form. Culturing pearls is a commercial industry in some countries.

Value of Mollusks

Mollusks have many uses. They are food for fish, sea stars, birds, and humans. Many people make their living raising or collecting mollusks to sell for food. Other invertebrates, such as hermit crabs, use empty mollusk shells as shelter. Many mollusk shells are used for jewelry and decoration. Pearls are produced by several species of mollusks, but most are made by mollusks called pearl oysters, shown in **Figure 6.** Mollusk shells also provide information about the conditions in an ecosystem, including the source and distribution of water pollutants. The internal shell of a cuttlefish is the cuttlebone, which is used in birdcages to provide birds with calcium. Squid and octopuses are able to learn tasks, so scientists are studying their nervous systems to understand how learning takes place and how memory works.

Even though mollusks are beneficial in many ways, they also can cause problems for humans. Land slugs and snails damage plants. Certain species of snails are hosts of parasites that infect humans. Shipworms, a type of bivalve, make holes in submerged wood of docks and boats, causing millions of dollars in damage each year. Because clams, oysters, and other mollusks are filter feeders, bacteria, viruses, and toxic protists from the water can become trapped in the animals. Eating these infected mollusks can result in sickness or even death.

section 1 review

Summary

Mollusks

- The body plans of mollusks include a mantle, visceral mass, head, and foot.

Classification of Mollusks

- Gastropods typically have one shell, a foot, and eat using a radula.
- Bivalves have a hinged two-part shell, a muscular foot, and eat by filtering their food from the water.
- Cephalopods have a head, a foot which has been modified into tentacles, and a well-developed nervous system.

Value of Mollusks

- Mollusks are food for many animals, have commercial uses, and are used for research.

Self Check

1. **Explain** how a squid and other cephalopods can move so rapidly.
2. **Identify** some positive and negative ways that mollusks affect humans.
3. **Think Critically** Why is it unlikely that you would find garden slugs or land snails in a desert?

Applying Skills

4. **Interpret Scientific Illustrations** Observe the images of gastropods and bivalves in this section, and infer how bivalves are not adapted to life on land, but gastropods are.
5. **Use a Computer** Make a data table that compares and contrasts the following for gastropods, bivalves, and cephalopods: *methods for obtaining food, movement, circulation,* and *habitat.*

 Science Online bookc.mscience.com/self_check_quiz

section 1 review

1. Jet propulsion; water is ejected through the funnel or siphon in one direction, moving the animal in the opposite direction.
2. Mollusks are used for food, jewelry, and research. They damage boats and docks. Eating those that contain disease-causing organisms can cause illness.
3. The desert is too dry. Slugs and snails require a moist environment.
4. Bivalves filter food from the water. They move slowly or remain attached to one place. Gastropods use their radula and teeth to eat plants and algae.
5. Check data tables for accuracy.

Segmented Worms

Segmented Worm Characteristics

The worms you see crawling across sidewalks after a rain and those used for fishing are called annelids (A nuh ludz). The word *annelid* means "little rings" and describes the bodies of these worms. They have tube-shaped bodies that are divided into many segments.

Have you ever watched a robin try to pull an earthworm out of the ground or tried it yourself? Why don't they slip out of the soil easily? On the outside of each body segment are bristlelike structures called **setae** (SEE tee). Segmented worms use their setae to hold on to the soil and to move. Segmented worms also have bilateral symmetry, a body cavity that holds the organs, and two body openings—a mouth and an anus. Annelids can be found in freshwater, salt water, and moist soil. Earthworms, like the one in **Figure 7,** marine worms, and leeches are examples of annelids.

 **Reading Check** *What is the function of setae?*

Earthworm Body Systems

The most well-known annelids are earthworms. They have a definite anterior, or front end, and a posterior, or back end. Earthworms have more than 100 body segments. The segments can be seen on the outside and the inside of the body cavity. Each body segment, except for the first and last segments, has four pairs of setae. Earthworms move by using their setae and two sets of muscles in the body wall. One set of muscles runs the length of the body, and the other set circles the body. When an earthworm contracts its long muscles, it causes some of the segments to bunch up and the setae to stick out. This anchors the worm to the soil. When the circular muscles contract, the setae are pulled in and the worm can move forward.

Figure 7 One species of earthworm that lives in Australia can grow to be 3.3 m long.

What **You'll Learn**

- **Identify** the characteristics of segmented worms.
- **Describe** the structures of an earthworm and how it takes in and digests food.
- **Explain** the importance of segmented worms.

Why **It's Important**

Earthworms condition and aerate the soil, which helps increase crop yields.

Review Vocabulary
aerate: to supply with air

New Vocabulary
- setae
- crop
- gizzard

INTERACTIVE CHALKBOARD
PowerPoint® Presentations

Bellringer

Section Focus Transparencies also are available on the Interactive Chalkboard CD-ROM.
L2 ELL

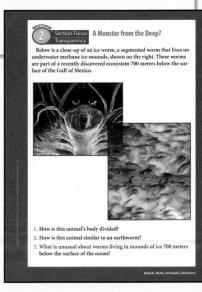

Tie to Prior Knowledge

Earthworm Observations Most students have seen earthworms. Discuss their observations about worms, where worms live, and what they eat. L2

Reading Check

Answer to hold onto soil and move

Section 2 Resource Manager

Chapter *FAST FILE* Resources
Transparency Activity, pp. 47, 51–52
Directed Reading for Content Mastery, p. 18
Lab Activity, pp. 9–12
Enrichment, p. 31
Reinforcement, p. 27

Performance Assessment in the Science Classroom, p. 55

Caption Answer

Figure 8 In addition to fertilizing, worms also aerate soil.

Discussion

Annelids Display specimens (or pictures on a bulletin board) of annelids (clam worms, tube worms, fan worms, leeches, *Tubifex* worms, redworms and earthworms). Have students discuss how they are similar.

Activity

Sensory Maze Have several students set up a maze in the classroom, using desks and chairs. Blindfold volunteers who have not seen the maze, and ask them to find their way through it. Use this activity to help students understand that earthworms find food and escape predators without being able to see. L2 LS **Kinesthetic**

Quick Demo

Earthworm Anatomy

Materials preserved earthworm, dissecting tray, dissecting knife, dissecting probe, stereomicroscope (optional)

Estimated Time 20 minutes

Procedure Dissect a preserved earthworm, and have students examine its digestive, circulatory, excretory, reproductive, and nervous systems. L2 LS **Visual-Spatial**

Fun Fact

Even though earthworms do not have eyes, they have light receptors in the head that sense the presence of light.

Figure 8 Earthworm castings— also called vermicompost—are used as an organic fertilizer in gardens.
Infer *why earthworms are healthy to have in a garden or compost pile.*

Digestion and Excretion As an earthworm burrows through the soil, it takes soil into its mouth. Earthworms get energy from the bits of leaves and other organic matter found in the soil. The soil ingested by an earthworm moves to the **crop,** which is a sac used for storage. Behind the crop is a muscular structure called the **gizzard,** which grinds the soil and the bits of organic matter. This ground material passes to the intestine, where the organic matter is broken down and the nutrients are absorbed by the blood. Wastes leave the worm through the anus. When earthworms take in soil, they provide spaces for air and water to flow through it and mix the soil. Their wastes pile up at the openings to their burrows. These piles are called castings. Castings, like those in **Figure 8,** help fertilize the soil.

Circulation and Respiration Earthworms have a closed circulatory system, as shown in **Figure 9.** Two blood vessels along the top of the body and one along the bottom of the body meet in the front end of the earthworm. There, they connect to heartlike structures called aortic arches, which pump blood through the body. Smaller vessels go into each body segment.

Earthworms don't have gills or lungs. Oxygen and carbon dioxide are exchanged through their skin, which is covered with a thin film of watery mucus. It's important never to touch earthworms with dry hands or remove their thin mucous layer, because they could suffocate. But as you can tell after a rainstorm, earthworms don't survive in puddles of water either.

Figure 9 An earthworm's circulatory system includes five aortic arches that pump blood throughout its body.

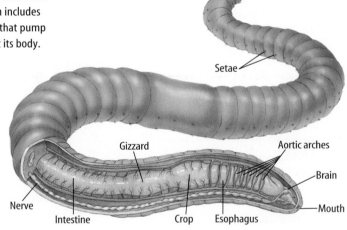

Setae

Gizzard

Aortic arches

Brain

Mouth

Nerve

Intestine

Crop

Esophagus

Differentiated Instruction

Challenge Have students research the major complex invertebrates in the chapter. Have them make identification cards of the ones in which they are most interested. On one side of the card, they can draw a picture of the invertebrate and on the other, give the name and major characteristics. A game can be played by keeping track of the number of organisms students can identify. L3

Teacher FYI

Soil Aeration Earthworm aeration of the soil is so beneficial that their presence in hundreds or thousands per hectare is a characteristic of a productive farm. *Lumbricus terrestris* ingests its own weight in soil and decaying matter every day. Earthworms survive in thin films of water in slightly moist soil, but if the soil becomes flooded, the worms can drown.

Nerve Response and Reproduction Earthworms have a small brain in their front segment. Nerves in each segment join to form a main nerve cord that connects to the brain. Earthworms respond to light, temperature, and moisture.

Earthworms are hermaphrodites (hur MA fruh dites)—meaning they produce sperm and eggs in the same body. Even though each worm has male and female reproductive structures, an individual worm can't fertilize its own eggs. Instead, it has to receive sperm from another earthworm in order to reproduce.

Marine Worms

More than 8,000 species of marine worms, or polychaetes, (PAH lee keets) exist, which is more than any other kind of annelid. Marine worms float, burrow, build structures, or walk along the ocean floor. Some polychaetes even produce their own light. Others, like the ice worms in **Figure 10,** are able to live 540 m deep. Polychaetes, like earthworms, have segments with setae. However, the setae occur in bundles on these worms. The word polychaete means "many bristles."

Sessile, bottom-dwelling polychaetes, such as the Christmas tree worms shown in **Figure 11,** have specialized tentacles that are used for exchanging oxygen and carbon dioxide and gathering food. Some marine worms build tubes around their bodies. When these worms are startled, they retreat into their tubes. Free-swimming polychaetes, such as the bristleworm shown in **Figure 11,** have a head with eyes; a tail; and parapodia (per uh POH dee uh). Parapodia are paired, fleshy outgrowths on each segment, which aid in feeding and locomotion.

Figure 10 Ice worms, a type of marine polychaete, were discovered first in 1997 living 540 m deep in the Gulf of Mexico.

Figure 11 These Christmas tree worms filter microorganisms from the water to eat. This bristleworm swims backwards and forwards, so it has eyes at both ends of its body.

Christmas tree worms

Bristleworm

Teacher FYI

Polychaetes Traits Polychaetes live in cracks and crevices in coral reefs, sand, mud, piles of rock, and in open water. Some build their own tube structures and burrows. Many are free-moving. Some polychaetes are brightly colored, iridescent, or even luminescent.

Visual Learning

Figure 11 Have students compare and contrast the marine worms found in this figure. [L1] **LS Visual-Spatial**

Discussion

Wormy Words Have students discuss the meaning of "wormy" slang and colloquial expressions in the English language. Examples are: "the worm in the apple" (one bad thing in an otherwise good situation); "worm your way out of something" (get out of unpleasant situations using devious methods); describing a person as a "leech" (one who clings to another without contributing). [L2]

IDENTIFYING
Misconceptions

Insects not Worms Make sure students understand that grubs and caterpillars are not annelids. They are insects in larval stages.

Differentiated Instruction

Challenge Have students research the economic importance of earthworms and how they are raised commercially. [L3]

Learning Disabled Have students make a picture dictionary illustrating the meaning of key words used in each section of this chapter. Have them begin by looking up the prefixes *exo-* and *endo-* in the dictionary. [L2] **LS Visual-Spatial**

Reading Check

Answer The anesthetic numbs the wound so the animal won't feel a leech's bite. Therefore, a leech can feed without the animal even knowing it. This allows the leech to get more food, and provides protection for the leech, since the animal is not trying to remove it.

Discussion

Earthworms and Leeches How do earthworms and leeches differ? Earthworms have setae; leeches do not. Leeches have anterior and posterior suckers; earthworms do not. Why are both classified as annelids? Each has a body cavity that holds organs and a segmented body. L2

Caption Answer

Figure 12 Chemicals in a leech's saliva contains an anticoagulant.

Discussion

Segmentation How does an annelid's segmentation help it move? Segmentation increases the flexibility of an earthworm because separate parts can move independently of one another. L2

Science Online

Topic: Beneficial Leeches
Visit bookc.msscience.com for Web links to information about the uses of chemicals from leech saliva.

Activity Describe a possible use for leech saliva, and design a 30-second commercial on how you might sell it.

Leeches

A favorite topic for scary movies is leeches. If you've ever had to remove a leech from your body after swimming in a fresh-water pond, lake, or river, you know it isn't fun. Leeches are segmented worms, but their bodies are not as round or as long as earthworms are, and they don't have setae. They feed on the blood of other animals. A sucker at each end of a leech's body is used to attach itself to an animal. If a leech attaches to you, you probably won't feel it. Leeches produce many chemicals, including an anesthetic (a nus THEH tihk) that numbs the wound so you don't feel its bite. After the leech has attached itself, it cuts into the animal and sucks out two to ten times its own weight in blood. Even though leeches prefer to eat blood, they can survive by eating aquatic insects and other organisms instead.

Reading Check *Why is producing an anesthetic an advantage to a leech?*

Leeches and Medicine

Sometimes, leeches are used after surgery to keep blood flowing to the repaired area, as shown in **Figure 12.** For example, the tiny blood vessels in the ear quickly can become blocked with blood clots after surgery. To keep blood flowing in such places, physicians might attach leeches to the surgical site. As the leeches feed on the blood, chemicals in their saliva prevent the blood from coagulating. Besides the anti-clotting chemical, leech saliva also contains a chemical that dilates blood vessels, which improves the blood flow and allows the wound to heal more quickly. These chemicals are being studied to treat patients with heart or circulatory diseases, strokes, arthritis, or glaucoma.

Figure 12 Medical leeches are used sometimes to prevent blood from clotting or accumulating in damaged skin.
Explain *how a leech can prevent blood clots.*

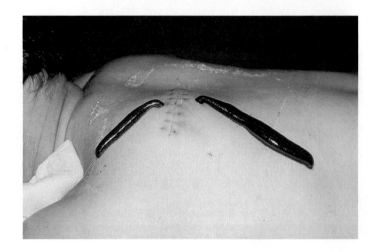

46 ◆ C CHAPTER 2 Mollusks, Worms, Arthropods, Echinoderms

Science Journal

Annelids Have students research and report on annelids other than earthworms and leeches. Some examples are feather worms, fanworms, peacock worms, and giant tube worms that live in deep-sea vents. Have them include the structural differences among the worms in their reports. L2
IS **Linguistic**

Differentiated Instruction

Challenge Have students research and report on *Hirudo medicinalis.* This leech produces the anti-coagulant hirudin. *Hirudo medicinalis,* the medicinal leech, feeds primarily on the blood of mammals, but it also sucks blood from amphibians, reptiles, and fish. It has three jaws with sharp teeth that make a Y-shaped incision in the skin of the host. After it feeds, the leech detaches from its host and may not feed again for as long as 18 months. L3

Value of Segmented Worms

Different kinds of segmented worms are helpful to other animals in a variety of ways. Earthworms help aerate the soil by constantly burrowing through it. By grinding and partially digesting the large amount of plant material in soil, earthworms speed up the return of nitrogen and other nutrients to the soil for use by plants.

Researchers are developing drugs based on the chemicals that come from leeches because leech saliva prevents blood clots. Marine worms and their larvae are food for many fish, invertebrates, and mammals.

Origin of Segmented Worms

Some scientists hypothesize that segmented worms evolved in the sea. The fossil record for segmented worms is limited because of their soft bodies. The tubes of marine worms are the most common fossils of the segmented worms. Some of these fossils date back about 620 million years.

Similarities between mollusks and segmented worms suggest that they could have a common ancestor. These groups were the first animals to have a body cavity with space for body organs to develop and function. Mollusks and segmented worms have a one-way digestive system with a separate mouth and anus. Their larvae, shown in **Figure 13,** are similar and are the best evidence that they have a common ancestor.

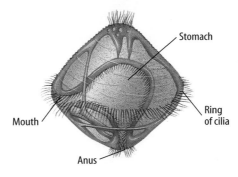

Stomach
Ring of cilia
Mouth
Anus

Mollusk larva

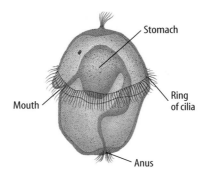

Stomach
Ring of cilia
Mouth
Anus

Annelid larva

Figure 13 Some mollusk larvae have many structures that are similar to those of some annelid larvae.

Visual Learning

Figure 13 Have students compare the structures of the larvae. L2

3 Assess

DAILY INTERVENTION

Check for Understanding
Kinesthetic Using modeling clay or dough, have students construct a new species of annelid. Their species must possess all of the characteristics of annelids including segments, bilateral symmetry, a body cavity that holds organs, and two digestive openings. Setae are optional. L2

Reteach
Mollusk and Segmented Worms Have students make a chart that compares the structures, environment, and ways of life (free-living or parasitic) of mollusks and segmented worms L2 P

✓ Assessment

Content Have students work in groups to list earthworm body systems, and external features. Use **Performance Assessment in the Science Classroom,** p. 169. L2

---

section 2 review

Summary

Segmented Worm Characteristics

- Segmented worms have tube-shaped bodies divided into many segments, bilateral symmetry, a body cavity with organs, and two body openings.

- Earthworms have a definite anterior and posterior end, a closed circulatory system, a small brain, and eat organic matter in the soil. Most segments have four pairs of setae.

- Polychaetes are marine worms with many setae occurring in bundles.

- Leeches are segmented worms that feed on the blood of other animals. They have no setae, but a sucker at each end of the body.

Self Check

1. **Define** setae and state their function.

2. **Describe** how an earthworm takes in and digests its food.

3. **Compare and contrast** how earthworms and marine worms exchange oxygen and carbon dioxide.

4. **Think Critically** What advantages do marine worms with tubes have over free-swimming polychaetes?

Applying Math

5. **Use Proportions** Suppose you find six earthworms in 10 cm³ of soil. Based on this sample, calculate the number of earthworms you would find in 10 m³ of soil.

---

section 2 review

1. Setae are bristlelike structures on the outside of a segmented worm's body. They are used to hold on to the soil and to move.

2. It takes in soil, which moves through the digestive system. Food (plant and animal material in the soil) is removed from the soil and digested. Waste material leaves through the anus.

3. Earthworms obtain oxygen through their moist skin. Marine worms have specialized tentacles for obtaining oxygen.

4. Tube worms have a protective covering.

5. 6,000 earthworms

as you read

What You'll Learn

- **Determine** the characteristics that are used to classify arthropods.
- **Explain** how the structure of the exoskeleton relates to its function.
- **Distinguish** between complete and incomplete metamorphosis.

Why It's Important

Arthropods, such as those that carry diseases and eat crops, affect your life every day.

Review Vocabulary
venom: toxic fluid injected by an animal

New Vocabulary
- appendage
- exoskeleton
- molting
- spiracle
- metamorphosis

Characteristics of Arthropods

There are more than a million different species of arthropods, (AR thruh pahdz) making them the largest group of animals. The word *arthropoda* means "jointed foot." The jointed **appendages** of arthropods can include legs, antennae, claws, and pincers. Arthropod appendages are adapted for moving about, capturing prey, feeding, mating, and sensing their environment. Arthropods also have bilateral symmetry, segmented bodies, an exoskeleton, a body cavity, a digestive system with two openings, and a nervous system. Most arthropod species have separate sexes and reproduce sexually. Arthropods are adapted to living in almost every environment. They vary in size from microscopic dust mites to the large, Japanese spider crab, shown in **Figure 14.**

Segmented Bodies The bodies of arthropods are divided into segments similar to those of segmented worms. Some arthropods have many segments, but others have segments that are fused together to form body regions, such as those of insects, spiders, and crabs.

Exoskeletons All arthropods have a hard, outer covering called an **exoskeleton.** It covers, supports, and protects the internal body and provides places for muscles to attach. In many land-dwelling arthropods, such as insects, the exoskeleton has a waxy layer that reduces water loss from the animal.

An exoskeleton cannot grow as the animal grows. From time to time, the exoskeleton is shed and replaced by a new one in a process called **molting.** While the animals are molting, they are not well protected from predators because the new exoskeleton is soft. Before the new exoskeleton hardens, the animal swallows air or water to increase its exoskeleton's size. This way the new exoskeleton allows room for growth.

Figure 14 The Japanese spider crab has legs that can span more than 3 m.

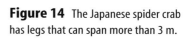

Insects

More species of insects exist than all other animal groups combined. More than 700,000 species of insects have been classified, and scientists identify more each year. Insects have three body regions—a head, a thorax, and an abdomen, as shown in **Figure 15.** However, it is almost impossible on some insects to see where one region stops and the next one begins.

Head
Thorax
Abdomen

Figure 15 One of the largest types of ants is the carpenter ant. Like all insects, it has a head, thorax, and abdomen.

Head An insect's head has a pair of antennae, eyes, and a mouth. The antennae are used for touch and smell. The eyes are simple or compound. Simple eyes detect light and darkness. Compound eyes, like those in **Figure 16,** contain many lenses and can detect colors and movement. The mouthparts of insects vary, depending on what the insect eats.

Thorax Three pairs of legs and one or two pairs of wings, if present, are attached to the thorax. Some insects, such as silverfish and fleas, don't have wings, and other insects have wings only for part of their lives. Insects are the only invertebrate animals that can fly. Flying allows insects to find places to live, food sources, and mates. Flight also helps them escape from their predators.

✔ Reading Check *How does flight benefit insects?*

Abdomen The abdomen has neither wings nor legs but it is where the reproductive structures are found. Females lay thousands of eggs, but only a fraction of the eggs develop into adults. Think about how overproduction of eggs might ensure that each insect species will continue.

Insects have an open circulatory system that carries digested food to cells and removes wastes. However, insect blood does not carry oxygen because it does not have hemoglobin. Instead, insects have openings called **spiracles** (SPIHR ih kulz) on the abdomen and thorax through which air enters and waste gases leave the insect's body.

Figure 16 Each compound eye is made up of small lenses that fit together. Each lens sees a part of the picture to make up the whole scene. Insects can't focus their eyes. Their eyes are always open and can detect movements.

Stained LM Magnification: 400×

SECTION 3 Arthropods **C ◆ 49**

Science Journal

Insect Societies Some insects, including ants, bees, termites, and wasps, live in highly organized societies. Each member has a specific job necessary for the survival of the colony. Have students choose a social insect and describe in their Science Journals the role of each member of the society. L2 **IS** **Linguistic**

Mini LAB

Purpose Students observe metamorphosis in fruit flies. [L1] [LS]
Visual-Spatial

Materials small piece of banana, baby food jar, cheesecloth, rubber band, magnifying lens

Teaching Strategy Fruit fly cultures may be purchased from a biological supply company.

Troubleshooting Be sure containers have flies at all stages of metamorphosis. Students may have a difficult time seeing the egg stage. Point out this stage to students, and have them observe the eggs with a magnifying lens.

Analysis
1. complete metamorphosis
2. The flies are most active in the larva and adult stages.

Assessment

Performance Have students observe mealworms over a period of five to six weeks and compare their metamorphosis with that of fruit flies. Both are complete metamorphoses. The stages are longer in mealworms. Use **Performance Assessment in the Science Classroom,** p. 99.

✔ **Reading Check**

Answer when in their nymph form

Mini LAB

Observing Metamorphosis

Procedure 🧫 🧤
1. Place a 2-cm piece of ripe **banana** in a **jar** and leave it open.
2. Check the jar every day for two weeks. When you see fruit flies, cover the mouth of the jar with **cheesecloth.**
3. Identify, describe, and draw all the stages of metamorphosis that you observe.

Analysis
1. What type of metamorphosis do fruit flies undergo?
2. In which stages are the flies the most active?

From Egg to Adult Many insects go through changes in body form as they grow. This series of changes is called **metamorphosis** (me tuh MOR fuh sihs). Grasshoppers, silverfish, lice, and crickets undergo incomplete metamorphosis, shown in **Figure 17.** The stages of incomplete metamorphosis are egg, nymph, and adult. The nymph form molts several times before becoming an adult. Many insects—butterflies, beetles, ants, bees, moths, and flies—undergo complete metamorphosis, also shown in **Figure 17.** The stages of complete metamorphosis are egg, larva, pupa, and adult. Caterpillar is the common name for the larva of a moth or butterfly. Other insect larvae are called grubs, maggots, or mealworms. Only larval forms molt.

✔ **Reading Check** *When do grasshoppers molt?*

Figure 17 The two types of metamorphosis are shown here.

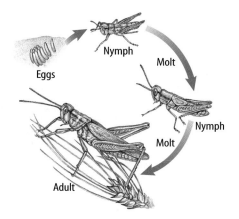

In incomplete metamorphosis, nymphs are smaller versions of their parents.

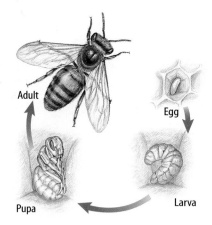

Many insects go through complete metamorphosis.

Visual Learning

Figure 17 Have students make a table in which they compare and contrast the two types of metamorphoses shown in this figure. [L2] [LS] **Visual-Spatial**

Differentiated Instruction

Visually Impaired Purchase a variety of scientifically accurate, arthropod models. As a visually impaired student touches and describes each feature of a model, have a sighted student name the feature and record the description. Together, they should devise a classification system for the arthropod models. [L2] COOP LEARN [LS] **Kinesthetic, Interpersonal**

Figure 18 Feeding adaptations of insects include different mouthparts.

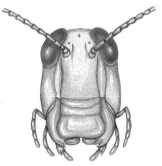

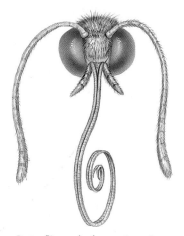

Grasshoppers have left and right mouthparts called mandibles that enable them to chew through tough plant tissues.

Butterflies and other nectar eaters have a long siphon that enables them to drink nectar from flowers.

Mosquitoes have mouths that are adapted for piercing skin and sucking blood.

Obtaining Food

Insects feed on plants, the blood of animals, nectar, decaying materials, wood in houses, and clothes. Mouthparts of insects, such as those in **Figure 18,** are as diverse as the insects themselves. Grasshoppers and ants have large mandibles (MAN duh bulz) for chewing plant tissue. Butterflies and honeybees are equipped with siphons for lapping up nectar in flowers. Aphids and cicadas pierce plant tissues and suck out plant fluids. Praying mantises eat other animals. External parasites, such as mosquitoes, fleas, and lice, drink the blood and body fluids of other animals. Silverfish eat things that contain starch and some moth larvae eat wool clothing.

Insect Success

Because of their tough, flexible, waterproof exoskeletons; their ability to fly; rapid reproductive cycles; and small sizes, insects are extremely successful. Most insects have short life spans, so genetic traits can change more quickly in insect populations than in organisms that take longer to reproduce. Because insects generally are small, they can live in a wide range of environments and avoid their enemies. Many species of insects can live in the same area and not compete with one another for food, because many are so specialized in what they eat.

Protective coloration, or camouflage, allows insects to blend in with their surroundings. Many moths resting on trees look like tree bark or bird droppings. Walking sticks and some caterpillars resemble twigs. When a leaf butterfly folds its wings it looks like a dead leaf.

Disease Carriers Some insects may carry certain diseases to humans. Some species of mosquitoes can carry malaria or yellow fever, and can cause problems around the world. Research to learn about one disease that is carried by an insect, where it is a problem, and the steps that are being taken for prevention and treatment. Make a bulletin board of all the information that you and your classmates gather.

Fun Fact

Only female mosquitoes bite. The blood is used to nourish their eggs. Mosquitoes can detect you twenty feet away by the carbon dioxide you exhale. They use other sensors to make sure you are a good source of a meal, rather than a metal exhaust pipe. Their sensors detect many things including heat, lactic acid, and water vapor.

Activity

Butterfly Awareness Have students design a poster to increase awareness of butterflies and the need to protect them. They could use the monarch butterfly and draw a map showing the migration route of the monarch from the United States to central Mexico. The poster should also include plants that butterflies feed on and pollinate. L2 IS **Visual-Spatial** P

Disease Carriers Possible topics: malaria, myiasis, relapsing fever, African sleeping sickness, leishmaniasis, yellow fever, dengue fever

Fun Fact

Insects are found in every biome except the deep ocean. Some insect species can survive in extremely cold climates because they have a natural antifreeze in their body fluids. Fleas, lice, and midges are all found in extremely cold areas.

Science Journal

Healing Powers Have students research the use of green bottle fly (*Lucilia sericata*) maggots to promote healing of open sores. They can use scientific and medical magazines, newspaper articles, and television programs for information. L2
IS **Linguistic**

Teacher FYI

Insect Wings Insect wings are not modified limbs as are wings in bats and birds. They are thin outgrowths of the exoskeleton. The wings of many insects are made of a double layer of chitin with a supporting network of hollow veins filled with air or blood.

Arachnids

Spiders, scorpions, mites, and ticks are examples of arachnids (uh RAK nudz). They have two body regions—a head-chest region called the cephalothorax (se fuh luh THOR aks) and an abdomen. Arachnids have four pairs of legs but no antennae. Many arachnids are adapted to kill prey with venom glands, stingers, or fangs. Others are parasites.

Scorpions Arachnids that have a sharp, venom-filled stinger at the end of their abdomen are called scorpions. The venom from the stinger paralyzes the prey. Unlike other arachnids, scorpions have a pair of well-developed appendages—pincers—with which they grab their prey. The sting of a scorpion is painful and can be fatal to humans.

Applying Math   **Use Percentages**

SILK ELASTICITY A strand of spider's silk can be stretched from 65 cm to 85 cm before it loses its elasticity—the ability to snap back to its original length. Calculate the percent of elasticity of spider's silk.

Solution

1 *This is what you know:*
- original length of silk strand = 65 cm
- stretched length of silk strand = 85 cm

2 *This is what you need to find out:* percent of elasticity

3 *This is the procedure you need to use:*
- Find the difference between the stretched and original length. 85 cm − 65 cm = 20 cm
- $\dfrac{\text{difference in length}}{\text{original length}} \times 100 = \%$ of elasticity
- $\dfrac{20 \text{ cm}}{65 \text{ cm}} \times 100 = 30.7 \%$ of elasticity

4 *Check your answer:* Multiply 30.7% by 65 cm and you should get 20 cm.

Practice Problems

1. A 40-cm strand of nylon can be stretched to a length of 46.5 cm before losing its elasticity. Calculate the percent of elasticity for nylon and compare it to that of spider's silk.

2. Knowing the elasticity of spider's silk, what was the original length of a silk strand when the difference between the two strands is 44 cm?

For more practice, visit bookc.msscience.com/ math_practice

Science Journal

Careers Students may be interested in careers related to arthropods. Suggest that they research different types of careers in the field of entomology and record in their Science Journals what skills and education are needed and what the jobs entail. L2 LS **Linguistic**

Cultural Diversity

Origin of Silk Silk moth cocoons are one continuous strand of silk. According to Chinese legends, silk cloth originated around 3000 B.C. It is said that a cocoon fell into an empress' tea. The tea dissolved the substance that glued the cocoon together, revealing the long silk strand. Several strands were woven into a thread and, eventually, silk fabric was woven.

Spiders Because spiders can't chew their food, they release enzymes into their prey that help digest it. The spider then sucks the predigested liquid into its mouth.

Oxygen and carbon dioxide are exchanged in book lungs, illustrated in **Figure 19.** Openings on the abdomen allow these gases to move into and out of the book lungs.

Mites and Ticks Most mites are animal or plant parasites. However, some are not parasites, like the mites that live in the follicles of human eyelashes. Most mites are so small that they look like tiny specs to the unaided eye. All ticks are animal parasites. Ticks attach to their host's skin and remove blood from their hosts through specialized mouthparts. Ticks often carry bacteria and viruses that cause disease in humans and other animals. Diseases carried by ticks include Lyme disease and Rocky Mountain spotted fever.

Centipedes and Millipedes

Two groups of arthropods—centipedes and millipedes—have long bodies with many segments and many legs, antennae, and simple eyes. They can be found in damp environments, including in woodpiles, under vegetation, and in basements. Centipedes and millipedes reproduce sexually. They make nests for their eggs and stay with them until the eggs hatch.

Compare the centipede and millipede in **Figure 20.** How many pairs of legs does the centipede have per segment? How many pairs of legs does the millipede have per segment? Centipedes hunt for their prey, which includes snails, slugs, and worms. They have a pair of venomous claws that they use to inject venom into their prey. Their pinches are painful to humans but usually aren't fatal. Millipedes feed on plants and decaying material and often are found under the damp plant material.

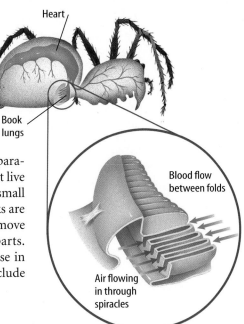

Figure 19 Air circulates between the moist folds of the book lungs bringing oxygen to the blood.

Figure 20 Centipedes are predators—they capture and eat other animals. Millipedes eat plants or decaying plant material.

Centipede

Millipede

SECTION 3 Arthropods **C** ◆ **53**

Visualizing Arthropod Diversity

Have students examine the pictures and read the captions. Then ask the following questions.

What different types of locomotion are used by arthropods? Students should note that arthropods walk, fly and swim. Barnacles usually do not move from place to place under their own power.

What characteristic of a Monarch butterfly allows it to survive the changing weather in its environment? A monarch's wings allow it to migrate to a warmer climate when temperatures become too cold.

Activity

Model Arthropods Have students work in pairs to make a model of one of the arthropods pictured. Students should research the characteristics of the arthropod they have chosen to model, and incorporate their findings into their model. Have students present their models to the class. L2

Activity

Venn Diagram Have students make a Venn diagram that compares the characteristics of three of the pictured arthropods. Have students do further research to increase the number of characteristics included in their diagram. L2

NATIONAL GEOGRAPHIC **VISUALIZING ARTHROPOD DIVERSITY**

Figure 21

Some 600 million years ago, the first arthropods lived in Earth's ancient seas. Today, they inhabit nearly every environment on Earth. Arthropods are the most abundant and diverse group of animals on Earth. They range in size from nearly microscopic mites to spindly, giant Japanese spider crabs with legs spanning more than 3 m.

GRASS SPIDER Grass spiders spin fine, nearly invisible webs just above the ground.

MONARCH BUTTERFLY Monarchs are a common sight in much of the United States during the summer. In fall, they migrate south to warmer climates.

LOBSTER Like crabs, lobsters are crustaceans that belong to the group called Decapoda, which means "ten legs." It's the lobster's tail, however, that interests most seafood lovers.

GOOSENECK BARNACLE Gooseneck barnacles typically live attached to objects that float in the ocean. They use their long, feathery setae to strain tiny bits of food from the water.

HISSING COCKROACH Most cockroaches are considered to be pests by humans, but hissing cockroaches, such as this one, are sometimes kept as pets.

HORSESHOE CRAB Contrary to their name, horseshoe crabs are not crustaceans. They are more closely related to spiders than to crabs.

CENTIPEDE One pair of legs per segment distinguishes a centipede from a millipede, which has two pairs of legs per body segment.

54

Active Reading

Jigsaw Place students in five cooperative groups. Each group is to be responsible for studying and summarizing one of the five types of arthropods discussed in this section—insects, arachnids, centipedes, millipedes, and crustaceans. Once finished, each group is to direct the discussion on the type of arthropod it was responsible for learning about. Instruct groups to include drawings and several examples of their type of arthropod. L2 COOP LEARN
IS Interpersonal

Crustaceans

Crabs, crayfish, shrimp, barnacles, pill bugs, and water fleas are crustaceans. Crustaceans and other arthropods are shown in **Figure 21.** Crustaceans have one or two pairs of antennae and mandibles, which are used for crushing food. Most crustaceans live in water, but some, like the pill bugs shown in **Figure 22,** live in moist environments on land. Pill bugs are common in gardens and around house foundations. They are harmless to humans.

Crustaceans, like the blue crab shown in **Figure 22,** have five pairs of legs. The first pair of legs are claws that catch and hold food. The other four pairs are walking legs. They also have five pairs of appendages on the abdomen called swimmerets. They help the crustacean move and are used in reproduction. In addition, the swimmerets force water over the feathery gills where the oxygen and carbon dioxide are exchanged. If a crustacean loses an appendage, it will grow back, or regenerate.

Value of Arthropods

Arthropods play several roles in the environment. They are a source of food for many animals, including humans. Some humans consider shrimp, crab, crayfish, and lobster as food delicacies. In Africa and Asia, many people eat insect larvae and insects such as grasshoppers, termites, and ants, which are excellent sources of protein.

Agriculture would be impossible without bees, butterflies, moths, and flies that pollinate crops. Bees manufacture honey, and silkworms produce silk. Many insects and spiders are predators of harmful animal species, such as stableflies. Useful chemicals are obtained from some arthropods. For example, bee venom is used to treat rheumatic arthritis.

Not all arthropods are useful to humans. Almost every cultivated crop has some insect pest that feeds on it. Many arthropods—mosquitoes, tsetse flies, fleas, and ticks—carry human and other animal diseases. In addition, weevils, cockroaches, carpenter ants, clothes moths, termites, and carpet beetles destroy food, clothing, and property.

Insects are an important part of the ecological communities in which humans live. Removing all of the insects would cause more harm than good.

Pill bugs

Crab

Figure 22 The segments in some crustaceans, such as this crab, aren't obvious because they are covered by a shieldlike structure. Pill bugs—also called roly polys—are crustaceans that live on land.

Compare and contrast *pill bugs to centipedes and millipedes.*

Discussion

Insect Survival How does meta-morphosis contribute to the suc-cess and survival of insect species? There is no competition between larvae and adults for food; insects can survive harsh and cold weather while protected as pupae. L2

3 Assess

DAILY INTERVENTION

Check for Understanding

Linguistic Have students explain why arthropods molt several times during their lives. L2 LS

Reteach

Arthropod Characteristics Give each group a dissecting tray con-taining a preserved millipede, centipede, crayfish, grasshopper, and spider. Have the students list the characteristics of the animals and determine how the five organisms are similar and how they are different. L1

COOP LEARN LS **Kinesthetic**

✓ Assessment

Content Ask students to write in their Science Journals how incomplete and complete meta-morphosis are similar and how they are different. Both are a series of changes. In complete metamorphoses, the young look very different from the adults. Use **Performance Assessment in the Science Classroom,** p. 175. L2

Figure 23 More than 15,000 species of trilobites have been classified. They are one of the most recognized types of fossils.

Controlling Insects One common way to control problem insects is by insecticides. However, many insecticides also kill helpful insects. Another problem is that many toxic substances that kill insects remain in the environment and accumulate in the bodies of animals that eat them. As other animals eat the contaminated animals, the insecticides can find their way into human food. Humans also are harmed by these toxins.

Different types of bacteria, fungi, and viruses are being used to control some insect pests. Natural predators and parasites of insect pests have been somewhat successful in controlling them. Other biological controls include using sterile males or naturally occurring chemicals that interfere with the reproduction or behavior of insect pests.

Origin of Arthropods Because of their hard body parts, arthropod fossils, like the one in **Figure 23,** are among the old-est and best-preserved fossils of many-celled animals. Some are more than 500 million years old. Because earthworms and leeches have individual body segments, scientists hypothesize that arthropods probably evolved from an ancestor of seg-mented worms. Over time, groups of body segments fused and became adapted for locomotion, feeding, and sensing the envi-ronment. The hard exoskeleton and walking legs allowed arthropods to be among the first successful land animals.

section 3 review

Summary

Characteristics of Arthropods

- All arthropods have jointed appendages, bilateral symmetry, a body cavity, a digestive system, a nervous system, segmented bodies, and an exoskeleton.

Arthropod Types

- Insects have three body segments—head, thorax, and abdomen—a pair of antennae, and three pairs of legs. They go through com-plete or incomplete metamorphosis.
- Arachnids have two body segments—a cephalothorax and an abdomen—four pairs of legs, and no antennae.
- Centipedes and millipedes have long bodies with many segments and legs.
- Crustaceans have five pairs of legs and five pairs of appendages called swimmerets.

Self Check

1. **Infer** the advantages and disadvantages of an exoskeleton.
2. **Compare and contrast** the stages of complete and incomplete metamorphosis.
3. **List** four ways arthropods obtain food.
4. **Evaluate** the impact of arthropods.
5. **Concept Map** Make an events-chain concept map of complete metamorphosis and one of incomplete metamorphosis.
6. **Think Critically** Choose an insect you are familiar with and explain how it is adapted to its environment.

Applying Math

7. **Make a Graph** Of the major arthropod groups, 88% are insects, 7% are arachnids, 3% are crustaceans, 1% are centipedes and millipedes, and all others make up 1%. Show this data in a circle graph.

Science Online bookc.msscience.com/self_check_quiz

section 3 review

1. advantages: prevents dehydration, supports and protects body; disad-vantages: body outgrows exoskele-ton, animal vulnerable to predators while new exoskeleton hardens
2. Incomplete has a nymph stage between egg and adult; complete has a larva and pupa stage

between egg and adult.
3. Arthropods obtain food by chewing, piercing and sucking, lapping up nectar, and eating other animals.
4. Arthropods are a food source, they pollinate crops, prey on harmful organisms, and can be used medici-nally. Arthropods destroy crops, carry

disease, and destroy property.
5. Make sure students include all stages in both concept maps.
6. Answers will vary. Look for under-standing of insect adaptations.
7. Graph segments should be propor-tional and labeled.

Observing a Crayfish

A crayfish has a segmented body and a fused head and thorax. It has a snout and eyes on movable eyestalks. Most crayfish have pincers.

Real-World Question

How does a crayfish use its appendages?

Goals

- **Observe** a crayfish.
- **Determine** the function of pincers.

Materials

crayfish in a small aquarium
uncooked ground beef
stirrer

Safety Precautions

Procedure

1. Copy the data table and use it to record all of your observations during this lab.

Crayfish Observations

Body Region	Number of Appendages	Function
Head	5 pairs	sense environment; hold and chew food
Thorax	5 pairs	capture food; defense; walking
Abdomen	5 pairs	create water currents to help crayfish move; reproduction

2. Your teacher will provide you with a crayfish in an aquarium. Leave the crayfish in the aquarium while you do the lab. Draw your crayfish.

3. Gently touch the crayfish with the stirrer. How does the body feel?
4. **Observe** how the crayfish moves in the water.
5. **Observe** the compound eyes. On which body region are they located?
6. Drop a small piece of ground beef into the aquarium. Observe the crayfish's reaction. Wash your hands.
7. Return the aquarium to its proper place.

Conclude and Apply

1. **Infer** how the location of the eyes is an advantage for the crayfish.
2. **Explain** how the structure of the pincers aids in getting food.
3. **Infer** how the exoskeleton provides protection.

Communicating Your Data

Compare your observations with those of other students in your class. **For more help, refer to the** Science Skill Handbook.

Real-World Question

Purpose Students observe crayfish structure and determine appendage use. L2

IS Visual-Spatial

Process Skills observe, interpret data, infer, compare and contrast

Time Required 35 minutes

Procedure

Alternate Materials Preserved crayfish may be used.

Teaching Strategy Crayfish may be obtained from a local stream or a biological supply company. If obtained locally, return them to the stream when the activity is completed.

Troubleshooting Students may not be able to count the appendages of the crayfish in the aquarium. Use a transparency of a crayfish on the overhead projector to help them.

Conclude and Apply

1. Crayfish conceal themselves under rocks and in mud. The eyes at the end of stalks allow the crayfish to see without revealing their bodies.
2. The two-piece structure works like a clamp to capture prey and the serrated edges help hold prey.
3. The hard exoskeleton protects it from predators and from falling debris.

Assessment

Performance To expand students' understanding of crayfish, have them put a plastic bag containing ice cubes at one end of a long aquarium and a bag of warm water at the other end. Observe crayfish response. Have students infer how this response is reflected in nature. Remove bags when finished. Use **Performance Assessment in the Science Classroom,** p. 89.

Communicating Your Data

Have students put together a bulletin board on which crayfish drawings can be displayed. Copy the data table onto the board and fill it in as a class.

1 Motivate

INTERACTIVE CHALKBOARD
PowerPoint® Presentations

Bellringer

Section Focus Transparencies also are available on the Interactive Chalkboard CD-ROM.

L2 ELL

SECTION 4 Section Focus Transparency **Tangled Up with Reefs**

The crown-of-thorns sea star lives and feeds on the coral reefs of the Pacific and Indian Oceans. These sea stars have few predators and can cause great damage to the reefs. When there are few corals left to feed on, the number of crown-of-thorns sea stars often declines. Unfortunately, damaged portions of the reef may never recover.

1. Why is it a problem for reefs that crown-of-thorns sea stars have relatively few predators?
2. Why might there be few predators of this sea star?
3. Name some other animals that have a skin similar to the sea star's.

Mollusks, Worms, Arthropods, Echinoderms

Tie to Prior Knowledge

Dried Echinoderms Even if students have not seen living echinoderms, they have probably seen dried sea stars and sand dollar skeletons. Use their knowledge of echinoderms to introduce this lesson. L2

Fun Fact

The sunflower star is one of the largest echinoderms. With 24 arms, it can reach a diameter over 2 feet!

---

section 4 Echinoderms

as you read

What You'll Learn

- **List** the characteristics of echinoderms.
- **Explain** how sea stars obtain and digest food.
- **Discuss** the importance of echinoderms.

Why It's Important

Echinoderms are a group of animals that affect oceans and coastal areas.

Review Vocabulary
epidermis: outer, thinnest layer of skin

New Vocabulary
- water-vascular system
- tube feet

Echinoderm Characteristics

Echinoderms (ih KI nuh durm) are found in oceans all over the world. The term *echinoderm* is from the Greek words *echinos* meaning "spiny" and *derma* meaning "skin." Echinoderms have a hard endoskeleton covered by a thin, bumpy, or spiny epidermis. They are radially symmetrical, which allows them to sense food, predators, and other things in their environment from all directions.

All echinoderms have a mouth, stomach, and intestines. They feed on a variety of plants and animals. For example, sea stars feed on worms and mollusks, and sea urchins feed on algae. Others feed on dead and decaying matter called detritus (de TRI tus) found on the ocean floor.

Echinoderms have no head or brain, but they do have a nerve ring that surrounds the mouth. They also have cells that respond to light and touch.

Water-Vascular System A characteristic unique to echinoderms is their water-vascular system. It allows them to move, exchange carbon dioxide and oxygen, capture food, and release wastes. The **water-vascular system,** as shown in **Figure 24,** is a network of water-filled canals with thousands of tube feet connected to it. **Tube feet** are hollow, thin-walled tubes that each end in a suction cup. As the pressure in the tube feet changes, the animal is able to move along by pushing out and pulling in its tube feet.

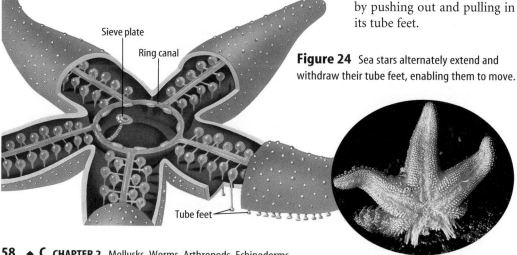

Sieve plate

Ring canal

Tube feet

Figure 24 Sea stars alternately extend and withdraw their tube feet, enabling them to move.

Section 4 Resource Manager

Chapter *FAST FILE* Resources

Transparency Activity, p. 49

Directed Reading for Content Mastery, pp. 19, 20

MiniLAB, p. 4

Enrichment, p. 32

Reinforcement, p. 28

Lab Worksheet, pp. 7–8

Lab Management and Safety, p. 73

Types of Echinoderms

Approximately 6,000 species of echinoderms are living today. Of those, more than one-third are sea stars. The other groups include brittle stars, sea urchins, sand dollars, and sea cucumbers.

Sea Stars Echinoderms with at least five arms arranged around a central point are called sea stars. The arms are lined with thousands of tube feet. Sea stars use their tube feet to open the shells of their prey. When the shell is open slightly, the sea star pushes its stomach through its mouth and into its prey. The sea star's stomach surrounds the soft body of its prey and secretes enzymes that help digest it. When the meal is over, the sea star pulls its stomach back into its own body.

✔ **Reading Check** *What is unusual about the way that sea stars eat their prey?*

Sea stars reproduce sexually when females release eggs and males release sperm into the water. Females can produce millions of eggs in one season.

Sea stars also can repair themselves by regeneration. If a sea star loses an arm, it can grow a new one. If enough of the center disk is left attached to a severed arm, a whole new sea star can grow from that arm.

Brittle Stars Like the one in **Figure 25,** brittle stars have fragile, slender, branched arms that break off easily. This adaptation helps a brittle star survive attacks by predators. While the predator is eating a broken arm, the brittle star escapes. Brittle stars quickly regenerate lost parts. They live hidden under rocks or in litter on the ocean floor. Brittle stars use their flexible arms for movement instead of their tube feet. Their tube feet are used to move particles of food into their mouth.

Figure 25 A brittle star's arms are so flexible that they wave back and forth in the ocean currents. They are called brittle stars because their arms break off easily if they are grabbed by a predator.

SECTION 4 Echinoderms **C ◆ 59**

Mini LAB

Modeling the Strength of Tube Feet

Procedure
1. Hold your arm straight out, palm up.
2. Place a **heavy book** on your hand.
3. Have your partner time how long you can hold your arm up with the book on it.

Analysis
1. Describe how your arm feels after a few minutes.
2. If the book models the sea star and your arm models the clam, infer how a sea star successfully overcomes a clam to obtain food.

Try at Home

---

2 Teach

Mini LAB

Purpose to model how sea stars can open clam shells held closed by muscles L1 IS **Kinesthetic**

Materials heavy books, clock with a second hand

Teaching Strategies
• Make sure the books students use are heavy but not too heavy to lift.
• As students try this lab, suggest they imagine this is a life-or-death struggle as it is for the sea star and clam.

Analysis
1. arm muscles tire
2. Sea stars pull on a clam by using the suction power of their tube feet. Eventually, the muscles of the clam tire and the shell opens.

Assessment

Performance Have students wet suction cups and press them against a variety of surfaces. Ask students whether they can pick up an object with a suction cup and to compare this to tube feet. Yes; tube feet act like suction cups. Use **Performance Assessment in the Science Classroom,** p. 97.

Try at Home

✔ **Reading Check**

Answer They expel their stomach to eat.

Visual Learning

Figure 25 Have students study the brittle star in its natural environment. Then, have them make a list of its adaptations to this environment. L2 P

Differentiated Instruction

Learning Disabled Have learning disabled students make a picture dictionary illustrating the meaning of unfamiliar terms in this chapter. Have them write their words on cards and keep the cards in alphabetical order. L1 IS **Visual-Spatial**

Figure 26 Like all echinoderms, sand dollars and sea urchins are radially symmetrical.

Sand dollars live on ocean floors where they can burrow into the sand.

Sea urchins use tube feet and their spines to move around on the bottom of the ocean.

Science Online

Topic: Humans and Echinoderms

Visit bookc.msscience.com for Web links to information about how echinoderms are used by humans.

Activity Choose one or two uses and write an essay on why echinoderms are important to you.

Sea Urchins and Sand Dollars Another group of echinoderms includes sea urchins, sea biscuits, and sand dollars. They are disk- or globe-shaped animals covered with spines. They do not have arms, but sand dollars have a five-pointed pattern on their surface. **Figure 26** shows living sand dollars, covered with stiff, hairlike spines, and sea urchins with long, pointed spines that protect them from predators. Some sea urchins have sacs near the end of the spines that contain toxic fluid that is injected into predators. The spines also help in movement and burrowing. Sea urchins have five toothlike structures around their mouth.

Sea Cucumbers The animal shown in **Figure 27** is a sea cucumber. Sea cucumbers are soft-bodied echinoderms that have a leathery covering. They have tentacles around their mouth and rows of tube feet on their upper and lower surfaces. When threatened, sea cucumbers may expel their internal organs. These organs regenerate in a few weeks. Some sea cucumbers eat detritus, and others eat plankton.

✔ Reading Check

What makes sea cucumbers different from other echinoderms?

Figure 27 Sea cucumbers have short tube feet, which they use to move around.
Describe *the characteristics of sea cucumbers.*

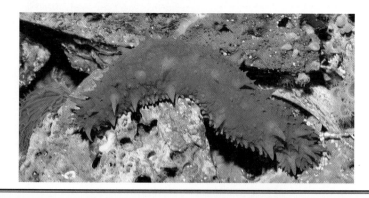

Differentiated Instruction

Challenge Have students find out about other echinoderm defenses such as the amount of slime produced by the sea star *Pteraster tesselatus*, the venom in the spines of the sea urchin *Asthenosoma*, and the modified poison spines that are pincerlike appendages of the sea urchin *Toxopneustes*. Also, sea cucumbers expel their internal organs as a type of defense. L3

Teacher FYI

Many ancient echinoderms became extinct at the end of the Permian period. A number of factors caused the extinction, including climate changes and the formation of Pangaea.

Value of Echinoderms

Echinoderms are important to the marine environment because they feed on dead organisms and help recycle materials. Sea urchins control the growth of algae in coastal areas. Sea urchin eggs and sea cucumbers are used for food in some places. Many echinoderms are used in research and some might be possible sources of medicines. Sea stars are important predators that control populations of other animals. However, because sea stars feed on oysters and clams, they also destroy millions of dollars' worth of mollusks each year.

Origin of Echinoderms Like the example in **Figure 28,** a good fossil record exists for echinoderms. Echinoderms date back more than 400 million years. The earliest echinoderms might have had bilateral symmetry as adults and may have been attached to the ocean floor by stalks. Many larval forms of modern echinoderms are bilaterally symmetrical.

Scientists hypothesize that echinoderms more closely resemble animals with backbones than any other group of invertebrates. This is because echinoderms have complex body systems and an embryo that develops the same way that the embryos of animals with backbones develop.

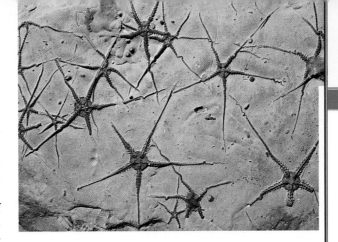

Figure 28 *Ophiopinna elegans* was a brittle star that lived about 165 million years ago.
Explain *the origins of echinoderms.*

section 4 review

Summary

Echinoderm Characteristics

- Echinoderms have a hard endoskeleton and are covered by thin, spiny skin.
- They are radially symmetrical. They have no brain or head, but have a nerve ring, and respond to light and touch.
- They have a specialized water-vascular system, which helps them move, exchange gases, capture food, and release wastes.

Types of Echinoderms

- The largest group of echinoderms is sea stars.
- Other groups include brittle stars, sea urchins and sand dollars, and sea cucumbers.

Self Check

1. **Explain** how echinoderms move and get their food.
2. **Infer** how sea urchins are beneficial.
3. **List** the methods of defense that echinoderms have to protect themselves from predators.
4. **Think Critically** Why would the ability to regenerate lost body parts be an important adaptation for sea stars, brittle stars, and other echinoderms?

Applying Skills

5. **Form a Hypothesis** Why do you think echinoderms live on the ocean floor?
6. **Communicate** Choose an echinoderm and write about it. Describe its appearance, how it gets food, where it lives, and other interesting facts.

Science online bookc.msscience.com/self_check_quiz

DAILY INTERVENTION

Check for Understanding

Linguistic Have students explain why echinoderms have few predators. L2 LS

Reteach

Echinoderm Characteristics Have students look at either photographs or specimens of various echinoderms and list the major characteristics of each type. L2

✓ Assessment

Oral Infer why echinoderms are bottom dwellers. The tube feet are on the ventral side. Use **Performance Assessment in the Science Classroom,** p. 89. L2

Virtual Labs

Classify *How are mollusks, worms, arthropods, and echinoderms classified?*

section 4 review

1. through the use of tube feet
2. They control the growth of algae. Their eggs are used as food by some people.
3. They have hard endoskeletons and spines, they regenerate rapidly, some have poison glands, and sea cucumbers can expel and regenerate their digestive systems.
4. Sea stars are dependent upon their arms (which contain tube feet) to move and obtain food. They could not survive without them.
5. With the exception of the brittle star, echinoderms have no means of movement except for their tube feet. Living on the ocean floor allows them to feed on other organisms and hide under debris.
6. Check students' work.

BENCH TESTED

▶ Real-World Question

Purpose Students experiment to determine the foods preferred by earthworms. L2 IS **Kinesthetic and Logical-Mathematical**

Process Skills identify and control variables, compare and contrast, observe and infer

Time Required one class period

▶ Procedure

Materials Be certain students do not pack the materials into their jars tightly. Soil and humus should be sprinkled into the jar to allow sufficient air pockets to form.

Alternate Materials Decomposing leaf litter can replace humus, and melon or cantaloupe rinds can replace banana peels.

Safety Precautions Students should thoroughly wash their hands after handling lab materials. Caution students not to eat foods during science class. Caution students to moisten their hands before handling earthworms and to handle them gently.

Teaching Strategies

- Ask students to capture worms from their home gardens or yards to be used in the activity.
- Inspect each group's jar before they start the final stages of the experiment.

LAB

What do w⊙rms eat?

Goals
- **Construct** five earthworm habitats.
- **Test** different foods to determine which ones earthworms eat.

Materials
orange peels
apple peels
banana skin
kiwi fruit skin
watermelon rind
*skins of five
    different fruits
widemouthed jars (5)
potting soil
water
humus
*peat moss
earthworms
black construction paper
    (5 sheets)
masking tape
marker
rubber bands (5)
*Alternate materials

Safety Precautions

WARNING: *Do not handle earthworms with dry hands. Do not eat any materials used in the lab.*

▶ Real-World Question

Earthworms are valuable because they improve the soil in which they live. There can be 50,000 earthworms living in one acre. Their tunnels increase air movement through the soil and improve water drainage. As they eat the decaying material in soil, their wastes can enrich the soil. Other than decaying material, what else do earthworms eat? Do they have favorite foods?

▶ Procedure

1. Pour equal amounts of soil into each of the jars. Do not pack the soil. Leave several centimeters of space at the top of each jar.

2. Sprinkle equal amounts of water into each jar to moisten the soil. Avoid pouring too much water into the jars.

3. Pour humus into each of your jars to a depth of 2 cm. The humus should be loose.

4. Add watermelon rinds to the first jar, orange peels to the second, apple peels to the third, kiwi fruit skins to the fourth, and a banana peel to the fifth jar. Each jar should have 2 cm of fruit skins on top of the layer of humus.

Alternative Inquiry Lab

Asking Questions To extend this lab, make it an inquiry lab. Build on student experiences by encouraging them to use what they have learned to brainstorm questions about the eating habits of worms. Have each student choose one question to explore. Unsafe or impractical questions should be eliminated. Ask them to choose the materials they need to explore their questions. Students should have their plan approved before continuing. Conduct the experiments after all of the necessary materials have been gathered.

5. Add five earthworms to each jar.

6. Wrap a sheet of black construction paper around each jar and secure it with a rubber band.

7. Using the masking tape and marker, label each jar with the type of fruit it contains.

8. Copy the data table below in your Science Journal.

9. Place all of your jars in the same cool, dark place. Observe your jars every other day for a week and record your observations in your data table.

Fruit Wastes

Date	Watermelon rind	Orange peels	Apple peels	Kiwi skins	Banana peels
		Answers will vary.			

⊙ Analyze Your Data

1. **Record** the changes in your data table.

2. **Compare** the amount of skins left in each jar.

3. **Record** which fruit skin had the greatest change. The least?

⊙ Conclude and Apply

1. **Infer** the type of food favored by earthworms.

2. **Infer** why some of the fruit skins were not eaten by the earthworms.

3. **Identify** a food source in each jar other than the fruit skins.

4. **Predict** what would happen in the jars over the next month if you continued the experiment.

Communicating Your Data

Use the results of your experiment and information from your reading to help you write a recipe for an appetizing dinner that worms would enjoy. Based on the results of your experiment, add other fruit skins or foods to your menu you think worms might like.

Tie to Prior Knowledge Most students know that worms create rich soil by decomposing organic matter.

⊙ Analyze Your Data

Expected Outcome Softer fruit skins such as apples and pears will be consumed by the worms first, and thicker skins will be decomposed last or possibly not at all.

Answers to Questions

1. Check students' data tables.

2. The apple peel will disappear during the week. The other types of fruit skins may show varying degrees of decomposition.

3. Apple peels; answers on the least change will vary depending on thickness of peel, usually watermelon rind, but accept all reasonable answers.

Error Analysis Have each student group occasionally examine the jars of other groups to compare the decay process occurring in the jars. Ask groups to list plausible explanations to explain differences in decomposition rates.

⊙ Conclude and Apply

1. apple peels

2. Watermelon rinds, orange peels, and banana skins are thicker and difficult for earthworms to digest.

3. soil and humus

4. The less digestible fruit skins would begin to decay, enabling the earthworms to consume them.

☑ Assessment

Oral Have students explain the role earthworms play in the formation of nutrient-rich soil. Earthworms help decompose organic matter into nutrient-rich soil, and they eat soil and enrich it as it passes through their digestive systems. Use **Performance Assessment in the Science Classroom,** p. 89. L2

Communicating Your Data

Ask students to research vermicomposting, or composting using worms. They can find what foods should be avoided when composting, which types of worms are the best to use, and the best way to set up a vermicomposting bin. L2

Science and Language Arts

from "The Creatures on My Mind"
by Ursula K. Le Guin

Understanding Literature

Personal Experience Narrative
Answers might include that insects lack the same sensory system as do humans; others may say that there is no way of knowing how insects feel.

Respond to the Reading

1. Possible answer: by flying into the light fixture
2. adult stage
3. **Linking Science and Writing** Have students consider the circumstances of the experience. Was a real or imagined danger involved?

 **Arthropods**
Although many people are horrified by arthropods, particularly insects, the majority of these animals are beneficial to Earth's ecosystems. Most of the world's flowering plants are pollinated by arthropods. Other arthropods, such as larger crustaceans like lobster and shrimp, are used for food. Smaller crustaceans are major components of ocean and wetland food chains.

However, some arthropods do pose threats to animals as well as to agriculture. For example, some insects can devastate crops, and others can carry diseases such as malaria, yellow fever (via mosquitoes) and typhus (via lice).

When I stayed for a week in New Orleans... I had an apartment with a balcony... But when I first stepped out on it, the first thing I saw was a huge beetle. It lay on its back directly under the light fixture. I thought it was dead, then saw its legs twitch and twitch again. Big insects horrify me. As a child I feared moths and spiders, but adolescence cured me, as if those fears evaporated in the stew of hormones. But I never got enough hormones to make me easy with the large, hard-shelled insects: wood roaches, June bugs, mantises, cicadas. This beetle was a couple of inches long; its abdomen was ribbed, its legs long and jointed; it was dull reddish brown; it was dying. I felt a little sick seeing it lie there twitching, enough to keep me from sitting out on the balcony that first day... And if I had any courage or common sense, I kept telling myself, I'd... put it out of its misery. We don't know what a beetle may or may not suffer...

Understanding Literature

Personal Experience Narrative In this passage, the author uses her personal experience to consider her connection to other living things. In this piece, the author recounts a minor event in her life when she happens upon a dying beetle. The experience allows the author to pose some important questions about another species and to think about how beetles might feel when they die. How do you think the beetle is feeling?

Respond to the Reading

1. How do you suppose the beetle injured itself?
2. From the author's description, in what stage of development is the beetle?
3. **Linking Science and Writing** Write about a personal experience that caused you to think about an important question or topic in your life.

INTEGRATE Life Science The author names several arthropod species in the passage, including insects and an arachnid. Beetles, June bugs, mantises, cicadas, and moths are all insects. The spider is an arachnid. Of the arthropods the author names, can you tell which ones go through a complete metamorphosis?

64 ◆ **C CHAPTER 2** Mollusks, Worms, Arthropods, Echinoderms

Resources for Teachers and Students

Bugs: Insects, Spiders, Centipedes, Millipedes and Other Closely Related Arthropods, by Frank Lowenstein and Sheryl Lechner, Black Dog & Leventhal Publishing, December 1999

National Audubon Society Field Guide to North American Insects and Spiders, by Lorus J. Milne and Susan Rayfield (Illustrator), Knopf Publishing, November 1980

Reviewing Main Ideas

Section 1 — Mollusks

1. Mollusks are soft-bodied invertebrates that usually are covered by a hard shell. They move using a muscular foot.

2. Mollusks with one shell are gastropods. Bivalves have two shells. Cephalopods have an internal shell and a foot that is divided into tentacles.

Section 2 — Segmented Worms

1. Segmented worms have tube-shaped bodies divided into sections, a body cavity that holds the internal organs, and bristlelike structures called setae to help them move.

2. An earthworm's digestive system has a mouth, crop, gizzard, intestine, and anus. Polychaetes are marine worms. Leeches are parasites that attach to animals and feed on their blood.

Section 3 — Arthropods

1. More than a million species of arthropods exist, which is more than any other group of animals. Most arthropods are insects.

2. Arthropods are grouped by number of body segments and appendages. Exoskeletons cover, protect, and support arthropod bodies.

3. Young arthropods develop either by complete metamorphosis or incomplete metamorphosis.

Section 4 — Echinoderms

1. Echinoderms have a hard, spiny exoskeleton covered by a thin epidermis.

2. Most echinoderms have a water-vascular system that enables them to move, exchange carbon dioxide and oxygen, capture food, and give off wastes.

Visualizing Main Ideas

Copy and complete the following concept map about insects.

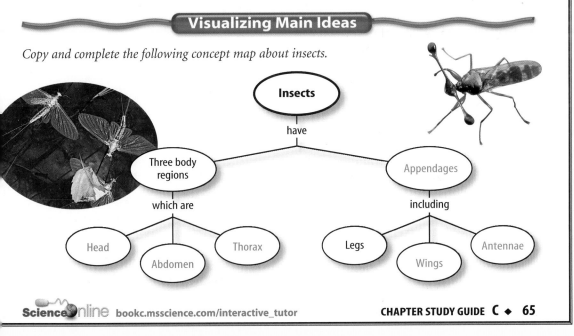

Insects

have

Three body regions — which are — Head, Abdomen, Thorax

Appendages — including — Legs, Wings, Antennae

Reviewing Main Ideas

Summary statements can be used by students to review the major concepts of the chapter.

Visualizing Main Ideas

See student page.

Science online

Visit bookc.msscience.com
/self_check_quiz
/interactive_tutor
/vocabulary_puzzlemaker
/chapter_review
/standardized_test

Assessment Transparency

For additional assessment questions, use the *Assessment Transparency* located in the transparency book.

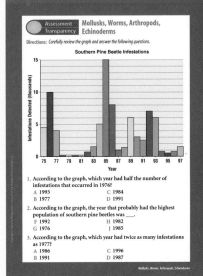

Assessment

Assessment Transparency — Mollusks, Worms, Arthropods, Echinoderms

Directions: Carefully review the graph and answer the following questions.

Southern Pine Beetle Infestations

1. According to the graph, which year had half the number of infestations that occurred in 1976?
   A 1993   C 1984
   B 1977   D 1991

2. According to the graph, the year that probably had the highest population of southern pine beetles was ___.
   F 1992   H 1982
   G 1976   J 1985

3. According to the graph, which year had twice as many infestations as 1977?
   A 1986   C 1996
   B 1991   D 1987

Using Vocabulary

1. mantle
2. setae, crop
3. exoskeleton
4. spiracles
5. Tube feet
6. radula
7. open circulatory system

Checking Concepts

8. C	12. D
9. D	13. A
10. A	14. A
11. C	15. B

Using Vocabulary

appendage p. 48	molting p. 48
closed circulatory	open circulatory
system p. 40	system p. 38
crop p. 44	radula p. 39
exoskeleton p. 48	setae p. 43
gill p. 38	spiracle p. 49
gizzard p. 44	tube feet p. 58
mantle p. 38	water-vascular
metamorphosis p. 50	system p. 58

Fill in the blanks with the correct vocabulary word or words.

1. Mollusk shells are secreted by the _____.

2. As earthworms move through soil using their _____, they take in soil, which is stored in the _____.

3. The _____ covers and protects arthropod bodies.

4. Insects exchange oxygen and carbon dioxide through _____.

5. _____ act like suction cups and help sea stars move and feed.

6. Snails use a(n) _____ to get food.

7. The blood of mollusks moves in a(n) _____.

Checking Concepts

Choose the word or phrase that best answers the question.

8. What structure covers organs of mollusks?
   A) gills
   B) food
   C) mantle
   D) visceral mass

9. What structures do echinoderms use to move and to open shells of mollusks?
   A) mantle
   B) calcium plates
   C) spines
   D) tube feet

10. Which organism has a closed circulatory system?
    A) earthworm
    B) octopus
    C) slug
    D) snail

11. What evidence suggests that arthropods might have evolved from annelids?
    A) Arthropods and annelids have gills.
    B) Both groups have species that live in salt water.
    C) Segmentation is present in both groups.
    D) All segmented worms have setae.

Use the photo below to answer questions 12 and 13.

12. Which of the following correctly describes the arthropod pictured above?
    A) three body regions, six legs
    B) two body regions, eight legs
    C) many body segments, ten legs
    D) many body segments, one pair of legs per segment

13. What type of arthropod is this animal?
    A) annelid
    B) arachnid
    C) insect
    D) mollusk

14. Which is an example of an annelid?
    A) earthworm
    B) octopus
    C) slug
    D) snail

15. Which sequence shows incomplete metamorphosis?
    A) egg—larvae—adult
    B) egg—nymph—adult
    C) larva—pupa—adult
    D) nymph—pupa—adult

 Scienceonline bookc.msscience.com/vocabulary_puzzlemaker

Use the ExamView® Pro Testmaker CD-ROM to:
- create multiple versions of tests
- create modified tests with one mouse click for inclusion students
- edit existing questions and add your own questions
- build tests aligned with state standards using built-in State Curriculum Tags
- change English tests to Spanish with one mouse click and vice versa

Thinking Critically

Use the photo below to answer question 16.

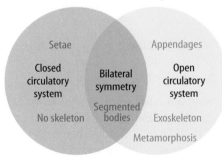

16. **Describe** how this animal obtains food.

17. **Compare** the ability of clams, oysters, scallops, and squid to protect themselves.

18. **Compare and contrast** an earthworm gizzard to teeth in other animals.

19. **Explain** the evidence that mollusks and annelids may share a common ancestor.

20. **Infer** how taking in extra water or air after molting, but before the new exoskeleton hardens, helps an arthropod.

21. **Classify** the following animals into arthropod groups: *spider, pill bug, crayfish, grasshopper, crab, silverfish, cricket, wasp, scorpion, shrimp, barnacle, tick,* and *butterfly.*

22. **Compare and Contrast** Copy and complete this Venn diagram to compare and contrast arthropods to annelids.

Annelids   **Arthropods**

- Setae
- Closed circulatory system
- No skeleton
- Bilateral symmetry
- Segmented bodies
- Appendages
- Open circulatory system
- Exoskeleton
- Metamorphosis

23. **Recognize Cause and Effect** If all the earthworms were removed from a hectare of soil, what would happen to the soil? Why?

24. **Research Information** The suffix *-ptera* means "wings." Research the meaning of the prefix listed below and give an example of a member of each insect group.

Diptera	Homoptera
Orthoptera	Hemiptera
Coleoptera	

Performance Activities

25. **Construct** Choose an arthropod that develops through complete metamorphosis and construct a three-dimensional model for each of the four stages.

Applying Math

Use the table below to answer questions 26 and 27.

Described Species	
Type of Organism	**Number of Described Species**
Anthropods	1,065,000
Land plants	270,000
Fungi	72,000
Mollusks	70,000
Nematodes	25,000
Birds	10,000
Mammals	5,000
Bacteria	4,000
Other	145,000

26. **Arthropods** Using the table above, what percentage of organisms are arthropods? Mollusks?

27. **Species Distribution** Make a bar graph that shows the number of described species listed in the table above.

Thinking Critically

16. Gastropods use their radula to tear plant materials and scrape algae and plant material.

17. Clams burrow into the sand; oysters attach themselves by strong sticky threads to rocks; scallops eject water and move by rapidly opening and closing their shells; a squid ejects water and escapes by jet propulsion. Oysters, clams, and scallops also have hard shells.

18. Grit in the earthworm gizzard grinds soil in the same way that teeth break up and grind food in the mouth.

19. A space in the body to hold organs is present in both groups. The larvae of both groups are similar.

20. It provides room in which to grow before the next molt.

21. arachnids: spider, tick, scorpion; crustaceans: pill bug, crayfish, crab, shrimp, barnacle; insects: grasshopper, silverfish, cricket, wasp, butterfly

22. See student page.

23. The soil would become packed and hardened. It would be less fertile because of the lack of earthworm wastes.

24. Gastropods have only one shell.

25. Diptera: two wings, flies; Orthoptera: straight wings, grasshoppers; Coleoptera: shielded wings, beetles; Homoptera: whole wings, leaf hoppers; Hemiptera: half wings, water bugs

Performance Activities

26. Models will vary. Use **PASC**, p. 123.

Applying Math

National Math Standards
1, 5, 9

27. 64% arthropods, 4% mollusks (1,666,000 total species described)

28. Check students' graphs.

FAST FILE

Answer Sheet A practice answer sheet can be found at bookc.msscience.com/answer_sheet.

SAMPLE

Part 1 Multiple Choice

1. C
2. B
3. C
4. D
5. A
6. C
7. D
8. C
9. D
10. A
11. B

Part 1 Multiple Choice

Record your answers on the answer sheet provided by your teacher or on a sheet of paper.

1. Which of the following is not a mollusk?
   - **A.** clam
   - **B.** snail
   - **C.** crab
   - **D.** squid

Use the illustration below to answer questions 2 and 3.

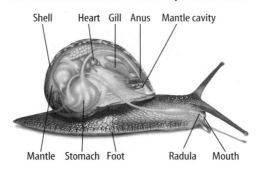

Shell Heart Gill Anus Mantle cavity

Mantle Stomach Foot Radula Mouth

2. This mollusk uses which of the following to exchange carbon dioxide with oxygen from the water?
   - **A.** radula
   - **B.** gill
   - **C.** mantle
   - **D.** shell

3. Which structure covers the body organs of this mollusk?
   - **A.** radula
   - **B.** gill
   - **C.** mantle
   - **D.** shell

4. Which is the largest group of mollusks?
   - **A.** cephalopods
   - **B.** bivalves
   - **C.** monovalves
   - **D.** gastropods

5. Which openings allow air to enter an insect's body?
   - **A.** spiracles
   - **B.** gills
   - **C.** thorax
   - **D.** setae

Use the photo below to answer questions 6 and 7.

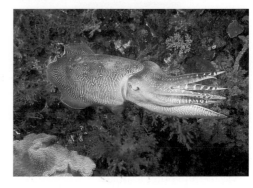

6. This organism is an example of what type of mollusk?
   - **A.** gastropod
   - **B.** bivalve
   - **C.** cephalopod
   - **D.** monovalve

7. How do these animals move?
   - **A.** a muscular foot
   - **B.** tentacles
   - **C.** contraction and relaxation
   - **D.** jet propulsion

8. What does the word annelid mean?
   - **A.** segmented
   - **B.** bristled
   - **C.** little rings
   - **D.** worms

9. What are bristlelike structures on the outside of each body segment of annelids called?
   - **A.** crops
   - **B.** gizzards
   - **C.** radula
   - **D.** setae

10. What is the largest group of animals?
    - **A.** arthropods
    - **B.** cephalopods
    - **C.** gastropods
    - **D.** annelids

11. What is it called when an arthropod loses its exoskeleton and replaces it with a new one?
    - **A.** shedding
    - **B.** molting
    - **C.** manging
    - **D.** exfoliating

68 ◆ **C** STANDARDIZED TEST PRACTICE

Part 2 Short Response/Grid In

12. they use tube feet to pry open the shells of their prey, push their stomach outside of their body into the prey and digest its soft body

13. regeneration

14. they scrape and tear food using their radula

15. a closed circulatory system to carry food and oxygen

16. jet propulsion; they take in water and force it out through an opening near the head

17. Sexually; they are hermaphrodites, but cannot fertilize themselves.

18. Blood and oxygen are not contained in blood vessels, the blood completely surrounds the organs; insects, snails, leeches

19. An irritant in some mollusks is coated by a material that forms smooth, hard layers.

Part 2 | Short Response/Grid In

Record your answers on the answer sheet provided by your teacher or on a sheet of paper.

12. Describe how a sea star captures and consumes its prey.

13. Explain how sea stars repair or replace lost or damaged body parts.

14. Describe how gastropods, such as snails and garden slugs, eat.

Use the photo below to answer questions 15 and 16.

15. Describe this animal's vascular system. How is it used?

16. This animal has a unique method of movement. What is it and how does it work?

17. Describe the type of reproductive system found in earthworms.

18. What is an open circulatory system? Give three examples of animals that have an open circulatory system.

19. How are pearls formed in clams, oysters, and some other gastropods?

Science Online   bookc.msscience.com/standardized_test

Part 3 | Open Ended

Record your answers on a sheet of paper.

Use the photo below to answer questions 20 and 21.

20. Name and describe the phylum that this sea star belongs to.

21. This animal has a vascular system that is unique. Describe it.

22. What structures allow an earthworm to move? Describe its locomotion.

23. There are more species of insects than all other animal groups combined. In all environments, they have to compete with one another for survival. How do so many insects survive?

24. Insect bodies are divided into three segments. What are these three segments and what appendages and organs are in/on each part?

Test-Taking Tip

Show Your Work For constructed-response questions, show all of your work and any calculations on your answer sheet.

Question 22 Write out all of the adaptations that insects have for survival and determine which are the most beneficial to the success of the group.

STANDARDIZED TEST PRACTICE **C** ◆ **69**

Rubrics

The following rubrics are sample scoring devices for short response and open-ended questions.

Short Response

Points	Description
2	The student demonstrates a thorough understanding of the science of the task. The response may contain minor flaws that do not detract from the demonstration of a thorough understanding.
1	The student has provided a response that is only partially correct.
0	The student has provided a completely incorrect solution or no response at all.

Open Ended

Points	Description
4	The student demonstrates a thorough understanding of the science of the task. The response may contain minor flaws that do not detract from the demonstration of a thorough understanding.
3	The student demonstrates an understanding of the science of the task. The response is essentially correct and demonstrates an essential but less than thorough understanding of the science.
2	The student demonstrates only a partial understanding of the science of the task. Although the student may have used the correct approach to a solution or may have provided a correct solution, the work lacks an essential understanding of the underlying science concepts.
1	The student demonstrates a very limited understanding of the science of the task. The response is incomplete and exhibits many flaws.
0	The student provides a completely incorrect solution or no response at all.

Part 3 | Open Ended

20. echinoderm; bumpy skin, water-vascular system, radially symmetrical, mouth, stomach, and intestines, no brain

21. water-vascular system—a network of water-filled canals with thousands of tube feet

22. setae and two sets of muscles in the body; the long muscles contract and push the setae out anchoring the worm to the soil; the circular muscles contract and pull the setae in moving the worm forward

23. a short lifespan allows genetic traits to change quickly, specialized diet helps them avoid competition, flying, and other adaptations such as camouflage

24. a head with eyes, antennae, and mouthparts, thorax with one or two pair of wings, if present, and three pairs of legs, and abdomen with the digestive and reproductive organs

Section/Objectives	Standards		Labs/Features
Chapter Opener	**National**	**State/Local**	**Launch Lab:** Snake Hearing, p. 71 **Foldables,** p. 71
	See pp. 16T–17T for a Key to Standards.		
Section 1 Chordates and Vertebrates 🕐 2 sessions 📖 1 block 1. **List** the characteristics of all chordates. 2. **Identify** characteristics shared by vertebrates. 3. **Differentiate** between ectotherms and endotherms.	National Content Standards: UCP.1–UCP.4, A.1, A.2, C.1–C.3, C.5		**Lab:** Endotherms and Ectotherms, p. 76
Section 2 Fish 🕐 2 sessions 📖 1 block 4. **List** the characteristics of the three classes of fish. 5. **Explain** how fish obtain food and oxygen and reproduce. 6. **Describe** the importance and origin of fish.	National Content Standards: UCP.1–UCP.5, A.1, A.2, C.1–C.3, C.5, F.1		**Integrate Health,** p. 80 **MiniLAB:** Modeling How Fish Adjust to Different Depths, p. 81 **Applying Math:** Density of a Fish, p. 82
Section 3 Amphibians 🕐 2 sessions 📖 1 block 7. **Describe** the adaptations amphibians have for living in water and living on land. 8. **List** the kinds of amphibians and the characteristics of each. 9. **Explain** how amphibians reproduce and develop.	National Content Standards: UCP.1–UCP.5, A.1, A.2, C.1–C.3, C.5		**Science Online,** p. 87 **MiniLAB:** Describing Frog Adaptations, p. 88
Section 4 Reptiles 🕐 3 sessions 📖 1.5 blocks 10. **List** the characteristics of reptiles. 11. **Determine** how reptile adaptations enable them to live on land. 12. **Explain** the importance of the amniotic egg.	National Content Standards: UCP.1–UCP.5, A.1, A.2, C.1–C.3, C.5, F.4, F.5		**Science Online,** p. 91 **Visualizing Extinct Reptiles,** p. 94 **Integrate History,** p. 95 **Lab:** Water Temperature and the Respiration Rate of Fish, p. 96 **Science and Society:** Venom, p. 98

Lab Materials	Reproducible Resources	Section Assessment	Technology
Launch Lab: tuning fork	**Chapter FAST FILE Resources** Foldables Worksheet, p. 17 Directed Reading Overview, p. 19 Note-taking Worksheets, pp. 35–38	*GLENCOE'S* **ASSESSMENT** *ADVANTAGE*	**Teacher Works** includes: • Interactive Teacher Edition • Lesson Planner with calendar • Access to all program blacklines • Correlations to standards • Web links
Lab: fiberfill, cloth, thermometer	**Chapter FAST FILE Resources** Transparency Activity, p. 48 Lab Activity, pp. 9–10 Enrichment, p. 31 Reinforcement, p. 27 Directed Reading, p. 20 Lab Worksheet, pp. 5–6	**Portfolio** Science Journal, p. 73 **Performance,** Applying Skills, p. 75 **Content** Section Review, p. 75	Section Focus Transparency Virtual Labs CD-ROM Guided Reading Audio Program Interactive Chalkboard CD-ROM
MiniLAB: 2 balloons, large bowl, water	**Chapter FAST FILE Resources** Transparency Activity, p. 49 MiniLAB, p. 3 Enrichment, p. 32 Reinforcement, p. 28 Directed Reading, p. 20 **Mathematics Skill Activities,** p. 49	**Portfolio** Differentiated Instruction, p. 79 **Performance** MiniLAB, p. 81 Applying Math, p. 82 Applying Skills, p. 84 **Content** Section Review, p. 84	Section Focus Transparency Virtual Labs CD-ROM Guided Reading Audio Program Interactive Chalkboard CD-ROM Video Lab
MiniLAB: live frog, jar, water, magnifying glass	**Chapter FAST FILE Resources** Transparency Activity, p. 50 MiniLAB, p. 4 Lab Activity, pp. 11–15 Enrichment, p. 33 Reinforcement, p. 29 Directed Reading, p. 21	**Portfolio** Differentiated Instruction, p. 88 **Performance** MiniLAB, p. 88 Applying Skills, p. 89 **Content** Section Review, p. 89	Section Focus Transparency Virtual Labs CD-ROM Guided Reading Audio Program Interactive Chalkboard CD-ROM
Lab: goldfish, aquarium, water, small fishnet, 600-mL beakers (3), ice, stirring rod, thermometer	**Chapter FAST FILE Resources** Transparency Activity, p. 51 Enrichment, p. 34 Reinforcement, p. 30 Transparency Activity, pp. 53–54 Directed Reading, pp. 21, 22 Lab Worksheet, pp. 7–8	**Portfolio** Differentiated Instruction, p. 91 **Performance** Applying Math, p. 95 **Content** Section Review, p. 95	Section Focus Transparency Teaching Transparency Virtual Labs CD-ROM Guided Reading Audio Program Interactive Chalkboard CD-ROM

End of Chapter Assessment

GLENCOE'S **ASSESSMENT** *ADVANTAGE*

Blackline Masters	Technology	Professional Series
Chapter FAST FILE Resources Chapter Review, pp. 41–42 Chapter Tests, pp. 43–46 **Standardized Test Practice,** pp. 15–18	MindJogger Videoquiz Virtual Labs CD-ROM ExamView® Pro Testmaker TeacherWorks CD-ROM Interactive Chalkboard CD-ROM	**Performance Assessment in the Science Classroom (PASC)**

Transparencies

Section Focus

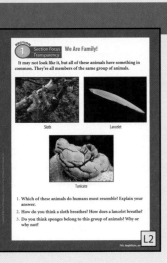

We Are Family!

It may not look like it, but all of these animals have something in common. They're all members of the same group of animals.

Sloth
Lancelet
Tunicate

1. Which of these animals do humans most resemble? Explain your answer.
2. How do you think a sloth breathes? How does a lancelet breathe?
3. Do you think sponges belong to this group of animals? Why or why not?

L2

A Fish Story of Enormous Proportion

Tales of sea serpents have been around as long as people have sailed the seas. The source of some of these tales may be the oarfish, the largest known bony fish. A deep-water species that is rarely seen, the oarfish can attain a length of 9 m and weights of 300 kg.

1. Why might someone think the oarfish is a sea serpent?
2. What characteristics of the oarfish show it to be a fish?
3. Do you think the oarfish eats plants? Why or why not?

L2

Sing At Your Own Risk

When male mud-puddle frogs sing for the females, bats sometimes listen in. The bats can use the sound to locate—and eat—the frogs. This is a natural event that helps maintain a stable frog population. However, the worldwide population of frogs is declining.

1. What kind of environment do frogs live in?
2. Why might frogs be especially sensitive to pollution in the air and water?

L2

This is a representation of key blackline masters available in the Teacher Classroom Resources. See Resource Manager boxes within the chapter for additional information.

Key to Teaching Strategies

The following designations will help you decide which activities are appropriate for your students.

L1 Level 1 activities should be appropriate for students with learning difficulties.

L2 Level 2 activities should be within the ability range of all students.

L3 Level 3 activities are designed for above-average students.

ELL ELL activities should be within the ability range of English-Language Learners.

COOP LEARN Cooperative Learning activities are designed for small group work.

LS Multiple Learning Styles logos, as described on page 12T, are used throughout to indicate strategies that address different learning styles.

P These strategies represent student products that can be placed into a best-work portfolio.

PBL Problem-Based Learning activities apply real-world situations to learning.

Assessment

Fish, Amphibians, and Reptiles

Directions: Carefully review the maps and answer the following questions.

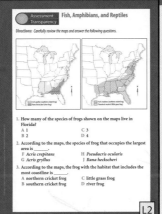

1. How many of the species of frogs shown on the maps live in Florida?
   A 1   C 3
   B 2   D 4
2. According to the maps, the species of frog that occupies the largest area is _____.
   F *Acris crepitans*   H *Pseudacris ocularis*
   G *Acris gryllus*   J *Rana heckscheri*
3. According to the maps, the frog with the habitat that includes the most coastline is _____.
   A northern cricket frog   C little grass frog
   B southern cricket frog   D river frog

L2

Teaching

Amniotic Egg

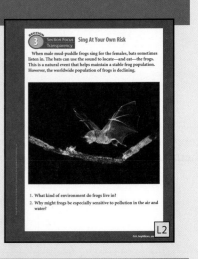

Embryo
Shell
Yolk sac
Air space
Egg membrane

L2

Hands-on Activities

Student Text Lab Worksheet

Activity Endotherms and Ectotherms

Lab Preview
Directions: Answer these questions before you begin the Activity.
1. List the three locations you will place your animal.

2. Where must ectotherms go if it is too hot?

Birds and mammals are endotherms. Fish, amphibians, and reptiles are ectotherms. How can you determine whether an animal you have never seen before is an endotherm or an ectotherm? What tests you conduct to find out?

What You'll Investigate
Is an animal you construct an endotherm or an ectotherm?

Materials
fiberfill
*cotton balls
*old cells
*tissue
cloth
thermometer
*alternate materials

Goals
• Construct an imaginary animal
• Determine whether your animal is an endotherm or an ectotherm.

Safety Precautions

Procedure
1. Design an animal that has a thermometer inside. Construct the animal cloth and some kind of stuffing material. Make sure that you will be able to remove and reinsert the thermometer.
2. Draw a picture of your animal and record data about its size and shape on a separate sheet of paper
3. Place your animal in three locations that have different temperatures. Record the locations in the data table in the Data and Observations section.
4. In each location, record the time and the temperature of your animal at the beginning and after 10 min.

L2

Laboratory Activities

Laboratory Activity Examining Vertebrates

What do you have in common with a fish, a frog, a turtle, a bird, and a guinea pig? You belong to the animal kingdom. Animals that have backbones are vertebrates. Vertebrates are classified in subphylum Vertebrata, phylum Chordata.

Strategy
You will observe representative animals from five classes of vertebrates.
You will record characteristics of each class based upon your observations.

Materials
guppy or goldfish in an aquarium
frog or chameleon in a terrarium
lizard or turtle
canary
guinea pig
food for each animal used
reference books

Procedure
1. Observe each animal for several minutes. Your teacher will give each animal food. Observe how it feeds.
2. Record answers to the following questions in Table 1 in the Data and Observations section. Use reference books for more information.
   a. Where does the animal live?
   b. How does the animal move about?
   c. How does it take in food?
   d. Is it an ectotherm or an endotherm?
   e. What is its body covering?
   f. How does it get oxygen?
   g. Have many appendages (limbs or fins) does it have?

Data and Observations
Table 1

Vertebrate Information					
Animal	Fish	Frog	Turtle	Bird	Guinea pig
Habitat					
Movement					
Food getting					
Ectotherm or endotherm					
Body covering					
Respiration					
Appendages					

L2

Meeting Different Ability Levels

Content Outline

Reinforcement

Enrichment

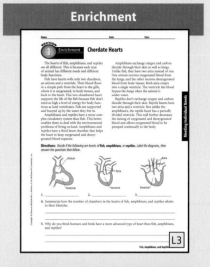

Directed Reading (English/Spanish)

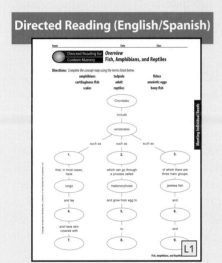

Study Guide

Reading Essentials

Assessment

Test Practice Workbook

Chapter Review

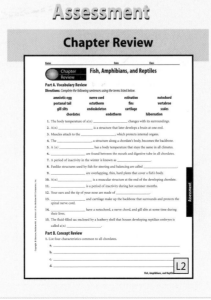

Chapter Tests

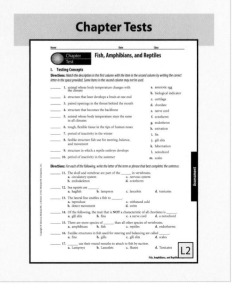

Science Content Background

Chordate Characteristics

In Phylum *Chordata*, students are most aware of animals with backbones, such as fish and mammals, that belong to the subphylum *Vertebrata*. There are two other *Chordata* subphyla. The *Urochordata* includes sea squirts, which have a spongelike appearance. They are a very remote ancestor on the Chordata tree. Their larva, however, are similar in form to tadpoles. The *Cephalochordata* includes lancelets, which are fishlike in appearance and who spend most of their time buried in sand. In addition to having a notochord, chordates have a dorsal hollow nerve cord at some time during their life cycles.

Fish, amphibians, and reptiles are ectotherms, which means their temperature varies with their surroundings. The internal temperature of ectotherms fluctuates more than it does for endotherms. The advantage for ectotherms is they spend less energy maintaining a constant body temperature. The disadvantage is that these organisms are more sluggish at cooler temperatures. Other names for ectotherms are cold-blooded animals and poikilotherms.

Fish Characteristics

Most fish have fins that occur in pairs. Fish breathe with gills and reproduce sexually, usually with external fertilization. Fish circulate blood in a closed system with a two-chambered heart, consisting of one atrium and one ventricle. The atrium receives blood from the body and pushes it to the ventricle. The ventricle pumps blood through the gills and then to the rest of the body. Some scientists define the fish heart as four-chambered. They include the area before the atrium and the area after the ventricle as chambers.

Amphibian Characteristics

Amphibians were the first land animals to evolve, and they developed adaptations that allow them to spend part of their life on land. Their three-chamber heart allows better circulation of oxygenated blood. This is necessary because walking as opposed to swimming uses more energy. Lungs and moist skin provide two methods for amphibians for the exchange of oxygen and carbon dioxide. Unlike fish and other vertebrates, most amphibians undergo a metamorphosis.

Teacher to Teacher

Jeff Remington
Palmyra Middle School
Palmyra, Pennsylvania

"I use Cartesian divers to demonstrate the concept of a swim bladder. Students pass them around and really seem to get the concept."

Jeff Remington

Gail Shumway/FPG International

Salamanders

Having frogs and toads as the poster organisms for amphibians makes many people forget about salamanders, even though there is an abundance of species. In North America, there are more species of salamanders than in the rest of the world combined. Because they don't lose their tails as adults, they are sometimes mistaken for reptiles. Salamanders need to maintain moist skin for breathing. They lay their eggs in water, but the larva very much resemble the adult except they have gills.

Importance of Amphibians

There is concern about the declining numbers of amphibians and the possibility of extinctions. Among the species that are endangered are the San Marcos salamander (*Eurycea nana*), Wyoming toad (*Bufo baxteri*), and Mississippi gopher frog (*Rana capito sevosa*).

 ## Reptiles

Reptile Characteristics

Reptiles have adaptations for life away from moist environments. Their thick, dry skin is covered with scales to prevent water loss. They cannot absorb oxygen through their skin, so they have well-developed lungs for gas exchange. While most have three-chambered hearts, some reptiles evolved the more efficient four-chamber heart. Compared to amphibians, the legs of reptiles are located more directly under the animal. This increases the efficiency of movement on land. The reptile egg is an amniotic egg. It contains moisture and barriers to prevent moisture loss. It gets its name from the amnion, which is a membrane that contains fluid that cushions the embryo and prevents dehydration. So unlike the amphibian egg, the reptile egg can survive and develop in dry terrestrial environments. Without an external watery environment for sperm to swim to the egg, reptiles evolved the capability for internal fertilization.

Lizards come in a variety of forms. While most lizards eat insects, iguanas are herbivores. The largest lizard is the Komodo dragon, which can be ten feet long and two hundred pounds. Only a couple of lizards inject venom when biting. These are the Gila monster of the southwestern United States and the beaded lizard of Mexico.

Importance of Reptiles

The following turtles are endangered species: Kemp's Ridley Sea Turtle (*Lepidochelys kempii*) and Leatherback Sea Turtle (*Dermochelys coriacea*).

---

chapter content resources

Internet Resources
For additional content background, visit
bookc.msscience.com to:
- access your book online
- find references to related articles in popular science magazines
- access Web links with related content background
- access current events with science journal topics

Print Resources
Fish and Amphibians (Discovery Channel Science) by Kathy Freely, Susan Wernert, Monique Peterson, Justine Ciovacco, Sharon Yates, Gareth Stevens, 2002
Herpetology: An Introductory Biology of Amphibians and Reptiles, Second Edition by George R. Zug, Laurie J. Vitt, Jonalee P. Caldwell, Academic Press, 2001
Amphibians: The World of Frogs, Toads, Salamanders, and Newts by Robert Hofrichter, Firefly Books, 2000
Fishes: A Field and Laboratory Manual on Their Structure, Identification, and Natural History by Gregor Cailliet, Milton Love, Alfred Ebeling, Waveland Press, 1996

Chapter Vocabulary

chordate, p. 72
notochord, p. 72
postanal tail, p. 72
nerve cord, p. 73
pharyngeal pouch, p. 73
endoskeleton, p. 73
cartilage, p. 73
vertebrate, p. 73
ectotherm, p. 75
endotherm, p. 75
fin, p. 77
scale, p. 77
hibernation, p. 85
estivation, p. 85
amniotic egg, p. 91

Science Journal Student responses will vary, but may include: fish live and breathe in water, amphibians change forms and live near water, and reptiles lay eggs and breathe air.

INTERACTIVE CHALKBOARD
with Image Bank

PowerPoint® Presentations

This CD-ROM is an editable Microsoft® PowerPoint® presentation that includes:

- a pre-made presentation for every chapter
- interactive graphics
- animations
- audio clips
- image bank
- all new section and chapter questions
- Standardized Test Practice
- transparencies
- pre-lab questions for all labs
- Foldables directions
- links to bookc.msscience.com

Fish, Amphibians, and Reptiles

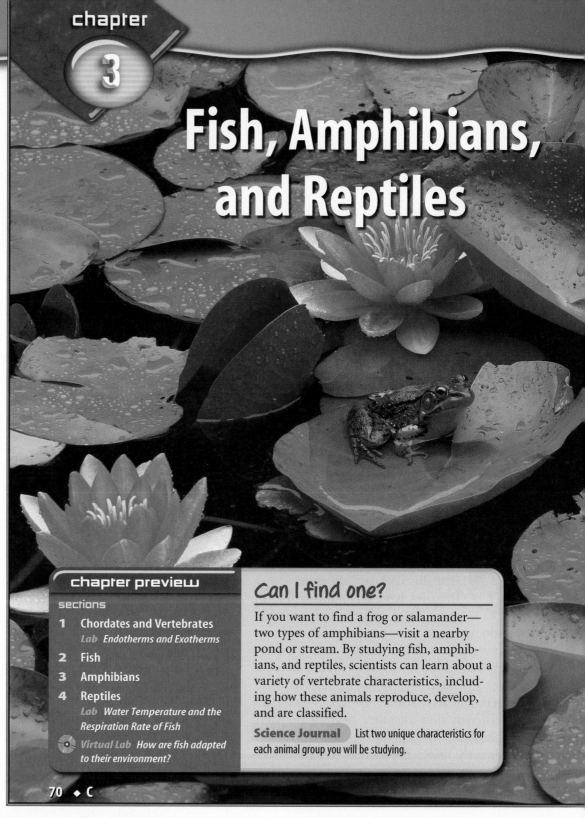

chapter preview

sections

1 Chordates and Vertebrates
   Lab Endotherms and Exotherms

2 Fish

3 Amphibians

4 Reptiles
   Lab Water Temperature and the Respiration Rate of Fish

   Virtual Lab How are fish adapted to their environment?

70 ◆ C

Can I find one?

If you want to find a frog or salamander—two types of amphibians—visit a nearby pond or stream. By studying fish, amphibians, and reptiles, scientists can learn about a variety of vertebrate characteristics, including how these animals reproduce, develop, and are classified.

Science Journal List two unique characteristics for each animal group you will be studying.

Theme Connection

Stability and Change The theme of stability and change is introduced in a discussion of chordates and vertebrates. The theme is developed through the discussion of adaptations that fish, amphibians, and reptiles have for living in their environments. The ecological importance of fish, amphibians, and reptiles is presented.

About the Photo

Bullfrogs The American Bullfrog, *Rana catesbeiana,* is one of the most well-known frogs due to its characteristic bass *jug-o-rum* sound. This call attracts females and marks territory. The bullfrog is native to the central and eastern United States and the southern portions of Ontario and Quebec. Bullfrogs are large, sometimes more than 6 inches. They range in color from dull green to dull gray to black.

Start-Up Activities

Snake Hearing

How much do you know about reptiles? For example, do snakes have eyelids? Why do snakes flick their tongues in and out? How can some snakes swallow animals that are larger than their own heads? Snakes don't have ears, so how do they hear? In this lab, you will discover the answer to one of these questions.

1. Hold a tuning fork by the stem and tap it on a hard piece of rubber, such as the sole of a shoe.
2. Hold it next to your ear. What, if anything, do you hear?
3. Tap the tuning fork again. Press the base of the stem firmly against your chin. In your Science Journal, describe what happens.
4. **Think Critically** Using the results from step 3, infer how a snake detects vibrations. In your Science Journal, predict how different animals can use vibrations to hear.

Preview this chapter's content and activities at bookc.msscience.com

Fish, Amphibians, and Reptiles Make the following Foldable to help you organize information about the animals you will be studying.

STEP 1 Fold one piece of paper lengthwise into thirds.

STEP 2 Fold the paper widthwise into fourths.

STEP 3 Unfold, lay the paper lengthwise, and draw lines along the folds.

STEP 4 Label your table as shown.

Fish	Amphibians	Reptiles

Make a Table As you read this chapter, complete the table describing characteristics of each type of animal.

Purpose Use the Launch Lab to introduce students to reptiles, one of the vertebrate classes they will study in this chapter. **L1**

ELL **IN** **Auditory-Musical**

Preparation Before beginning this lab, obtain several tuning forks. You may wish to cut up a discarded rubber car floor mat for students to use as a striking pad.

Materials one tuning fork for every two students

Teaching Strategy Advise students not to touch the prongs of the tuning fork after hitting it on the piece of rubber.

Think Critically

Sound is heard because vibrations travel through the bones in the jaw and skull to the fluid in the inner ear. Here, the vibrations are translated into nerve impulses and interpreted as sound by the brain. In many snakes and salamanders, the jawbone is sensitive to ground vibrations.

Assessment

Process Infer how you could best warn venomous snakes of your approach when hiking. Making heavy footsteps or striking the ground with a stick will produce vibrations to warn snakes and allow them to avoid hikers. Use **Performance Assessment in the Science Classroom,** p. 89.

 Dinah Zike Study Fold

Student preparation materials for this Foldable are available in the **Chapter FAST FILE Resources.**

1 Motivate

Bellringer

Section Focus Transparencies also are available on the Interactive Chalkboard CD-ROM.

L2 ELL

Section Focus Transparency We Are Family!

It may not look like it, but all of these animals have something in common. They're all members of the same group of animals.

Sloth   Lancelet

Tunicate

1. Which of these animals do humans most resemble? Explain your answer.
2. How do you think a sloth breathes? How does a lancelet breathe?
3. Do you think sponges belong to this group of animals? Why or why not?

Fish, Amphibians, and Reptiles

Tie to Prior Knowledge

Common Vertebrates Vertebrates are animals that are familiar to students. Ask them to name as many kinds of vertebrates as possible. Then ask what characteristics these animals have in common.
L2

Caption Answer

Figure 1 A sea squirt and a human are both chordates. At some stage in development all chordates have a notochord, postanal tail, nerve chord, and pharyngeal pouches.

✔ Reading Check

Answer It is replaced by a backbone.

Chordates and Vertebrates

as you read

What You'll Learn

- **List** the characteristics of all chordates.
- **Identify** characteristics shared by vertebrates.
- **Differentiate** between ectotherms and endotherms.

Why It's Important

Humans are vertebrates. Other vertebrates play important roles in your life because they provide food, companionship, and labor.

🔍 Review Vocabulary

motor responses: responses that involve muscular movement

New Vocabulary

- chordate
- notochord
- postanal tail
- nerve cord
- pharyngeal pouch
- endoskeleton
- cartilage
- vertebrae
- ectotherm
- endotherm

Figure 1 Sea squirts get their name because when they're taken out of the ocean, they squirt water out of their body.
Determine what you have in common with a sea squirt.

Chordate Characteristics

During a walk along the seashore at low tide, you often can see jellylike masses of animals clinging to rocks. Some of these animals may be sea squirts, as shown in **Figure 1,** which is one of the many types of animals known as chordates (KOR dayts). **Chordates** are animals that have four characteristics present at some stage of their development—a notochord, postanal tail, nerve cord, and pharyngeal pouches.

Notochord All chordates have an internal **notochord** that supports the animal and extends along the upper part of its body, as shown in **Figure 2.** The notochord is flexible but firm because it is made up of fluid-filled cells that are enclosed in a stiff covering. The notochord also extends into the **postanal tail**—a muscular structure at the end of the developing chordate. Some chordates, such as fish, amphibians, reptiles, birds, and mammals, develop backbones that partly or entirely replace the notochord. They are called vertebrates. In some chordates, such as the sea squirt, other tunicates, and the lancelets, the notochord is kept into adulthood.

✔ Reading Check
What happens to the notochord as a bat develops?

Section 1 Resource Manager

Chapter *FAST FILE* Resources
Transparency Activity, p. 48
Directed Reading for Content Mastery, pp. 19, 20
Note-taking Worksheets, pp. 35–38
Enrichment, p. 31

Reinforcement, p. 27
Lab Worksheet, pp. 5–6
Lab Activity, pp. 9–10
Earth Science Critical Thinking/Problem Solving, p. 12
Lab Management and Safety, p. 58

Nerve Cord Above the notochord and along the length of a developing chordate's body is a tubelike structure called the **nerve cord,** also shown in **Figure 2.** As most chordates develop, the front end of the nerve cord enlarges to form the brain and the remainder becomes the spinal cord. These two structures become the central nervous system that develops into complex systems for sensory and motor responses.

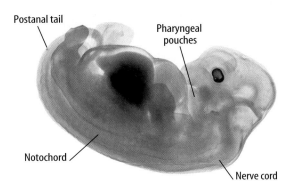
Postanal tail
Pharyngeal pouches
Notochord
Nerve cord

Pharyngeal Pouches All developing chordates have **pharyngeal pouches.** They are found in the region between the mouth and the digestive tube as pairs of openings to the outside. Many chordates have several pairs of pharyngeal pouches. Ancient invertebrate chordates used them for filter feeding. This is still their purpose in some living chordates such as lancelets. In fish, they have developed into internal gills where oxygen and carbon dioxide are exchanged. In humans, pharyngeal pouches are present only during embryonic development. However, one pair becomes the tubes that go from the ears to the throat.

Figure 2 At some time during its development, a chordate has a notochord, postanal tail, nerve cord, and pharyngeal pouches.

Figure 3 Vertebrae are separated by soft disks of cartilage.

Vertebrate Characteristics

Besides the characteristics common to all chordates, vertebrates have distinct characteristics. These traits set vertebrates apart from other chordates.

Structure All vertebrates have an internal framework called an **endoskeleton.** It is made up of bone and/or flexible tissue called **cartilage.** Your ears and the tip of your nose are made of cartilage. The endoskeleton provides a place for muscle attachment and supports and protects the organs. Part of the endoskeleton is a flexible, supportive column called the backbone, as shown in **Figure 3.** It is a stack of **vertebrae** alternating with cartilage. The backbone surrounds and protects the spinal nerve cord. Vertebrates also have a head with a skull that encloses and protects the brain.

Most of a vertebrate's internal organs are found in a central body cavity. A protective skin covers a vertebrate. Hair, feathers, scales, or horns sometimes grow from the skin.

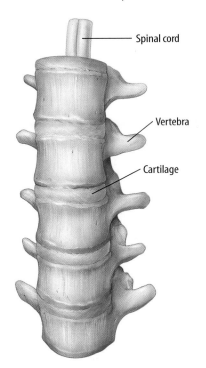
Spinal cord
Vertebra
Cartilage
Vertebrae column

SECTION 1 Chordates and Vertebrates C ◆ **73**

SECTION 1 Chordates and Vertebrates C ◆ **73**

SECTION 1 Chordates and Vertebrates C ◆ **73**

Animal Performance Organize the class into seven groups. Assign each group one of the seven groups of vertebrates shown on this page. Give students time to research information about the kinds of animals in their group. Then have each group develop a game, poem, song, or short play that presents the information about the animals they researched. L2 ELL COOP LEARN IS
Interpersonal, Linguistic

Discussion

Jawless Fish Lampreys and hagfish are the only jawless fish that survive today. How can you explain the small number of species in this group? Possible answers: Without paired fins, they are not good swimmers. Without jaws, they are not good predators. When jaws and paired fins evolved, species with these characteristics were more successful and became dominant. L2

Teacher FYI

Chordata **Subphyla** The phylum *Chordata* includes three subphyla: *Urochordata* (tunicates), *Cephalochordata* (lancelets), and *Vertebrata*.

Visual Learning

Table 1 Have students make a circle graph from this data, showing what percentage of species belongs to each vertebrate group. L2 IS **Logical-Mathematical**

Table 1 Types of Vertebrates

Group	Estimated Number of Species	Examples	
Jawless fish	60	lamprey, hagfish	
Jawed cartilaginous fish	500 to 900	shark, ray, skate	
Bony fish	20,000	salmon, bass, guppy, sea horse, lungfish	
Amphibians	4,000	frog, toad, salamander	
Reptiles	7,970	turtle, lizard, snake, crocodile, alligator	
Birds	8,700	stork, eagle, sparrow, turkey, duck, ostrich	
Mammals	4,600	human, whale, bat, mouse, lion, cow, otter	

74 ◆ **C CHAPTER 3** Fish, Amphibians, and Reptiles

Differentiated Instruction

Challenge Have students list the characteristics of each vertebrate group. Which help contribute to the success of the group? Which keep the group from being more successful? L3

Active Reading

Learning Journal Have students draw a vertical line down each page of their Learning Journals. Have them record research notes, lecture notes, or vocabulary terms in the left column, and their responses to, interpretations of, questions about, or analyses in the right column. Direct students to write a Learning Journal related to chordates and vertebrates. L2

Vertebrate Groups Seven main groups of vertebrates are found on Earth today, as shown in **Table 1.** Vertebrates are either ectotherms or endotherms. Fish, amphibians, and reptiles are ectotherms, also known as cold-blooded animals. An **ectotherm** has an internal body temperature that changes with the temperature of its surroundings. Birds and mammals are endotherms, which sometimes are called warm-blooded animals. An **endotherm** has a nearly constant internal body temperature.

Vertebrate Origins Some vertebrate fossils, like the one in **Figure 4,** are of water-dwelling, armored animals that lived about 420 million years ago (mya). Lobe-finned fish appeared in the fossil record about 395 mya. The oldest known amphibian fossils date from about 370 mya. Reptile fossils have been found in deposits about 350 million years old. One well-known group of reptiles—the dinosaurs—first appeared about 230 mya.

In 1861, a fossil imprint of an animal with scales, jaws with teeth, claws on its front limbs, and feathers was found. The 150-million-year-old fossil was an ancestor of birds, and was named *Archaeopteryx* (ar kee AHP tuh rihks).

Mammal-like reptiles appeared about 235 mya. However, true mammals appeared about 190 mya, and modern mammals originated about 38 million years ago.

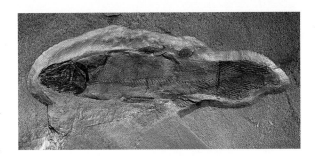

Figure 4 Placoderms were the first fish with jaws. These predatory fish were covered with heavy armor.

Discussion

Basking Ectotherms do not perspire or pant. How do they control body temperature? The temperature of an ectotherm changes with its surroundings. If an ectotherm becomes too cold, it moves to warmer surroundings. An example is a lizard on a rock in the Sun. If it becomes too warm, the ectotherm moves to cooler surroundings. L2

3 Assess

DAILY INTERVENTION

Check for Understanding

Linguistic Have students write a paragraph explaining why vertebrates are classified as chordates, but not all chordates are classified as vertebrates. L2 LS

Reteach

Fish and Cat Skeletons Provide a skeleton of a fish (ectothermic vertebrate) and a cat (endothermic vertebrate). Have students observe the skeletons and determine how they are similar and how they are different. L2 LS
Visual-Spatial

Assessment

Oral Ask students to explain temperature control in ectotherms and endotherms, comparing the way energy is absorbed and used. In ectotherms heat energy is absorbed from sunlight, as opposed to chemical release of energy by digestion and respiration in endotherms. L2

---

section 1 review

Summary

Chordate Characteristics

- Chordates have four common characteristics at some point in their development: a notochord, postanal tail, nerve cord, and pharyngeal pouches.

Vertebrate Characteristics

- All vertebrates have an endoskeleton, a backbone, a head with a skull to protect the brain, internal organs in a central body cavity, and a protective skin.
- Vertebrates can be ectothermic or endothermic.
- There are seven main groups of vertebrates.

Self Check

1. **Explain** the difference between a vertebra and a notochord.
2. **Compare and contrast** some of the physical differences between ectotherms and endotherms.
3. **Think Critically** If the outside temperature decreases by 20°C, what will happen to a reptile's body temperature?

Applying Skills

4. **Concept Map** Construct a concept map using these terms: *chordates, bony fish, amphibians, cartilaginous fish, reptiles, birds, mammals, lancelets, tunicates, invertebrate chordates, jawless fish,* and *vertebrates.*

---

section 1 review

1. The notochord is made up of fluid-filled cells enclosed in a stiff covering; a vertebra is made of bone or cartilage.

2. The body temperature of an ectotherm changes with its surroundings. The body temperature of an endotherm remains the same regardless of its surroundings.

3. Its body temperature will decrease by about 20°.

4. Check students' concept maps to make sure they used all listed terms and classified organisms correctly.

BENCH TESTED

▶ Real-World Question

Purpose Students construct a model animal and determine if it is an endotherm or an ectotherm.
L2 **IS** **Logical-Mathematical**

Process Skills observe and infer, construct, describe, compare

Time Required 45 minutes

▶ Procedure

Alternate Materials Students can use scraps of wool clothing, cotton balls, socks, shredded paper, or tissue paper for the stuffing.

Teaching Strategy Prepare locations in the classroom that have a wide range of temperatures such as near a heating vent or radiator, on a windowsill, and in a refrigerator.

Troubleshooting Students should use only one kind of stuffing so that their results are comparable with others.

▶ Conclude and Apply

1. Answers will vary.
2. If the temperature did not change dramatically, the model represents an endotherm. If the temperature did change dramatically, it is a model of an ectotherm.
3. Thicker "animals" should maintain the temperature of their inner core better than flat "animals."
4. Answers will vary.

Birds and mammals are endotherms. Fish, amphibians and reptiles are ectotherms.

▶ Real-World Question

How can you determine whether an animal you have never seen before is an endotherm or an ectotherm? What tests might you conduct to find the answer?

Goals

■ **Construct** an imaginary animal.
■ **Determine** whether your animal is an endotherm or an ectotherm.

Materials

fiberfill   cloth
*cotton balls   thermometer
*old socks   *Alternate materials
*tissue

Safety Precautions 🔧 🥽 👕 🧤

▶ Procedure

1. Design an animal that has a thermometer inside. Construct the animal using cloth and some kind of stuffing material. Make sure that you will be able to remove and reinsert the thermometer.

2. Draw a picture of your animal and record data about its size and shape.

Animal Temperature		
Location	Beginning Time/ Temperature	Ending Time/ Temperature
	Answers will vary.	

3. Copy the data table in your Science Journal.

4. Place your animal in three locations that have different temperatures. Record the locations in the data table.

5. In each location, record the time and the temperature of your animal at the beginning and after 10 min.

▶ Conclude and Apply

1. **Describe** your results. Did the animal's temperature vary depending upon the location?

2. Based on your results, is your animal an endotherm or an ectotherm? Explain.

3. **Compare** your results to those of others in your class. Were the results the same for animals of different sizes? Did the shape of the animal, such as one being flatter and another more cylindrical, matter?

4. Based on your results and information in the chapter, do you think your animal is most likely a bird, a mammal, a reptile, an amphibian, or a fish? Explain.

Communicating **Your Data**

Compare your conclusions with those of other students in your class. **For more help, refer to the** Science Skill Handbook.

✓ Assessment

Performance Have students build a second animal with an internal temperature opposite to the first. For example, if they first constructed an endotherm, ask them to construct an ectotherm and vice versa. Use **Performance Assessment in the Science Classroom**, p. 97. L2

Communicating **Your Data**

Encourage students to compare the shape and contents of their animals and discuss how differences in these variables affected their results. L2

Fish Characteristics

Did you know that more differences appear among fish than among any other vertebrate group? In fact, there are more species of fish than species of other vertebrate groups. All fish are ectotherms. They are adapted for living in nearly every type of water environment on Earth—freshwater and salt water. Some fish, such as salmon, spend part of their life in freshwater and part of it in salt water. Fish are found at varying depths, from shallow pools to deep oceans.

A streamlined shape, a muscular tail, and fins allow most fish to move rapidly through the water. **Fins** are fanlike structures attached to the endoskeleton. They are used for steering, balancing, and moving. Paired fins on the sides allow fish to move right, left, backward, and forward. Fins on the top and bottom of the body give the fish stability. Most fish secrete a slimy mucus that also helps them move through the water.

Most fish have scales. **Scales** are hard, thin plates that cover the skin and protect the body, similar to shingles on the roof of a house. Most fish scales are made of bone. **Figure 5** illustrates how they can be tooth shaped, diamond shaped, cone shaped, or round. The shape of the scales can be used to help classify fish. The age of some species can be estimated by counting the annual growth rings of the scales.

Figure 5 Four types of fish scales are shown here.

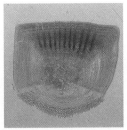

Sharks are covered with placoid scales such as these. Shark teeth are modified forms of these scales.

Lobe-finned fish and gars are covered by ganoid scales. These scales don't overlap like other fish scales.

Ctenoid (TEN oyd) scales have a rough edge, which is thought to reduce drag as the fish swims through the water.

Cycloid scales are thin and overlap, giving the fish flexibility. These scales grow as the fish grows.

SECTION 2 Fish **C ◆ 77**

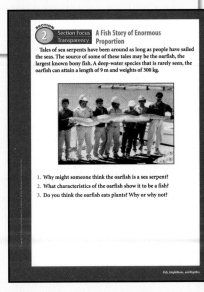

Use an Analogy

House Shingles Show students a picture of shingles on a house. Explain that most fish are covered with scales arranged much like the shingles on a roof. Scales are firmly attached to the skin tissue from which they grow. In most fish species, the outer part of each scale overlaps the next scale, like shingles on a house. The exception are ganoid scales, found on lobe-finned fish. L2 LS **Logical-Mathematical**

Activity

Jawless Fish Table Organize the class into groups of four. Have each group make a table comparing the characteristics of jawless fish, cartilaginous fish, and bony fish. They should compare body shapes and coverings, placement of fins, methods of feeding, sense organs, and any other characteristics they read about. L2 COOP LEARN LS **Interpersonal**

Caption Answer

Figure 7 Fish breathe with gills—feathery filaments containing many tiny blood vessels. A fish takes water into its mouth and then it passes over the gills. There oxygen from the water is exchanged with the carbon dioxide in the blood.

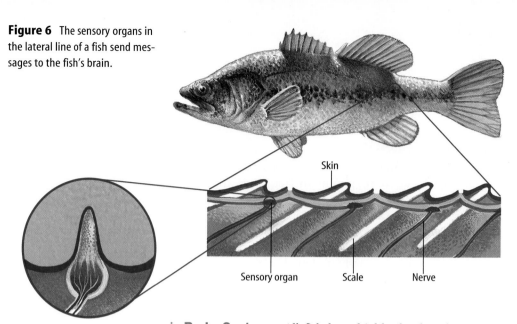

Figure 6 The sensory organs in the lateral line of a fish send messages to the fish's brain.

Skin
Sensory organ   Scale   Nerve

Body Systems All fish have highly developed sensory systems. Most fish have a lateral line system, as shown in **Figure 6.** A lateral line system is made up of a shallow, canal-like structure that extends along the length of the fish's body and is filled with sensory organs. The lateral line enables a fish to sense its environment and to detect movement. Some fish, such as sharks, also have a strong sense of smell. Sharks can detect blood in the water from several kilometers away.

Fish have a two-chambered heart in which oxygen-filled blood mixes with carbon dioxide-filled blood. A fish's blood isn't carrying as much oxygen as blood that is pumped through a three- or four-chambered heart.

Gas Exchange Most fish have organs called gills for the exchange of carbon dioxide and oxygen. Gills are located on both sides of the fish's head and are made up of feathery gill filaments that contain many tiny blood vessels. When a fish takes water into its mouth, the water passes over the gills, where oxygen from the water is exchanged with carbon dioxide in the blood. The water then passes out through slits on each side of the fish. Many fish, such as the halibut in **Figure 7,** are able to take in water while lying on the ocean floor.

Figure 7 Even though a halibut's eyes are on one side of the fish, gills are on both sides. **Describe** how a fish breathes.

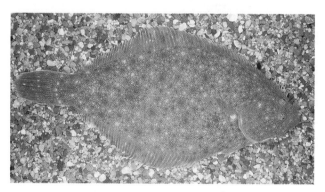

78 ◆ C CHAPTER 3 Fish, Amphibians, and Reptiles

LAB DEMONSTRATION

Purpose to demonstrate water flow across a fish's gill

Materials guppy or goldfish, water, food coloring, clear container

Preparation Place guppy or goldfish in a clear container with an adequate amount of water.

Procedure Have students observe the fish as it swims, noting the opening and closing of its mouth and gill covers. Place a drop of food coloring in front of the fish's mouth.

Expected Outcome Students will see colored water come out of the fish's gills.

Assessment

How long did it take for colored water to come out of the gills? Answers will vary, but soon after the food coloring is added. What does the appearance of colored water indicate? That the water with food coloring flowed over the fish's gills before being expelled. L2

Figure 8 Fish obtain food in different ways.

A whale shark's mouth can open to 1.4 m wide.

Sawfish are rare. They use their toothed snouts to root out bottom fish to eat.

Parrot fish use their hard beaks to bite off pieces of coral.

Electric eels produce a powerful electric shock that stuns their prey.

Feeding Adaptations Some of the adaptations that fish have for obtaining food are shown in **Figure 8.** Some of the largest sharks are filter feeders that take in small animals as they swim. The archerfish shoots down insects by spitting drops of water at them. Even though some fish have strong teeth, most do not chew their food. They use their teeth to capture their prey or to tear off chunks of food.

Reproduction Fish reproduce sexually. Reproduction is controlled by sex hormones. The production of sex hormones is dependent upon certain environmental factors such as temperature, length of daylight, and availability of food.

Female fish release large numbers of eggs into the water. Males then swim over the eggs and release sperm. This behavior is called spawning. The joining of the egg and sperm cells outside the female's body is called external fertilization. Certain species of sharks and rays have internal fertilization and lay fertilized eggs. Some fish, such as guppies and other sharks, have internal fertilization but the eggs develop and hatch inside the female's body. After they hatch, they leave her body.

Some species do not take care of their young. They release hundreds or even millions of eggs, which increases the chances that a few offspring will survive to become adults. Fish that care for their young lay fewer eggs. Some fish, including some catfish, hold their eggs and young in their mouths. Male sea horses keep the fertilized eggs in a pouch until they hatch.

Differentiated Instruction

Challenge Have students research and write a report in their Science Journals on reproduction in guppies, catfish, and sea horses. L2 LS **Linguistic** P

Teacher FYI

Shark Teeth A shark's teeth are adapted to its feeding habits. Struggles that occur while trying to capture prey can cause the loss of teeth. A shark's mouth has 6 to 20 rows of backward slanting teeth. When one tooth breaks or wears down, a replacement moves forward. A single shark may grow more than 20,000 teeth in its lifetime.

Use an Analogy

Tree Cross Section Show students a cross section of a tree and explain its similarity to a cycloid or ctenoid fish scale. Tell students that as a fish grows, more material is added to the scales to make them larger. In temperate climates, a new layer of material is added each year, forming rings. Because one ring is added each year, scale rings can be counted to estimate the age of some fish just as tree rings can be counted to estimate the age of a tree. L2 LS **Logical-Mathematical**

Teacher FYI

Non Ectotherms Most fish are ectotherms, but tuna, mako sharks, and swordfish are exceptions. They are able to maintain their body temperatures slightly above that of the surrounding water. They can adapt to different temperatures at different ocean depths and swim faster and longer than both their competition and their prey. This allows them to hunt in much colder water than their competitors can.

Visual Learning

Figure 8 Have students make a list comparing and contrasting the fish shown. L2

Fun Fact

At one time, it was believed that for every land animal there was a corresponding water animal. This is one reason for names such as catfish, sea horse, and dogfish.

Airplane Wings Fish with paired fins use them the same way airplanes use wings and propellers to generate thrust, to direct the body up and down, and to change direction. L2

Fish Fats Accept all reasonable responses. Encourage students to use the Food Guide Pyramid as a guide for developing a healthful meal.

Career A dietician plans food and nutrition programs, and supervises the preparation and serving of meals. Part of their work is to prevent and treat illnesses by promoting healthy eating habits and suggesting diet modifications. Dieticians need at least a bachelor's degree in dietetics, food and nutrition, or a related area. Coursework generally includes chemistry, biochemistry, biology, microbiology, physiology, foods, and nutrition.

IDENTIFYING Misconceptions

Shark Attacks Movies may have given students the impression that all sharks eat humans. Of the 370 known species, only 27 have been known to attack humans. Have students find out which sharks attack humans and what safety rules are used to prevent shark attacks. L2

✔ Reading Check

Answer because of overfishing and the slow shark reproduction rate

Caption Answer

Figure 9 They are bottom feeders eating dead and dying fish and other marine organisms.

Fish Fats Many fish contain oil with omega-3 fatty acids, which seems to reverse the effects of too much cholesterol. A diet rich in fish that contain this oil might prevent the formation of fatty deposits in the arteries of humans. In your Science Journal, develop a menu for a meal that includes fish.

Figure 9 Hagfish have cartilaginous skeletons. They feed on marine worms, mollusks, and crustaceans, in addition to dead and dying fish.
Infer how hagfish eat.

Curriculum Connection

Language Arts Divide the class into groups. Assign each group a well-known shark—great white, bull, hammerhead, or nurse. Have each group research characteristics, feeding habits, and behavior of the sharks and report back to the class. L2 COOP LEARN IS **Interpersonal**

Types of Fish

Fish vary in size, shape, color, living environments, and other factors. Despite their diversity, fish are grouped into only three categories—jawless fish, jawed cartilaginous (kar tuh LA juh nuss) fish, and bony fish.

Jawless Fish

Lampreys, along with the hagfish in **Figure 9,** are jawless fish. Jawless fish have round, toothed mouths and long, tubelike bodies covered with scaleless, slimy skin. Most lampreys are parasites. They attach to other fish with their suckerlike mouth. They then feed by removing blood and other body fluids from the host fish. Hagfish feed on dead or dying fish and other aquatic animals.

Jawless fish have flexible endoskeletons made of cartilage. Hagfish live only in salt water, but some species of lamprey live in salt water and other species live in freshwater.

Jawed Cartilaginous Fish

Sharks, skates, and rays are jawed cartilaginous fish. These fish have endoskeletons made of cartilage like jawless fish. Unlike jawless fish, these fish have movable jaws that usually have well-developed teeth. Their bodies are covered with tiny scales that make their skins feel like fine sandpaper.

Sharks are top predators in many ocean food chains. They are efficient at finding and killing their food, which includes other fish, mammals, and some reptiles. Because of overfishing and the fact that shark reproduction is slow, shark populations are decreasing at an alarming rate.

✔ **Reading Check** *Why are shark populations decreasing?*

Figure 10 Bony fish come in many sizes, shapes, and colors. However, all bony fish have the same basic body structure.

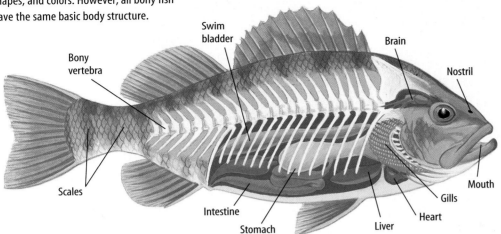

Labels: Swim bladder, Brain, Nostril, Bony vertebra, Mouth, Gills, Heart, Liver, Stomach, Intestine, Scales

Bony Fish

About 95 percent of all species of fish are bony fish. They have skeletons made of bone. The body structure of a typical bony fish is shown in **Figure 10.** A bony flap covers and protects the gills. It closes as water moves into the mouth and over the gills. When it opens, water exits from the gills.

Swim Bladder An important adaptation in most bony fish is the swim bladder. It is an air sac that allows the fish to adjust its density in response to the density of the surrounding water. The density of matter is found by dividing its mass by its volume. If the density of the object is greater than that of the liquid it is in, the object will sink. If the density of the object is equal to the density of the liquid, the object will neither sink nor float to the surface. If the density of the object is less than the density of the liquid, the object will float on the liquid's surface.

The transfer of gases—mostly oxygen in deepwater fish and nitrogen in shallow-water fish—between the swim bladder and the blood causes the swim bladder to inflate and deflate. As the swim bladder fills with gases, the fish's density decreases and it rises in the water. When the swim bladder deflates, the fish's density increases and it sinks. Glands regulate the gas content in the swim bladder, enabling the fish to remain at a specific depth with little effort. Deepwater fish often have oil in their swim bladders rather than gases. Some bottom-dwelling fish and active fish that frequently change depth have no swim bladders.

Mini LAB

Modeling How Fish Adjust to Different Depths

Procedure
1. Fill a **balloon** with air.
2. Place it in a **bowl of water**.
3. Fill **another balloon** partially with water, then blow air into it until it is the same size as the air-filled balloon.
4. Place the second balloon in the bowl of water.

Analysis
1. Infer what structure these balloons model.
2. Compare where in the water (on the surface, or below the surface) two fish would be if they had swim bladders similar to the two balloons.

Try at Home

Mini LAB

Purpose Students use a model to determine how fish use a swim bladder to control their depth. L1 ELL COOP LEARN IS **Kinesthetic and Interpersonal**

Materials 2 balloons, water, bowl

Teaching Strategies
• The bowl will need to be large enough to hold both balloons.
• Encourage students to experiment with different proportions of water and air in the balloon to simulate changes occurring within a fish's swim bladder.

Analysis
1. a swim bladder
2. A fish with a swim bladder filled with air would be near the surface; one with water and air would be farther beneath the surface.

Assessment

Process Ask students to infer the habitat of fish, such as blennies, that have no swim bladder. These fish are bottom dwellers. Use **Performance Assessment in the Science Classroom,** p. 89.

Try at Home

Fun Fact

The smallest freshwater fish is the dwarf pygmy goby, which measures 9 mm long. The largest living fish is the whale shark.

Differentiated Instruction

Challenge Have students research the different types of fishing such as fly-fishing, deep-sea fishing, spin-fishing, trolling, and down-rigging. If possible, have them interview persons who participate in these sports and report their finding to the class. L3

Cultural Diversity

Commercial Fishing Fish are a vital food source worldwide. Fishing is an important economic activity, and fish are part of the diet in many countries. Have students research the fishing industry in various countries and mark a world map to show where most commercial fishing occurs. L2 ELL IS **Visual-Spatial**

Activity

Freshwater Fish Have students research species of fish that live in the lakes and rivers of their state. Have them find or draw pictures of each species and make a bulletin board that illustrates where each species is found. L2

ELL **IS** **Visual-Spatial**

Fun Fact

A swim bladder works the same way a scuba diver's buoyancy compensator does. A scuba diver adds air to his or her compensator to rise, and releases air from the compensator to sink. Also, the diver may effect small changes in depth by inhaling or exhaling.

Discussion

Fish Bladders Bottom-dwelling fish often lack a swim bladder. What is the advantage of this? Swim bladders help fish maintain buoyancy. A bottom-dwelling fish would be at a disadvantage if it were buoyant. L2

Applying Math

National Math Standards

Correlation to Mathematics Objectives

1, 7

Teaching Strategy

Follow the steps in the example problem. Divide the mass of the fish by the volume of the fish.

Answers to Practice Problems

1. Divide the mass of the fish (215 g) by the volume (180 cm³). The fish will have a density of 1.19 g/cm³. The fish will sink in salt water because it is denser than the salt water.

2. The density of the fish is 1.023 g/cm³. The fish is a saltwater fish, because it is less dense than salt water and more dense than fresh water.

Figure 11 Coelacanths (SEE luh kanthz) have been found living in the Indian Ocean north of Madagascar.

Lobe-Finned Fish One of the three types of bony fish is the lobe-finned fish, as shown in **Figure 11**. Lobe-finned fish have fins that are lobelike and fleshy. These organisms were thought to have been extinct for more than 70 million years. But in 1938, some South African fishers caught a lobe-finned fish in a net. Several living lobe-finned fish have been studied since. Lobe-finned fish are important because scientists hypothesize that fish similar to these were the ancestors of the first land vertebrates—the amphibians.

Applying Math   Solve a One-Step Equation

DENSITY OF A FISH A freshwater fish has a mass of 645 g and a volume of 700 cm³. What is the fish's density, and will it sink or float in freshwater?

Solution

1. *This is what you know:*
   - density of freshwater = 1g/cm³
   - mass of fish = 645 g
   - volume of fish = 700 cm³

2. *This is the equation you need to use:*

$$\frac{\text{mass of object (g)}}{\text{volume of object (cm}^3)} = \text{density of object (g/cm}^3)$$

3. *Substitute the known values:*

$$\frac{645 \text{ g}}{700 \text{ cm}^3} = 0.921 \text{ g/cm}^3$$

4. *Check your answer:* Multiply 0.921 g/cm³ by 700 cm³. You should get 645 g. The fish will float in freshwater. Its density is less than that of freshwater.

Practice Problems

1. Calculate the density of a saltwater fish that has a mass of 215 g and a volume of 180 cm³. Will this fish float or sink in salt water? The density of ocean salt water is about 1.025 g/cm³.

2. A fish with a mass of 440 g and a volume of 430 cm³ floats in its water. Is it a freshwater fish or a saltwater fish?

For more practice, visit bookc.msscience.com/math_practice

82 ◆ **C** CHAPTER 3 Fish, Amphibians, and Reptiles

Differentiated Instruction

Learning Disabled Have students make a mobile of the different types of fish mentioned in this section (jawless, cartilaginous, and bony). Beneath each type, have them write the fact they find most interesting about it. The same thing can be done with amphibians and reptiles. L2 **IS** **Kinesthetic and Visual-Spatial**

Curriculum Connection

Language Arts Read aloud poems about fish. Several can be found in John Hersey's book *Blues*. Others include "The Fish" by Elizabeth Bishop, "The Red Mullet" by Robert Penn Warren, "The Lung Fish" by John Ciardi, and "Pike" by Ted Hughes. Ask students how the poet used the fish in each poem. Have them find other poems about fish to share. L2

Figure 12 Australian lungfish are one of the six species of lungfish.
Identify *the unique adaptation of a lungfish.*

Lungfish A lungfish, as shown in **Figure 12,** has one lung and gills. This adaptation enables them to live in shallow waters that have little oxygen. The lung enables the lungfish to breathe air when the water evaporates. Drought conditions stimulate lungfish to burrow into the mud and cover themselves with mucus until water returns. Lungfish have been found along the coasts of South America and Australia.

Ray-Finned Fish Most bony fish have fins made of long, thin bones covered with skin. Ray-finned fish, like those in **Figure 13,** have a lot of variation in their body plans. Most predatory fish have long, flexible bodies, which enable them to pursue prey quickly. Many bottom fish have flattened bodies and mouths adapted for eating off the bottom. Fish with unusual shapes, like the sea horse and anglerfish, also can be found. Yellow perch, tuna, salmon, swordfish, and eels are ray-finned fish.

Figure 13 Bony fish have a diversity of body plans.

Most bony fish are ray-finned fish, like this rainbow trout.

Sea horses use their tails to anchor themselves to sea grass. This prevents the ocean currents from washing them away.

Anglerfish have a structure that looks like a lure to attract prey fish. When the prey comes close, the anglerfish quickly opens its mouth and captures the prey.

SECTION 2 Fish **C ◆ 83**

Teacher FYI

Fish v. Fishes There is sometimes confusion about the use of the words *fish* and *fishes*. Many biologists use the following rules. When referring to a single individual of a single species, use *fish*. When referring to many individuals of a single species, the plural is also *fish*. When referring to several individuals of more than one species, the plural is *fishes*.

Quick Demo

Fish Parts

Materials preserved fish or model or drawing of a fish showing both internal and external features, dissecting tray, dissecting probes, dissecting knife

Estimated Time 15 minutes

Procedure If you are using a model or drawing point out the parts of the fish, first external, then internal parts. If you are using a preserved specimen, prepare the dissection before class. Allow students to come up to view the dissection, pointing out the different parts.

Virtual Labs

Fish Life *How are fish adapted to their environment?*

Differentiated Instruction

Challenge Have students survey a local fish market to find out what varieties of fish are available. Have them determine the procedures that are used to ensure that fish are fresh when they are sold. L3

Cultural Diversity

Fish Appreciation Asians have long celebrated the beauty of carp and goldfish. Elaborately decorated fishbowls and kites with carp designs can be found throughout China, Japan, and Korea. Have students research other ways the beauty of carp and goldfish are used. Water gardens; Asian chefs create works of edible art that look like carp. L2

Figure 14 Lancelets are small, eel-like animals. They spend most of their time buried in the sand and mud at the bottom of the ocean.

Importance and Origin of Fish

Fish play a part in your life in many ways. They provide food for many animals, including humans. Fish farming and commercial fishing also are important to the U.S. economy. Fishing is a method of obtaining food as well as a form of recreation enjoyed by many people. Many fish eat large amounts of insect larvae, such as mosquitoes, which keeps insect populations in check. Some, such as grass carp, are used to keep the plant growth from clogging waterways. Captive fish are kept in aquariums for humans to admire their bright colors and exotic forms.

Reading Check *How are fish helpful to humans?*

Most scientists agree that fish evolved from small, soft-bodied, filter-feeding organisms similar to present-day lancelets, shown in **Figure 14.** The earliest fossils of fish are those of jawless fish that lived about 450 million years ago. Fossils of these early fish usually are found where ancient streams emptied into the sea. This makes it difficult to tell whether these fish ancestors evolved in freshwater or in salt water.

Today's bony fish are probably descended from the first jawed fish called the acanthodians (a kan THOH dee unz). They appeared in the fossil record about 410 mya. Another group of ancient fish—the placoderms—appeared about 400 mya. For about 50 million years, placoderms dominated most water ecosystems then disappeared. Modern sharks and rays probably descended from the placoderms.

section 2 review

Summary

Fish Characteristics

- All fish have a streamlined shape, a muscular tail, fins, scales, well-developed sensory systems, and gills.
- All fish reproduce sexually and feed in many different ways.

Types of Fish

- There are three categories of fish: jawless fish, jawed cartilaginous fish, and bony fish.
- There are three types of bony fish: lobe-finned fish, lungfish, and ray-finned fish.

Self Check

1. **List** examples for each of the three classes of fish.
2. **Explain** how jawless fish and cartilaginous jawed fish take in food.
3. **Describe** the many ways that fish are important to humans.
4. **Think Critically** Female fish lay thousands of eggs. Why aren't lakes and oceans overcrowded with fish?

Applying Skills

5. **Concept Map** Make an events-chain concept map to show what must take place for the fish to rise from the bottom to the surface of the lake.

section 2 review

1. jawless fish—lamprey; cartilaginous fish—shark; bony fish—tuna
2. Jawless fish are parasites that attach to other fish. Cartilaginous fish are predators.
3. Possible answers: food, pets, controlling the growth of insect and plant pests
4. Many eggs are not fertilized; some eggs and young fish are eaten.
5. The sequence is as follows: A fish lying on the bottom of the lake transfers gases from the bloodstream into the swim bladder. As the swim bladder fills with gas, the fish rises in the water.

Amphibians

Amphibian Characteristics

The word *amphibian* comes from the Greek word *amphibios,* which means "double life." They are well named, because amphibians spend part of their lives in water and part on land. Frogs, toads, and the salamander shown in **Figure 15** are examples of amphibians. What characteristics do these animals have that allow them to live on land and in water?

Amphibians are ectotherms. Their body temperature changes when the temperature of their surroundings changes. In cold weather, amphibians become inactive and bury themselves in mud or leaves until the temperature warms. This period of inactivity during cold weather is called **hibernation.** Amphibians that live in hot, dry environments become inactive and hide in the ground when temperatures become too hot. Inactivity during the hot, dry months is called **estivation.**

✔ Reading Check *How are hibernation and estivation similar?*

Respiration Amphibians have moist skin that is smooth, thin, and without scales. They have many capillaries directly beneath the skin and in the lining of the mouth. This makes it possible for oxygen and carbon dioxide to be exchanged through the skin and the mouth lining. Amphibians also have small, simple, saclike lungs in the chest cavity for the exchange of oxygen and carbon dioxide. Some salamanders have no lungs and breathe only through their skin.

as you read

What You'll Learn

- **Describe** the adaptations amphibians have for living in water and living on land.
- **List** the kinds of amphibians and the characteristics of each.
- **Explain** how amphibians reproduce and develop.

Why It's Important

Because amphibians are sensitive to changes in the environment, they can be used as biological indicators.

🔎 Review Vocabulary

habitat: place where an organism lives and that provides the types of food, shelter, moisture, and temperature needed for survival

New Vocabulary

- hibernation
- estivation

Bellringer

Section Focus Transparencies also are available on the Interactive Chalkboard CD-ROM.
[L2] [ELL]

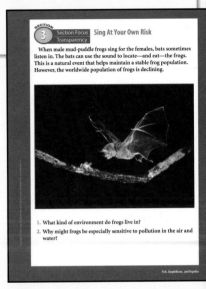

Tie to Prior Knowledge

Fish Adaptations Discuss the characteristics of lobe-finned fish. Show students a picture of a lobe-finned fish. Ask them what adaptations would be necessary for a fish to survive on land. [L2]

✔ Reading Check

Answer Both are periods of amphibian inactivity brought on by weather changes.

Figure 15 Salamanders often are mistaken for lizards because of their shape. However, like all amphibians, they have a moist, scaleless skin that requires them to live in a damp habitat.

SECTION 3 Amphibians **C ◆ 85**

Section 3 Resource Manager

Chapter *FAST FILE* Resources

Transparency Activity, p. 50

Directed Reading for Content Mastery, p. 21

Enrichment, p. 33

Reinforcement, p. 29

MiniLAB, p. 4

Lab Activity, pp. 11–15

Life Science Critical Thinking/Problem Solving, p. 7

Discussion

Naming Amphibians *Amphibian* means "one who leads a double life." Why is this an appropriate name for amphibians? Many begin their lives as aquatic tadpoles and then live most of their adult lives on land. L2

Inquiry Lab

Frog Hibernation

Purpose to explore and observe amphibian reactions to changes in temperature L2

Possible Materials aquarium, water, mud, dirt, wire screen, frog, heat lamp, jar big enough for frog, shallow tub large enough to put aquarium or jar into, ice or cold water, thermometer

Estimated Time one class session

Teaching Strategies

• Students can design a terrarium for the frog, with mud on one side deep enough for the frog to burrow into and shallow water on the other end.

• Students can predict how the frog will react when the temperature is raised or lowered. They also can predict how they will see this reaction, perhaps by observing the throat.

• Students can raise the temperature by putting the terrarium under a heat lamp. They can lower the temperature by placing the frog in a jar and slowly lowering the temperature in a cold-water bath. They can observe hibernation by putting the terrarium in a cold-water bath.

• Allow students to explore other questions as they arise.

• Have students obtain your approval for their lab ideas to ensure the safety of both the students and the frog.

For additional inquiry activities, see *Science Inquiry Labs.*

Figure 16 Red-eyed tree frogs are found in forests of Central and South America. They eat a variety of foods, including insects and even other frogs.

Figure 17 Amphibians go through metamorphosis as they develop.

Amphibian eggs are laid in a jellylike material to keep them moist.

After hatching, most young amphibians, like these tadpoles, do not look like adult forms.

Circulation The three-chambered heart in amphibians is an important change from the circulatory system of fish. In the three-chambered heart, one chamber receives oxygen-filled blood from the lungs and skin, and another chamber receives carbon dioxide-filled blood from the body tissues. Blood moves from both of these chambers to the third chamber, which pumps oxygen-filled blood to body tissues and carbon dioxide-filled blood back to the lungs. Limited mixing of these two bloods occurs.

Reproduction Even though amphibians are adapted for life on land, they depend on water for reproduction. Because their eggs do not have a protective, waterproof shell, they can dry out easily, so amphibians must have water to reproduce.

Amphibian eggs are fertilized externally by the male. As the eggs come out of the female's body, the male releases sperm over them. In most species the female lays eggs in a pond or other body of water. However, many species have developed special reproductive adaptations, enabling them to reproduce away from bodies of water. Red-eyed tree frogs, like the ones in **Figure 16,** lay eggs in a thick gelatin on the underside of leaves that hang over water. After the tadpoles hatch, they fall into the water below, where they continue developing. The Sonoran Desert toad waits for small puddles to form in the desert during the rainy season. It takes tadpoles only two to 12 days to hatch in these temporary puddles.

86 ◆ C CHAPTER 3 Fish, Amphibians, and Reptiles

Differentiated Instruction

Visually Impaired Use a model of a frog to help students locate and identify the function of different structures of amphibians. L2 IS **Kinesthetic**

Curriculum Connection

Language Arts Have students read "The Celebrated Jumping Frog of Calaveras County," written by Mark Twain while he lived in California. It appeared in the *New York Saturday Press* in November 1865. Every year, frog-jumping competitions are held in Calaveras County, California. Have students find out the distance frogs can jump. L2 IS **Linguistic**

Development Most amphibians go through a developmental process called metamorphosis (me tuh MOR fuh sus). Fertilized eggs hatch into tadpoles, the stage that lives in water. Tadpoles have fins, gills, and a two-chambered heart similar to fish. As tadpoles grow into adults, they develop legs, lungs, and a three-chambered heart. **Figure 17** shows this life cycle.

The tadpole of some amphibian species, such as salamanders, are not much different from the adult stage. Young salamanders look like adult salamanders, but they have external gills and usually a tail fin.

Frogs and Toads

Adult frogs and toads have short, broad bodies with four legs but no neck or tail. The strong hind legs are used for swimming and jumping. Bulging eyes and nostrils on top of the head let frogs and toads see and breathe while the rest of their body is submerged in water. On spring nights, males make their presence known with loud, distinctive croaking sounds. On each side of the head, just behind the eyes, are round tympanic membranes. These membranes vibrate somewhat like an eardrum in response to sounds and are used by frogs and toads to hear.

Most frog and toad tongues are attached at the front of their mouths. When they see prey, their tongue flips out and contacts the prey. The prey gets stuck in the sticky saliva on the tongue and the tongue flips back into the mouth. Toads and frogs eat a variety of insects, worms, and spiders, and one tropical species eats berries.

Science Online

Topic: Biological Indicators
Visit bookc.msscience.com for Web links to information about amphibians as biological indicators.

Activity What factors make amphibians good biological indicators?

Amphibians go through metamorphosis, which means they change form from larval stage to adult.

Most adult amphibians are able to move about and live on land.

SECTION 3 Amphibians **C ◆ 87**

Quick Demo

Frogs and Toads

Materials various photographs and models of different frogs and toads

Estimated Time 10 minutes

Procedure Have students look at the photographs and models to observe the differences between frogs and toads. They can sort them into groups, and also take note of the many types of frogs and toads. [L2]

Use an Analogy

Flypaper Tongues Explain that the tongue of a frog is very sticky, like the flypaper that is used to catch flies. This increases the ability of the frog to catch flying insects. [L1]

Activity

Frog Life Cycle Have students work in groups to prepare a poster showing the frog's life cycle. The poster should include drawings of each of the four stages of a frog's life cycle. Each stage should be explained with a paragraph. [L2] [IS] **Visual-Spatial and Linguistic**

IDENTIFYING Misconceptions

Toads and Warts Students may believe they can get warts from touching a toad. Explain that this is a myth which probably came about because many toads have bumpy, wartlike projections on their skin.

Differentiated Instruction

Challenge Have students write a report on the factors that may be contributing to the worldwide decline of frogs and other amphibians in recent years. [L3] [IS] **Linguistic**

Fun Fact

Is it a frog or a toad? Frogs have smooth, moist skin while toads have bumpy, dry skin. Frogs tend to have relatively longer hind legs than toads. This makes frogs capable of long leaps, while toads move in short hops. While toads return to water to lay their eggs, they can exist in drier terrestrial habitats than can frogs.

SECTION 3 Amphibians **C ◆ 87**

Mini LAB

Purpose Students observe frog adaptations. L1 IS **Visual-Spatial**

Materials one live frog in a jar for each student group, water, magnifying lens

Teaching Strategy Obtain references on amphibians for students to use in describing frog adaptations. Caution students to avoid moving the jar abruptly.

Analysis

1. bulging eyes and nostrils at the top of the head for seeing and breathing while in water, underside coloration for camouflage, webbed feet for swimming
2. strong legs for jumping, topside coloration for camouflage, wide mouth for capturing land insects

Assessment

Oral Ask students to list the metamorphic changes tadpoles undergo to adapt to life on land. Development of legs, lungs, wide mouth, and a digestive system designed for consuming insects instead of algae.

Teacher FYI

Caecilians Zoologists divide amphibians into three groups—frogs and toads, salamanders, and caecilians. Caecilians have no legs and look like large earthworms. There are about 150 species, which are found only in tropical regions. Most caecilians live in underground burrows, but some are aquatic.

Mini LAB

Describing Frog Adaptations

Procedure

1. Carefully observe a **frog** in a **jar.** Notice the position of its legs as it sits. Record all of your observations in your **Science Journal.**
2. Observe its mouth, eyes, nostrils and ears.
3. Observe the color of its back and belly.
4. Return the frog to your teacher.

Analysis

1. Describe the adaptations the frog has for living in water.
2. What adaptations does it have for living on land?

Figure 18 Poison frogs are brightly colored to show potential predators that they are poisonous. Toxins from poison frogs have been used in hunting for centuries.

Salamanders

Most species of salamanders and newts live in North America. These amphibians often are mistaken for lizards because of their long, slender bodies. The short legs of salamanders and newts appear to stick straight out from the sides of their bodies.

Land-living species of salamanders and newts usually are found near water. These amphibians hide under leaf litter and rocks during the day to avoid the drying heat of the Sun. At night, they use their well-developed senses of smell and vision to find and feed on worms, crustaceans, and insects.

Many species of salamanders breed on land, where fertilization is internal. Aquatic species of salamanders and newts release and fertilize their eggs in the water.

Importance of Amphibians

Most adult amphibians are insect predators and are helpful in keeping some insect populations in check. They also are a source of food for other animals, including other amphibians. Some people consider frog legs a delicacy.

Poison frogs, like the one in **Figure 18,** produce a poison that can kill large animals. They also are known as poison dart frogs or poison arrow frogs. The toxin is secreted through their skin and can affect muscles and nerves of animals that come in contact with it. Native people of the Emberá Chocó in Colombia, South America, cover blowgun darts that they use for hunting with the poison of one species of these frogs. Researchers are studying the action of these toxins to learn more about how the nervous system works. Researchers also are using amphibians in regeneration studies in hopes of developing new ways of treating humans who have lost limbs or were born without limbs.

Differentiated Instruction

Learning Disabled Have students make flash cards of the vocabulary words in this chapter using an illustration, the phonetic spelling, and the definition of each word. L1 IS **Linguistic and Visual-Spatial**

Challenge Have students research the use of amphibians in regeneration studies and report their findings to the class. L3 IS **Linguistic** P

Biological Indicators Because they live on land and reproduce in water, amphibians are affected directly by changes in the environment, including pesticides and other pollution. Amphibians also absorb gases through their skin, making them susceptible to air pollutants. Amphibians, like the one in **Figure 19,** are considered to be biological indicators. Biological indicators are species whose overall health reflects the health of a particular ecosystem.

 **Reading Check** *What is a biological indicator?*

Origin of Amphibians The fossil record shows that ancestors of modern fish were the first vertebrates on Earth. For about 150 million years, they were the only vertebrates. Then as the climate changed and competition for food and space increased, some lobe-finned fish might have traveled across land searching for water as their ponds dried up. Fossil evidence shows that from these lobe-finned fish evolved aquatic animals with four limbs. Amphibians probably evolved from these aquatic animals about 350 mya.

Because competition on land from other animals was minimal, evolution favored the development of amphibians. Insects, spiders, and other invertebrates were an abundant source of food on land. Land was almost free of predators, so amphibians were able to reproduce in large numbers, and many new species evolved. For 100 million years or more, amphibians were the dominant land animals.

Figure 19 Beginning in 1995, deformed frogs such as this were found. Concerned scientists hypothesize that an increase in the number of deformed frogs could be a warning of environmental problems for other organisms.

---

section 3 review

Summary

Amphibian Characteristics

- Amphibians have two phases of life—one in water and one on land.
- All amphibians have a three-chambered heart, reproduce in the water by laying eggs, and go through metamorphosis.

Types and Importance of Amphibians

- Frogs and toads have short, broad bodies, while salamanders have long, slender bodies.
- Amphibians are used for food, research, and are important as biological indicators.

Self Check

1. **List** the adaptations amphibians have for living in water and for living on land.
2. **Explain** how tadpole and frog hearts differ.
3. **Describe** two different environments where amphibians lay eggs.
4. **Think Critically** Why do you suppose frogs and toads seem to appear suddenly after a rain?

Applying Skills

5. **Concept Map** Make an events-chain concept map of frog metamorphosis. Describe each stage in your Science Journal.

---

section 3 review

1. water: moist, smooth skin; bulging eyes and nostrils on top of the head; strong hind legs for swimming; land: lungs; strong skeleton; strong hind legs for jumping; moist, smooth skin

2. Tadpoles have a two-chambered heart; frogs have a three-chambered heart.

3. Possible answers: underside of leaves in rainforest, in ponds or lakes, on the back of the female

4. They hunt food when the air is moist.

5. egg→legless tadpole→tadpole with legs→young frog with developing legs→adult frog on land

---

1 Motivate

INTERACTIVE CHALKBOARD
PowerPoint® Presentations

Bellringer

Section Focus Transparencies also are available on the Interactive Chalkboard CD-ROM.

L2 ELL

SECTION 4 Section Focus Transparency A Real Dragon!

The Komodo dragon is a large reptile that lives on a few islands in Indonesia. It's big and fast enough to kill deer, wild pigs, and water buffaloes; it is even known to have killed people. The Komodo dragon prefers to eat carrion, which is a polite way of saying it really likes rotten meat.

1. What other animals do you know that look like Komodo dragons?
2. Do you think the Komodo dragon could survive in a very cold environment? Why or why not?
3. What characteristics make Komodo dragons different from the amphibians you studied in the last section?

Fish, Amphibians, and Reptiles

Tie to Prior Knowledge

Common Reptiles Ask students what animals they can identify as reptiles. Answers should include alligators, crocodiles, lizards, snakes, and chameleons. Ask what these animals have in common. L2

✔ Reading Check

Answer By their behavior; they move to locations that are warmer or cooler.

---

as you read

What You'll Learn

- **List** the characteristics of reptiles.
- **Determine** how reptile adaptations enable them to live on land.
- **Explain** the importance of the amniotic egg.

Why It's Important

Reptiles provide information about how body systems work during extreme weather conditions

🔁 **Review Vocabulary**
bask: to warm by continued exposure to heat

New Vocabulary
- amniotic egg

Reptile Characteristics

Reptiles are ectotherms with a thick, dry, waterproof skin. Their skin is covered with scales that help reduce water loss and protect them from injury. Even though reptiles are ectotherms, they are able to modify their internal body temperatures by their behavior. When the weather is cold, they bask in the Sun, which warms them. When the weather is warm and the Sun gets too hot, they move into the shade to cool down.

✔ **Reading Check** *How are reptiles able to modify their body temperature?*

Some reptiles, such as turtles, crocodiles, and lizards, like the skink in **Figure 20,** move on four legs. Claws are used to dig, climb, and run. Reptiles, such as snakes and some lizards, move without legs.

Body Systems Scales on reptiles prevent the exchange of oxygen and carbon dioxide through the skin. Reptiles breathe with lungs. Even turtles and sea snakes that live in water must come to the surface to breathe.

The circulatory system of reptiles is more highly developed than that of amphibians. Most reptiles have a three-chambered heart with a partial wall inside the main chamber. This means that less mixing of oxygen-filled blood and carbon dioxide-filled blood occurs than in amphibians. This type of circulatory system provides more oxygen to all parts of the body. Crocodilians have a four-chambered heart that completely separates the oxygen-filled blood and the carbon dioxide-filled blood and keeps them from mixing.

Figure 20 Skinks, like this northern blue-tongue skink, are one of the largest lizard families with around 800 species.

Section 4 Resource Manager

Chapter *FAST FILE* Resources
Transparency Activity, pp. 51, 53–54
Directed Reading for Content Mastery, pp. 21, 22
Enrichment, p. 34
Reinforcement, p. 30

Lab Worksheet, pp. 7–8
Life Science Critical Thinking/Problem Solving, pp. 11, 13
Home and Community Involvement, p. 41

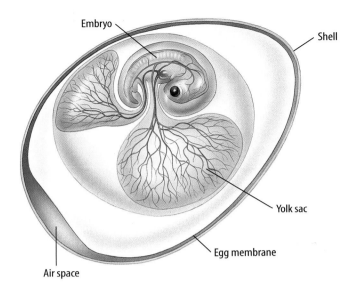

Embryo

Shell

Air space

Yolk sac

Egg membrane

Figure 21 The development of amniotic eggs enabled reptiles to reproduce on land.

Infer *how an amniotic egg helps reptiles be a more successful group.*

Amniotic Egg One of the most important adaptations of reptiles for living on land is the way they reproduce. Unlike the eggs of most fish and amphibians, eggs of reptiles are fertilized internally—inside the body of the female. After fertilization, the females of many reptiles lay eggs that are covered by tough, leathery shells. The shell prevents the eggs from drying out. This adaptation enables reptiles to lay their eggs on land.

The **amniotic egg** provides a complete environment for the embryo's development. **Figure 21** shows the structures in a reptilian egg. This type of egg contains membranes that protect and cushion the embryo and help it get rid of wastes. It also contains a large food supply—the yolk—for the embryo. Minute holes in the shell, called pores, allow oxygen and carbon dioxide to be exchanged. By the time it hatches, a young reptile looks like a small adult.

✓ Reading Check *What is the importance of an amniotic egg?*

Types of Modern Reptiles

Reptiles live on every continent except Antarctica and in all the oceans except those in the polar regions. They vary greatly in size, shape, and color. Reticulated pythons, 10 m in length, can swallow small deer whole. Some sea turtles weigh more than 350 kg and can swim faster than humans can run. Three-horned lizards have movable eye sockets and tongues as long as their bodies. The three living groups of reptiles are lizards and snakes, turtles, and crocodilians.

Science Online

Visit bookc.msscience.com for Web links to recent news about the nesting sites of turtles.

Activity Name two conservation organizations that are giving the turtles a helping hand, and how they are doing it.

Caption Answer

Figure 21 It allowed reptiles to move onto land where there was less competition for food and mates.

Use Science Words

Word Meaning The word *reptile* comes from the Latin word *repere*, meaning "to crawl." Have students use the word in a sentence describing its meaning. L2 IS **Linguistic**

Activity

Egg Parts Organize the class into groups of four. Give each group half of a hard-boiled chicken egg. Have students identify the three parts they observe, and tell the function of each. shell—protection, white—protects and cushions the embryo and gets rid of wastes, yolk—food supply for the embryo Explain to students that there is no embryo because commercial chicken eggs usually are not fertilized. L2 COOP LEARN IS **Interpersonal and Kinesthetic**

✓ Reading Check

Answer It enables the reptile to lay its eggs on land.

Differentiated Instruction

Challenge Have students research and report on a reptile in their state that is listed as threatened or endangered. Ask them to include information about the animal's history, reasons for the lower numbers, and actions being taken to help the species. L3 P

Teacher FYI

Slitlike Pupils The shape of a reptile's pupil can indicate whether the animal is active during night or day. Many nocturnal reptiles have slitlike pupils, which indicate that they are active at night.

Lizards and Snakes Some animals in the largest group of reptiles—the lizards and snakes like those shown in **Figure 22**—have a type of jaw not found in other reptiles, like the turtle also shown in **Figure 22.** The jaw has a special joint that unhinges and increases the size of their mouths. This enables them to swallow their prey whole. Lizards have movable eyelids, external ears, and legs with clawed toes on each foot. They feed on plants, other reptiles, insects, spiders, worms, and mammals.

Snakes have developed ways of moving without legs. They have poor hearing and most have poor eyesight. Recall how you could feel the vibrations of the tuning fork in the Launch Lab. Snakes do not hear sound waves in the air. They "hear" vibrations in the ground that are picked up by the lower jawbone and conducted to the bones of the snake's inner ear. From there, the vibrations are transferred to the snake's brain, where the sounds are interpreted.

Snakes are meat eaters. Some snakes wrap around and constrict their prey. Others inject their prey with venom. Many snakes feed on small mammals, and as a result, help control those populations.

Most snakes lay eggs after they are fertilized internally. In some species, eggs develop and hatch inside the female's body then leave her body shortly thereafter.

Figure 22 Examples of reptiles are shown below.

When frilled lizards are threatened, they flare out their collar. This behavior helps keep predators away.

Diamondback terrapins are one of the few species of turtles that live in brackish—slightly salty—water.

Rosy boas are one of only two species of boas found in the United States.

Cultural Diversity

Snakes In ancient Egypt, the poisonous asp was held in high esteem and its symbol is found in writings and artifacts. The Aztecs worshipped Quetzalcoatl, the mythical plumed serpent. In India, cobras were thought to be the reincarnated spirits of society's elite. Some cultures in Africa worship pythons. Have students find out how snakes are used in art or in celebrations in different cultures. L2

Curriculum Connection

History Have students research the impact hunting American alligators for their skin and meat had on the species early in the twentieth century. Ask them to find out what efforts were made to restore populations of these animals and the success of these efforts. L2

Turtles The only reptiles that have a two-part shell made of hard, bony plates are turtles. The vertebrae and ribs are fused to the inside of the top part of the shell. The muscles are attached to the lower and upper part of the inside of the shell. Most turtles can withdraw their heads and legs into the shell for protection against predators.

> ☑ **Reading Check** *What is the purpose of a turtle's shell?*

Turtles have no teeth but they do have powerful jaws with a beaklike structure used to crush food. They feed on insects, worms, fish, and plants. Turtles live in water and on land. Those that live on land are called tortoises.

Like most reptiles, turtles provide little or no care for their young. Turtles dig out a nest, deposit their eggs, cover the nest, and leave. Turtles never see their own hatchlings. Young turtles, like those in **Figure 23,** emerge from the eggs fully formed and live on their own.

Crocodilians Found in or near water in warm climates, crocodilians, such as crocodiles, gavials, and alligators, are similar in appearance. They are lizardlike in shape, and their backs have large, deep scales. Crocodilians can be distinguished from each other by the shape of their heads. Crocodiles have a narrow head with a triangular-shaped snout. Alligators have a broad head with a rounded snout. Gavials, as shown in **Figure 24,** have a very slender snout with a bulbous growth on the end. Crocodiles are aggressive and can attack animals as large as cattle. Alligators are less aggressive than crocodiles, and feed on fish, turtles, and waterbirds. Gavials primarily feed on fish. Crocodilians are among the world's largest living reptiles.

Crocodilians are some of the few reptiles that care for their young. The female guards the nest of eggs and when the eggs hatch, the male and female protect the young. A few crocodilian females have been photographed opening their nests in response to noises made by hatchlings. After the young hatch, a female carries them in her huge mouth to the safety of the water. She continues to keep watch over the young until they can protect themselves.

Figure 23 Most turtles are eaten shortly after they hatch. Only a few sea turtles actually make it into the ocean.

Figure 24 Indian gavials are one of the rarest crocodilian species on Earth. Adults are well adapted for capturing fish.

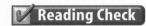

> ☑ **Reading Check**

Answer protection

Visual Learning

Figure 23 Have students list the reptilian characteristics of this turtle. L2

Quick Demo
Reptilian Products

Materials assorted items made from reptiles

Estimated Time 10 minutes

Procedure Display items or pictures of items made from the skins of snakes, alligators, and crocodiles, and the shells of turtles and tortoises. Ask students how these animals are important to our world and how people threaten their survival. L2

Differentiated Instruction

Learning Disabled Have students make a book with the general reptile characteristics on the first page, and the different groups of reptiles and their unique characteristics on subsequent pages. Pages should include lizards, snakes, turtles, and crocodilians. L2

Science Journal

Comparison Have students find pictures of crocodiles and alligators in magazines or reference books. Ask them to study their features, especially the shape of their heads. Have them make a drawing of both on the same sheet of paper. Then have them explain how they can be distinguished from each other based on the shape of their heads. L2
LS Visual-Spatial and Linguistic

Visualizing Extinct Reptiles

Have students examine the pictures and read the captions. Then ask the following questions.

How did the shape of these reptiles help them catch food in their environment? Long, streamlined bodies enabled them to move quickly through the water to capture prey.

Why are these animals classified as reptiles and not fish? Possible answers: They have amniotic eggs that are internally fertilized. They can modify their internal body temperature by basking in the Sun.

Activity

Reptile Poems Have students write a poem about extinct reptiles. Research topics such as reptile characteristics, how long ago they lived on Earth, and the location where fossils have been found. Include interesting statistics. For example, *Temnodontosaurus*, a plesiosaur, had the largest eyes of any animal that has ever lived. L2

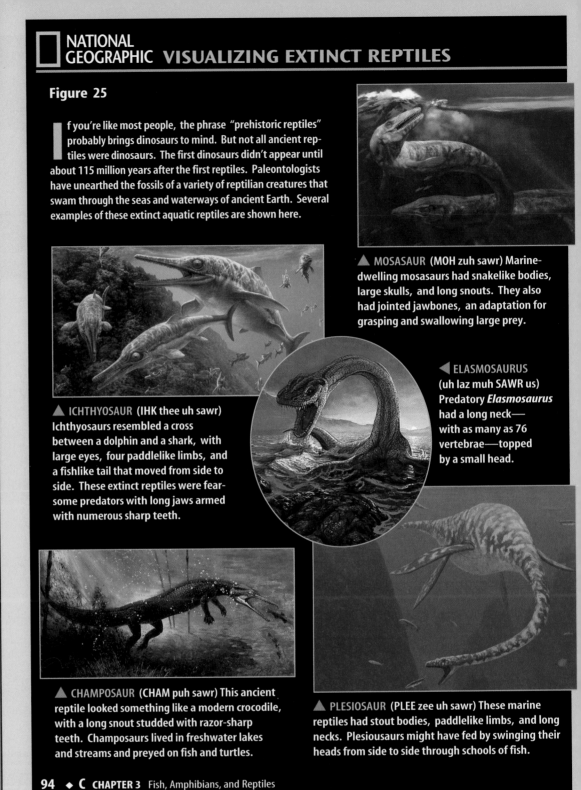

NATIONAL GEOGRAPHIC VISUALIZING EXTINCT REPTILES

Figure 25

If you're like most people, the phrase "prehistoric reptiles" probably brings dinosaurs to mind. But not all ancient reptiles were dinosaurs. The first dinosaurs didn't appear until about 115 million years after the first reptiles. Paleontologists have unearthed the fossils of a variety of reptilian creatures that swam through the seas and waterways of ancient Earth. Several examples of these extinct aquatic reptiles are shown here.

▲ **MOSASAUR (MOH zuh sawr)** Marine-dwelling mosasaurs had snakelike bodies, large skulls, and long snouts. They also had jointed jawbones, an adaptation for grasping and swallowing large prey.

▲ **ICHTHYOSAUR (IHK thee uh sawr)** Ichthyosaurs resembled a cross between a dolphin and a shark, with large eyes, four paddlelike limbs, and a fishlike tail that moved from side to side. These extinct reptiles were fearsome predators with long jaws armed with numerous sharp teeth.

◄ **ELASMOSAURUS (uh laz muh SAWR us)** Predatory *Elasmosaurus* had a long neck—with as many as 76 vertebrae—topped by a small head.

▲ **CHAMPOSAUR (CHAM puh sawr)** This ancient reptile looked something like a modern crocodile, with a long snout studded with razor-sharp teeth. Champosaurs lived in freshwater lakes and streams and preyed on fish and turtles.

▲ **PLESIOSAUR (PLEE zee uh sawr)** These marine reptiles had stout bodies, paddlelike limbs, and long necks. Plesiousaurs might have fed by swinging their heads from side to side through schools of fish.

94 ◆ **C CHAPTER 3** Fish, Amphibians, and Reptiles

Differentiated Instruction

Challenge Have students create an illustrated book of different types of extinct reptiles. Have students classify these animals. L3

The Importance of Reptiles

Reptiles are important predators in many environments. In farming areas, snakes eat rats and mice that destroy grains. Small lizards eat insects, and large lizards eat small animals that are considered pests.

Humans in many parts of the world eat reptiles and their eggs or foods that include reptiles, such as turtle soup. The number of reptile species is declining in areas where swamps and other lands are being developed for homes and recreation areas. Coastal nesting sites of sea turtles are being destroyed by development or are becoming unusable because of pollution. For years, many small turtles were collected in the wild and then sold as pets. People now understand that such practices disturb turtle populations. Today most species of turtles and their habitats are protected by law.

Origin of Reptiles Reptiles first appeared in the fossil record about 345 mya. The earliest reptiles did not depend upon water for reproduction. As a result, they began to dominate the land about 200 mya. Some reptiles even returned to the water to live, although they continued to lay their eggs on land. Dinosaurs—descendants of the early reptiles—ruled Earth during this era, then died out about 65 mya. Some of today's reptiles, such as the crocodilians, have changed little from their ancestors, some of which are illustrated in **Figure 25.**

INTEGRATE History

A Changing Environment Dinosaurs, reptiles that ruled Earth for 160 million years, died out about 65 million years ago. In your Science Journal, describe what changes in the environment could have caused the extinction of the dinosaurs.

INTEGRATE History

A Changing Environment Student answers should reflect the fact that dinosaurs were ectotherms. Temperatures decreased on Earth.

Discussion

Sea Turtles How do you think sea turtles get the oxygen they need for respiration? Turtles are reptiles and reptiles use lungs for gas exchange. They must come to the surface to obtain oxygen. L2

3 Assess

DAILY INTERVENTION

Check for Understanding
Linguistic Have students make a table of the characteristics of the different reptile groups.

Reteach

Ectotherm Differences Prepare a quiz game with photographs or descriptions of lizards, turtles, alligators, crocodiles, snakes, frogs, and salamanders. Have students classify the animals as amphibians or reptiles and name a characteristic of each. L2

Assessment

Oral The ability to change skin color is an adaptation in many reptiles. Ask students to explain how this adaptation may help reptiles survive. L2

---

section 4 review

Summary

Reptile Characteristics
- Reptiles are ectotherms with a thick, dry, waterproof skin that is covered with scales.
- Most have a three-chambered heart with a partial wall in the main chamber.
- Reptile young develop in an amniotic egg.

Types and Importance of Reptiles
- Lizards and snakes are the largest group of reptiles. Most lizards have legs, while snakes do not.
- Turtles have a two-part bony shell.
- Crocodilians are large reptiles and one of the few reptiles that care for their young.
- Reptiles are important predators. Some reptiles are food sources.

Self Check

1. **Describe** reptilian adaptations for living on land.
2. **Explain** how turtles differ from other reptiles.
3. **Infer** why early reptiles, including dinosaurs, were so successful as a group.
4. **Draw** the structure of an amniotic egg.
5. **Think Critically** Venomous coral snakes and some nonvenomous snakes have bright red, yellow, and black colors. How is this an advantage and a disadvantage to the nonvenomous snake?

Applying Math
6. **Solve One-Step Equations** *Brachiosaurus*, a dinosaur, was about 12 m tall and 22 m long. The average elephant is 3 m tall and 6 m long. How much taller and longer is the *Brachiosaurus* compared to an elephant?

 Science Online bookc.msscience.com/self_check_quiz

---

section 4 review

1. a thick, dry, scaly waterproof skin; four legs with claws (except snakes and some lizards); three-chambered heart; lungs; amniotic egg
2. Turtles are covered with a hard shell on top and bottom. Most can withdraw into this shell for protection.
3. They did not depend on water for reproduction.
4. Drawing should resemble egg in **Figure 22.**
5. Predators think they are venomous snakes and leave them alone. Disadvantage: nonvenomous

snakes may be killed because they are thought to be venomous.
6. The elephant is one-fourth the height of *Brachiosaurus*, and about one-third the length.

 LAB
Design Your Own

Real-World Question

Purpose Students design an experiment to determine the effect of water temperature on the respiration rate of fish. L2

LS Visual-Spatial

Process Skills design an experiment, form a hypothesis, observe and infer, communicate, compare, describe, graph, separate and control variables

Time Required two 30-minute class periods

Materials Large goldfish work best because their breathing is easily observed.

Safety Precautions Caution students not to handle the fish with their hands.

Form a Hypothesis

Possible Hypothesis Students might predict a slowing respiration rate or no change with a decrease in temperature. Few students will hypothesize an increase in the rate.

Test Your Hypothesis

Possible Procedures Students can place the fish in a large beaker of room-temperature water and record the respiration rate, the number of times the fish opens its mouth or gill covering in 20 seconds. Next, place the beaker into a large bowl filled with ice water. Measure the respiration rate each minute for 10 minutes. Allow the water in the beaker to return to room temperature before putting it into a hot-water bath. Measure the respiration rate.

Water Temperature and the Respiration Rate of Fish

Real-World Question

Imagine that last summer was hot with few storms. One day after many sunny, windless days, you noticed that a lot of dead fish were floating on the surface of your neighbor's pond. What might have caused these fish to die? How does water temperature affect the respiration rate of fish?

Form a Hypothesis

Fish obtain oxygen from the water. State a hypothesis about how water temperature affects the respiration rate of fish.

Test Your Hypothesis

Make a Plan

1. As a group, agree upon and write out a plan. You might make a plan that relates the amount of oxygen dissolved in water at different water temperatures and how this affects fish.

> **Goals**
> - **Design** and carry out an experiment to measure the effect of water temperature on the rate of respiration of fish.
> - **Observe** the breathing rate of fish.
>
> **Possible Materials**
> goldfish
> aquarium water
> small fishnet
> 600-mL beakers
> container of ice water
> stirring rod
> thermometer
> aquarium
>
> **Safety Precautions**
>
> Protect your clothing. Use the fishnet to transfer fish into beakers.

Alternative Inquiry Lab

Encourage Questions To extend this lab, make it an inquiry lab. Build on the experiences by encouraging your students to use what they have learned to brainstorm questions about a fish's breathing rate. Have each student choose one question to explore. Unsafe or impractical questions should be eliminated. Ask students to choose the materials they need to explore their questions. Students should have their plan approved before continuing. Conduct the experiments after all of the necessary materials have been gathered.

2. As a group, list the steps that you need to take to follow your plan. Be specific and describe exactly what you will do at each step. List your materials.

3. How will you measure the breathing rate of fish?

4. **Explain** how you will change the water temperature in the beakers. Fish respond better to a gradual change in temperature than an abrupt change. How will you measure the response of fish to changes in water temperature?

5. What data will your group collect? Prepare a data table in your Science Journal to record the data you collect. How many times will you run your experiment?

6. Read over your entire experiment to make sure the steps are in logical order. Identify any constants, variables, and controls.

Follow Your Plan

1. Make sure your teacher approves your setup and your plan before you start.

2. Carry out the experiment according to the approved plan.

3. While the experiment is going on, write down any observations that you make and complete the data table in your Science Journal.

◉ Analyze Your Data

1. **Compare** your results with the results of other groups in your class. Were the results similar?

2. **Infer** what you were measuring when you counted mouth or gill cover openings.

3. **Describe** how a decrease in water temperature affects respiration rate and behavior of the fish.

4. **Explain** how your results could be used to determine the kind of environment in which a fish can live.

◉ Conclude and Apply

1. **Explain** how fish can live in water that is totally covered by ice.

2. **Predict** what would happen to a fish if the water were to become very warm.

Construct a graph of your data on poster board and share your results with your classmates.

Teaching Strategies

• Placing a beaker with water and the fish into a large bowl of ice water will lower the temperature gradually without harming the fish.

• Allow water to return to room temperature before heating it.

• Heat fish's water gradually using a hot water bath.

Tie to Prior Knowledge Many students will be aware that fish have gills, but many will not know that a fish opening its mouth or gill covering indicates it is breathing.

Expected Outcomes The respiration rate of the fish should decrease and increase with a decrease and increase in water temperature, respectively.

◉ Analyze Your Data

Answers to Questions

1. Answers will vary, but results should be similar.

2. respiration rate

3. Respiration rate decreases and movement slows as temperature decreases.

4. Similar experiments could measure the temperature range in which various species of fish can breathe.

Error Analysis Students should compare their results and hypotheses and explain any differences in their data.

◉ Conclude and Apply

1. Ice is less dense than water, and a large body of water usually lies beneath the ice. The ice actually insulates the water, keeping the water temperature high enough for fish to breathe.

2. Warm water contains less oxygen, making it more difficult for a fish to breathe. Without enough dissolved oxygen, death could result.

Communicating Your Data

Encourage students to generate their graphs electronically.

✓ Assessment

Performance Have students research and report on the causes and effects of eutrophication. Eutrophication occurs when excess nutrients are added to the water from farms, lawns, and other sources. The nutrients cause an explosion of algae growth, and as the alga dies off, bacteria populations increase, depleting the water of oxygen and killing aquatic life. Use **Performance Assessment in the Science Classroom,** p. 159. L2

TIME

TIME

SCIENCE AND *Society*

SCIENCE ISSUES THAT AFFECT YOU!

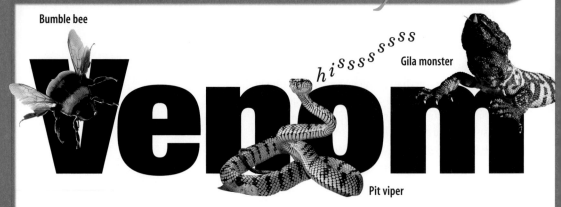

Bumble bee

hisssssss

Gila monster

Pit viper

Venom as Medicine

Hiss, rattle… Run! Just the sound of a snake sends most people on a sprint to escape what could be a painful bite. Why? The bites could contain venom, a toxic substance injected into prey or an enemy. Venom can harm—or even kill—the victim. Some venomous creatures use it to stun, kill, and digest their prey, while others use it as a means of protection.

Venom is produced by a gland in the body. Some fish use their sharp, bony spines to inject venom. Venomous snakes, such as pit vipers, have fangs. Venom passes through these hollow teeth into a victim's body. The Gila monster, the largest lizard in the United States, has enlarged, grooved teeth in its lower jaw through which its venom travels. It is one of only two species of venomous lizards.

Doctors and scientists have discovered a shocking surprise within this

sometimes deadly liquid. Oddly enough, the very same toxin that harms and weakens people can heal, too. In fact, doctors use the deadliest venom—that of some pit viper species—to treat certain types of heart attacks. Cobra venom has been used to soothe the effects of cancer, and other snake venoms reduce the spasms of epilepsy and asthma.

Some venoms also contain substances that help clot blood. Hemophiliacs—people whose blood will not clot naturally—rely on the medical benefits that venom-based medicines supply. Venoms also are used in biological research. For instance, venoms that affect the nervous system help doctors and researchers learn more about how nerves function.

It's still smart to steer clear of the rattle or the stinger—but it's good to know that the venom in them might someday help as many as it can hurt.

Research Besides venom, what other defenses do animals use to protect themselves or to subdue their prey? Explore how some animals that are native to your region use their built-in defenses.

Science online

For more information, visit bookc.msscience.com/time

Research Animals use a number of strategies to attract prey or protect themselves. The viceroy butterfly resembles the monarch butterfly, which is distasteful to birds. Many insects avoid predation by blending with their environment. Other organisms, like the angler fish, have structures that attract their own prey closer to them.

Resources for Teachers and Students

Life on Earth: A Natural History, by David Attenborough, Little Brown & Company, 1981

Life on Earth: A Natural History Written and Hosted by David Attenborough, 1996, British Broadcasting Corporation and BBC Enterprises, Ltd. Available through Warner Home Video

Reviewing Main Ideas

Section 1 — Chordates and Vertebrates

1. Chordates include lancelets, tunicates, and vertebrates. Chordates have a notochord, a nerve cord, pharyngeal pouches, and a postanal tail.

2. All vertebrates have an endoskeleton that includes a backbone and a skull that protects the brain.

3. An endotherm is an animal that has a nearly constant internal body temperature. An ectotherm has a body temperature that changes with the temperature of its environment.

Section 2 — Fish

1. Fish are vertebrates that have a streamlined body, fins, gills for gas exchange, and a highly developed sensory system.

2. Fish are divided into three groups—jawless fish, jawed cartilaginous fish, and bony fish.

3. Bony fish, with scales and a swim bladder, have the greatest number of known fish species.

Section 3 — Amphibians

1. The first vertebrates to live on land were the amphibians.

2. Amphibians have adaptations that allow them to live on land and in the water. The adaptations include moist skin, mucous glands, and lungs. Most amphibians are dependent on water to reproduce.

3. Most amphibians go through a metamorphosis from egg, to larva, to adult. During metamorphosis, legs develop, lungs replace gills, and the tail is lost.

Section 4 — Reptiles

1. Reptiles are land animals with thick, dry, scaly skin. They lay amniotic eggs with leathery shells.

2. Turtles with tough shells, meat-eating crocodilians, and snakes and lizards make up the reptile groups.

3. Early reptiles were successful because of their adaptations to living on land.

Visualizing Main Ideas

Copy and complete the concept map below that describes chordates.

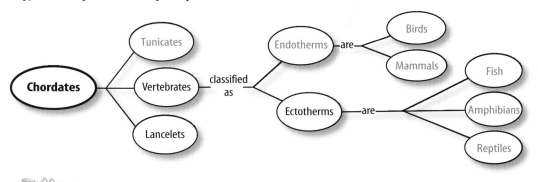

Reviewing Main Ideas

Summary statements can be used by students to review the major concepts of the chapter.

Visualizing Main Ideas

See student page.

Science Online

Visit bookc.msscience.com
/self_check_quiz
/interactive_tutor
/vocabulary_puzzlemaker
/chapter_review
/standardized_test

Assessment Transparency

For additional assessment questions, use the *Assessment Transparency* located in the transparency book.

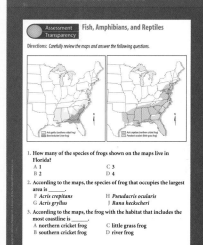

Using Vocabulary

1. nerve cord
2. estivation
3. endotherms
4. ectotherms
5. cartilage
6. amniotic eggs
7. notochord

Checking Concepts

8. D	11. C	14. A
9. A	12. A	15. A
10. A	13. A	16. C

Thinking Critically

17. The populations of insects and other animals they eat might increase. Populations of their predators might decrease.

18. The skin of amphibians absorbs oxygen, as well as poisonous gases or chemicals in the area. They often show signs of environmental pollutants quickly. Because of this, amphibians can be considered biological indicators—species that reflect the condition of the environment.

19. They have a notochord, postanal tail, nerve cord, and gill slits in some stage of development.

20. All vertebrates have, at some time in their lives, a notochord that becomes the vertebrae in vertebrates, a postanal tail, a nerve cord, and gill slits. They also all have an endoskeleton.

Using Vocabulary

amniotic egg p. 91	hibernation p. 85
cartilage p. 73	nerve cord p. 73
chordate p. 72	notochord p. 72
ectotherm p. 75	pharyngeal pouch p. 73
endoskeleton p. 73	postanal tail p. 72
endotherm p. 75	scale p. 77
estivation p. 85	vertebrae p. 73
fin p. 77	

Fill in the blanks with the correct vocabulary word or words.

1. All chordates have a notochord, pharyngeal pouches, postanal tail, and a(n) _____.

2. The inactivity of amphibians during hot, dry weather is _____.

3. All animals with a constant internal temperature are _____.

4. Reptiles are _____ with scaly skin.

5. Jawless fish have skeletons made of a tough, flexible tissue called _____.

6. Reptiles lay _____.

7. The structure that becomes the backbone in vertebrates is the _____.

Checking Concepts

Choose the word or phrase that best answers the question.

8. Which animals have fins, scales, and gills?
   A) amphibians   C) reptiles
   B) crocodiles   D) fish

9. Which is an example of a cartilaginous fish?
   A) hagfish   C) perch
   B) tuna   D) goldfish

10. What fish group has the greatest number of species?
    A) bony   C) jawed cartilaginous
    B) jawless   D) amphibians

11. Which of these fish have gills and lungs?
    A) shark   C) lungfish
    B) ray   D) perch

12. Biological indicators include which group of ectothermic vertebrates?
    A) amphibians
    B) cartilaginous fish
    C) bony fish
    D) reptiles

Use the photo below to answer question 13.

13. Which kinds of reptiles are included with the animal above?
    A) snakes   C) turtles
    B) crocodiles   D) alligators

14. What term best describes eggs of reptiles?
    A) amniotic   C) jellylike
    B) brown   D) hard-shelled

15. Vertebrates that have lungs and moist skin belong to which group?
    A) amphibians   C) reptiles
    B) fish   D) lizards

16. How can crocodiles be distinguished from alligators?
    A) care of the young
    B) scales on the back
    C) shape of the head
    D) habitats in which they live

 Science Online bookc.msscience.com/vocabulary_puzzlemaker

Use the ExamView® Pro Testmaker CD-ROM to:
- create multiple versions of tests
- create modified tests with one mouse click for inclusion students
- edit existing questions and add your own questions
- build tests aligned with state standards using built-in State Curriculum Tags
- change English tests to Spanish with one mouse click and vice versa

Thinking Critically

17. Infer Populations of frogs and toads are decreasing in some areas. What effects could this decrease have on other animal populations?

18. Explain why some amphibians are considered to be biological indicators.

19. Compare and contrast the ways tunicates and lancelets are similar to humans.

20. Describe the physical features common to all vertebrates.

21. Compare and contrast endotherms and ectotherms.

22. Explain how the development of the amniotic egg led to the success of early reptiles.

23. Communicate In your Science Journal, sequence the order in which these structures appeared in evolutionary history, then explain what type of organism had this adaptation and the advantage it provided: skin has mucous glands; skin has scales; dry, scaly skin.

24. Compare and Contrast Copy and complete this chart that compares the features of some vertebrate groups.

Vertebrate Groups

Feature	Fish	Amphibians	Reptiles
Heart	Two-chambered	Three-chambered	Three-chambered
Respiratory organ(s)	Gills	Skin and two lungs	Two lungs
Reproduction requires water	yes	yes	no

25. Explain how a fish uses its swim bladder.

26. Identify and Manipulate Variables and Controls Design an experiment to find out the effect of water temperature on frog egg development.

27. Classify To what animal group does an animal with a two-chambered heart belong?

28. Identify why it is necessary for a frog to live in a moist environment.

Performance Activities

29. Conduct a Survey Many people are wary of reptiles. Write questions about reptiles to find out how people feel about these animals. Give the survey to your classmates, then graph the results and share them with your class.

30. Display Cut out pictures of fish from magazines and mount them on poster board. Letter the names of each fish on 3-in × 5-in cards. Have your classmates try to match the names of the fish with their pictures. To make this activity more challenging, use only the scientific names of each fish.

Applying Math

Use the table below to answer questions 31 and 32.

Fish Species

Kinds of Fish	Number of Species
Jawless	45
Jawed cartilaginous	500
Bony	20,000

31. Fish Species Make a circle graph of the species of fish in the table above.

32. Fish Percentages What percent of fish species is bony fish? Jawed cartilaginous? Jawless?

 Science Online bookc.msscience.com/chapter_review

CHAPTER REVIEW C ◆ **101**

Thinking Critically

21. Endotherms maintain a constant body temperature while an ectotherm's body temperature changes with the environment.

22. The amniotic egg provides the developing embryo with protection from drying out and being eaten. An adequate supply of food is also provided. Reptile eggs can be laid anywhere on land, thus freeing reptiles from a reliance on water for reproduction.

23. Scales are present in fish, allowing them to move in water; skin with mucus glands is present in amphibians, which began to live on land; dry, scaly skin developed in reptiles that lived on land.

24. See student page.

25. By taking in or releasing gases, it raises and lowers itself in the water.

26. Students should design experiments with a control—a set temperature—and groups with higher or lower temperatures as the variables.

27. The animal is most likely a fish.

28. It allows exchange of oxygen and carbon dioxide within the environment.

Performance Activities

29. Student graphs will vary according to their survey audience. Use **PASC**, p. 107.

30. Students should find matching scientific names that describe the characteristics of each fish chosen. Use **PASC**, p. 145.

Applying Math

National Math Standards
5, 6

31. Students should find that 350° represents bony fish, 8.6° represents cartilagenous jawed fish, and about 0.8° represents jawless fish.

32. 97.3% are bony fish, 2.4% are cartilagenous jawed fish, and 0.22% are jawless fish

chapter **3** Standardized Test Practice

FAST FILE

Answer Sheet A practice answer sheet can be found at bookc.msscience.com/answer_sheet.

S A M P L E

Part 1 | Multiple Choice

1. C	6. D
2. A	7. A
3. D	8. C
4. B	9. A
5. B	10. C

Part 1 | Multiple Choice

Record your answers on the answer sheet provided by your teacher or on a sheet of paper.

1. What are fins attached to?
   A. ectoskeleton   C. endoskeleton
   B. notochord   D. spine

2. How many chambers does a fish heart contain, and does it carry more or less oxygen than other types of hearts?
   A. two, less   C. three, less
   B. four, less   D. four, more

Use the photo below to answer question 3.

3. What type of fish is shown in this picture?
   A. bony
   B. jawed cartilaginous
   C. large-mouth bass
   D. jawless

4. How do amphibians exchange carbon dioxide and oxygen?
   A. lungs only   C. gills only
   B. lungs and skin D. lungs and gills

5. How do frogs and toads hear?
   A. eardrum
   B. tympanic membrane
   C. skin
   D. tongue

6. Fish and amphibians do not have this type of egg so they must reproduce near water.
   A. external   C. porous
   B. membranous   D. amniotic

Use the photos below to answer questions 7 and 8.

7. What is the developmental process shown in this diagram?
   A. metamorphosis
   B. respiration
   C. ectotherm
   D. asexual reproduction

8. Where does this transition take place?
   A. land to air   C. water to land
   B. air to land   D. land to water

9. What is one way to distinguish a crocodile from an alligator?
   A. the shape of the snout
   B. number of eggs in nest
   C. size of teeth
   D. placement of nostrils

10. What are turtles missing that all other reptiles have?
    A. hair
    B. three-chambered heart
    C. teeth
    D. shelled eggs

Test-Taking Tip

Marking on Tests Be sure to ask if it is okay to mark in the test booklet when taking the test, but make sure you mark all of the answers on your answer sheet.

Question 6 Cross out answers you know are wrong or circle answers you know are correct. This will help you narrow your choices.

102 ◆ C STANDARDIZED TEST PRACTICE

Part 2 | Short Response

11. The lateral line system is a system of sensory organs that extend along the body. They detect movement and sense the environment.

12. Fish have feathery gill filaments that contain many tiny blood vessels for gas exchange when water passes over the gills.

13. When the swim bladder fills the fish, it becomes less dense, rising to a higher depth. When it empties, the fish becomes more dense and falls to a deeper depth.

14. Hibernation is a period of inactivity in cold weather and estivation is a period of inactivity in hot weather.

15. An amphibian heart changes from 2-chambered to 3-chambered and lungs replace gills.

16. construction, pollution, and habitat destruction

17. fewer offspring produced receive greater care

18. through vibrations in the ground that are picked up by the lower jawbone

19. ectothermic, modify their body temperature by behavior

20. The front end becomes the brain and the remainder becomes the spinal cord.

Part 2 | Short Response/Grid In

Record your answers on the answer sheet provided by your teacher or on a sheet of paper.

Use the illustration below to answer question 11.

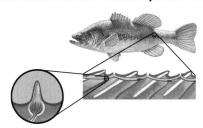

11. Describe the body system of the fish shown in this diagram. Why is it important to the fish?

12. What organs do fish have for the exchange of carbon dioxide and oxygen? How does the exchange take place?

13. How does a fish's swim bladder regulate its depth in water?

14. What is the difference between hibernation and estivation?

15. As an amphibian goes through metamorphosis, how do their heart and lungs change?

16. What is one possible reason for the decline in the number of reptiles in swamps and coastal areas?

17. What is the relationship between the number of young produced and the amount of care given by the parents in fish, amphibians, and reptiles?

18. How do snakes hear?

19. Are reptiles endothermic or ectothermic? Can reptiles modify their body temperature?

20. During chordate development, what structures originate from the nerve chord?

Part 3 | Open Ended

Record your answers on a sheet of paper.

21. Describe the composition and function of fish scales.

22. How did amphibians evolve and why were they the dominant land animals for a period of time?

23. Compare and contrast the circulatory systems of fish, amphibians, and reptiles. Which system provides the most oxygenated blood to the organs?

Use the illustration below to answer question 24.

24. Explain the composition and significance of the structure in this diagram.

25. Discuss the structure of a turtle's shell and what other body parts are attached to it.

26. What are two classifications of how organisms regulate body temperature? How does regulation of body temperature help to determine the climate in which an organism is found?

27. What are pharyngeal pouches and what animal group has them at some point during development? How has their function changed over time?

25. It is a two-part shell made of hard bony plates. The vertebrae and ribs are fused to the inside top and muscles are attached to the inside of both parts of the shell.

26. Ectotherm and endotherm; ectotherms' body temperatures change with their surroundings and they tend to live in warmer climates, and endotherms have a constant internal body temperature and can live in any environment.

27. All chordates have pharyngeal pouches at some point in development. They were used by ancient invertebrates for filter feeding, and this is still their purpose in some chordates. In fish they develop into gills and in humans they are only present during embryonic development.

Rubrics

For more help evaluating open-ended assessment questions, see the rubric on p. 10T.

Part 3 | Open Ended

21. They cover and protect the body of fish, most are made of bone and are tooth shaped, diamond shaped, cone shaped or round.

22. Lobe-finned fish had lungs and bony fins allowing them to survive a trip across land when resources became scarce. On land, insects and spiders were abundant with very little competition or predation so the amphibian became a dominant species.

23. All have hearts that pump oxygenated blood to the organs and tissues for gas exchange. Fish have a 2-chambered heart that allows for mixing of oxygenated and deoxygenated blood. Amphibians have a 3-chambered heart for less mixing of the blood. Most efficient for providing oxygenated blood to the organs is the reptilian 3-chambered heart with a partial wall.

24. The structure shown in this diagram is a backbone, a stack of vertebrae alternating with cartilage. It surrounds and protects the spinal nerve cord.

Section/Objectives	Standards		Labs/Features
	National	**State/Local**	
Chapter Opener	See pp. 16T–17T for a Key to Standards.		**Launch Lab:** Bird Gizzards, p. 105 **Foldables,** p. 105
Section 1 Birds ⏱ 2 sessions 📦 1 block 1. **Identify** the characteristics of birds. 2. **Identify** the adaptations birds have for flight. 3. **Explain** how birds reproduce and develop.	National Content Standards: UCP.1–UCP.5, A.1, A.2, C.1–C.5		**Integrate Astronomy,** p. 107 **MiniLAB:** Modeling Feather Function, p. 108 **Integrate Social Studies,** p. 109 **Science Online,** p. 110 **Visualizing Birds,** p. 112
Section 2 Mammals ⏱ 3 sessions 📦 1.5 blocks 4. **Identify** the characteristics of mammals and explain how they have enabled mammals to adapt to different environments. 5. **Distinguish** among monotremes, marsupials, and placentals. 6. **Explain** why many species of mammals are becoming threatened or endangered.	National Content Standards: UCP.1–UCP.3, UCP.5, A.1, A.2, F.1		**MiniLAB:** Inferring How Blubber Insulates, p. 116 **Applying Science:** Does a mammal's heart rate determine how long it will live?, p. 117 **Science Online,** p. 119 **Lab:** Mammal Footprints, p. 123 **Lab:** Bird Counts, pp. 124–125 **Science Stats:** Eggciting Facts, p. 126

Lab Materials	Reproducible Resources	Section Assessment	Technology
Launch Lab: cracked corn, sunflower seeds, nuts, or other seeds; gravel; old sock	**Chapter** *Fast File* **Resources** Foldables Worksheet, p. 15 Directed Reading Overview, p. 17 Note-taking Worksheets, pp. 29–31		Teacher**Works** includes: • Interactive Teacher Edition • Lesson Planner with calendar • Access to all program blacklines • Correlations to standards • Web links
MiniLAB: alcohol thermometers (2), polyester fiber or cotton, plastic bags (2), container of cold water, Science Journal *Need materials?* Contact Science Kit at 1-800-828-7777 or www.sciencekit.com on the Internet.	**Chapter** *Fast File* **Resources** Transparency Activity, p. 40 MiniLAB, p. 3 Lab Activity, pp. 9–10 Enrichment, p. 27 Reinforcement, p. 25 Directed Reading, p. 18 Transparency Activity, pp. 43–44 **Home and Community Involvement,** p. 27 **Earth Science Critical Thinking/ Problem Solving,** p. 12 **Life Science Critical Thinking/ Problem Solving,** pp. 12, 13	Portfolio Science Journal, p. 109 Assessment, p. 105 Performance MiniLAB, p. 108 Applying Skills, p. 113 Content Section Review, p. 113	Section Focus Transparency Teaching Transparency Virtual Labs CD-ROM Guided Reading Audio Program Interactive Chalkboard CD-ROM
MiniLAB: self-sealing plastic bags (2), vegetable shortening, ice water **Lab:** diagram of mammal footprints **Lab:** Internet and other sources of information on birds	**Chapter** *Fast File* **Resources** Transparency Activity, p. 41 MiniLAB, p. 4 Lab Activity, pp. 11–14 Enrichment, p. 28 Reinforcement, p. 26 Directed Reading, pp. 19, 20 Lab Worksheets, pp. 5–6, 7–8 **Lab Management and Safety,** p. 37 **Mathematics Skill Activities,** p. 7 **Cultural Diversity,** p. 9	Portfolio Assessment, p. 125 Performance MiniLAB, p. 116 Applying Science, p. 117 Applying Math, p. 126 Applying Math, p. 122 Content Section Review, p. 122	Section Focus Transparency Virtual Labs CD-ROM Guided Reading Audio Program Interactive Chalkboard CD-ROM Video Lab

End of Chapter Assessment

Blackline Masters	Technology	Professional Series
Chapter *Fast File* **Resources** Chapter Review, pp. 33–34 Chapter Tests, pp. 35–38 **Standardized Test Practice,** pp. 19–22	MindJogger Videoquiz Virtual Labs CD-ROM Exam*View*® Pro Testmaker TeacherWorks CD-ROM Interactive Chalkboard CD-ROM	**Performance Assessment in the Science Classroom (PASC)**

Transparencies

Section Focus

SECTION 1 — Section Focus Transparency — A Long Flight

Albatrosses are among the largest flying birds. They are able to ride the ocean winds in such a way that they can stay aloft for hours without flapping their wings. Albatrosses spend between five and ten years at sea before returning to shore to mate for the first time.

1. Describe the albatross pictured. How is it similar to other birds?
2. What might albatrosses eat?
3. What body characteristics enable birds to fly?

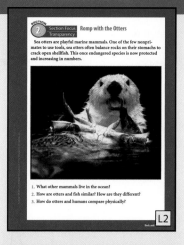

SECTION 2 — Section Focus Transparency — Romp with the Otters

Sea otters are playful marine mammals. One of the few nonprimates to use tools, sea otters often balance rocks on their stomachs to crack open shellfish. This once endangered species is now protected and increasing in numbers.

1. What other mammals live in the ocean?
2. How are otters and fish similar? How are they different?
3. How do otters and humans compare physically?

This is a representation of key blackline masters available in the Teacher Classroom Resources. See Resource Manager boxes within the chapter for additional information.

Key to Teaching Strategies

The following designations will help you decide which activities are appropriate for your students.

L1 Level 1 activities should be appropriate for students with learning difficulties.

L2 Level 2 activities should be within the ability range of all students.

L3 Level 3 activities are designed for above-average students.

ELL ELL activities should be within the ability range of English-Language Learners.

COOP LEARN Cooperative Learning activities are designed for small group work.

LS Multiple Learning Styles logos, as described on page 12T, are used throughout to indicate strategies that address different learning styles.

P These strategies represent student products that can be placed into a best-work portfolio.

PBL Problem-Based Learning activities apply real-world situations to learning.

Assessment

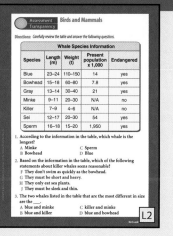

Assessment Transparency — Birds and Mammals

Directions: Carefully review the table and answer the following questions.

Whale Species Information

Species	Length (m)	Weight (t)	Present population x 1,000	Endangered
Blue	23–24	110–150	14	yes
Bowhead	15–18	60–80	7.8	yes
Gray	13–14	30–40	21	yes
Minke	9–11	20–30	N/A	no
Killer	7–9	4–6	N/A	no
Sei	12–17	20–30	54	yes
Sperm	16–18	15–20	1,950	yes

1. According to the information in the table, which whale is the longest?
   A Minke   C Sperm
   B Bowhead   D Blue
2. Based on the information in the table, which of the following statements about killer whales seems reasonable?
   F They don't swim as quickly as the bowhead.
   G They must be short and heavy.
   H They only eat sea plants.
   J They must be sleek and thin.
3. The two whales listed in the table that are the most different in size are the ___.
   A blue and minke   C killer and minke
   B blue and killer   D blue and bowhead

Teaching

SECTION 1 — Teaching Transparency — Hollow Bones of Birds

Hands-on Activities

Student Text Lab Worksheet

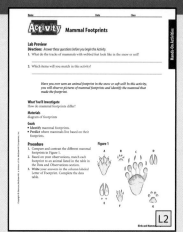

Activity — Mammal Footprints

Lab Preview
Directions: Answer these questions before you begin the Activity.
1. What do the tracks of mammals with webbed feet look like in the snow or soil?

2. Which items will you match in this activity?

Have you ever seen an animal footprint in the snow or soft soil? In this activity, you will observe pictures of mammal footprints and identify the mammal that made the footprint.

What You'll Investigate
How do mammal footprints differ?

Materials
diagram of footprints

Goals
• Identify mammal footprints.
• Predict where mammals live based on their footprints.

Procedure
1. Compare and contrast the different mammal footprints in Figure 1.
2. Based on your observations, match each footprint to an animal listed in the table in the Data and Observations section.
3. Write your answers in the column labeled Letter of Footprint. Complete the data table.

Figure 1

Laboratory Activities

LAB 1 — Laboratory Activity — Owl Pellets

The barn owl usually feeds on small mammals such as rodents, moles, and shrews. These mammals are swallowed whole. Some parts of the mammals dissolve in the owl's stomach. The indigestible parts, such as bones, hair, and feathers, are regurgitated in an owl pellet. You can find out what an owl eats by examining the owl pellet in this Laboratory Activity.

Strategy
You will dissect an owl pellet and identify animal skulls found in the owl pellet.
You will complete a table of the numbers and kinds of prey eaten by owls.

Materials
plastic gloves   white sheet of paper
forceps   dissecting needle
owl pellet   field guide to small mammals (that shows skeletons)

Procedure
1. Put on the plastic gloves. Use the forceps to place the owl pellet on the white paper.
2. Break the owl pellet apart. Carefully separate the bones of the animals from the feathers and fur.
3. Use the forceps and dissecting needle to clean skull bones. **CAUTION:** Use care when handling sharp objects.
4. Identify the skulls of the animals that the owl has eaten, using a field guide to small mammals. You can also refer to the mouse skeleton below to help you determine which are leg bones, which are ribs, and so on. Record the number of skulls of different animals in Table 1.
5. Make a class record of the kinds and numbers of animals found in the owl pellets.

Owl pellet

Mouse skeleton

Meeting Different Ability Levels

Content Outline

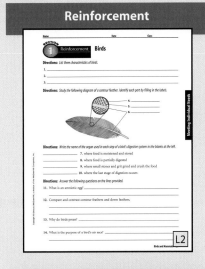

Reinforcement

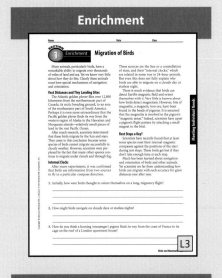

Enrichment

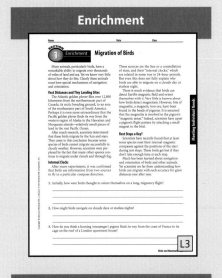

Directed Reading (English/Spanish)

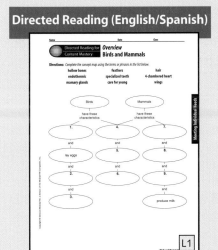

Study Guide

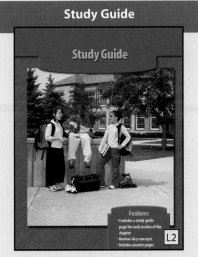

Reading Essentials

Assessment

Test Practice Workbook

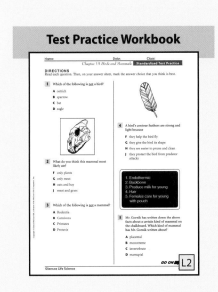

Chapter Review

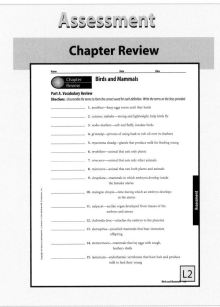

Chapter Tests

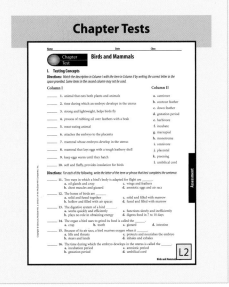

Science Content Background

Steve Lucas/International Stock

Birds

Bird Characteristics

As opposed to amphibians and reptiles, birds and mammals are endotherms—their bodies maintain a nearly constant internal body temperature. This has two advantages—metabolic functions work optimally at certain temperature ranges, and maintaining a warm temperature prevents endotherms from being sluggish on cold days. The disadvantage is that it can take a lot of energy to maintain this temperature.

If you observe birds, you will see their preening behavior, which involves smoothing feathers and spreading oil from the uropygial gland located at the base of their tails. The oil conditions the feathers, and smoothing feathers keeps them in their proper locations and in the proper shape. Sticky oil from oil spills hurts sea birds because their feathers get stuck in the wrong positions. This allows cold water to contact their skin, resulting in the birds needing more energy to stay warm. In cold areas or places without enough food, this can cause death to the birds.

Body Systems

Examinations of bird hearts reveal another way birds (and mammals) are different from all amphibians and most reptiles. Birds have a four-chambered heart. This is a more efficient pump because oxygenated and deoxygenated blood don't mix.

The Importance of Birds

Fossil evidence suggests that birds may have evolved from a group of dinosaurs. The scales on birds' feet and legs suggest their reptilian origins. In addition, birds' feathers are made of a protein called keratin, which is the same material that makes up reptile scales. Like reptiles, birds reproduce by internal fertilization and lay amniotic eggs.

Bird species are threatened by the actions of people. For example, the introduction of the brown tree snake onto the island of Guam has caused the loss of many bird species. The snake, which reproduces rapidly, climbs into trees and eats the eggs and chicks of many birds. The snake can find its way into airplanes and thus is easily spread to other islands. Nonflying birds are especially vulnerable to introduced animals. For example, about a century ago a lighthouse keeper's cat killed all the species of nonflying birds on one of New Zealand's islands.

Teacher to Teacher

Jeff Remington
Palmyra Middle School
Palmyra, Pennsylvania

"I pass around contour feathers, down feathers, and courtship feathers to have students determine form and function through inquiry."

Jeff Remington

---

section 2 Mammals

Characteristics of Mammals

Like the scales of reptiles and the feathers of birds, mammal hair is made of keratin. Hair helps these endotherms retain body heat. At times it is necessary to lose heat. Sweating and panting are two mechanisms that allow cooling of the body through evaporation of sweat from the skin or moisture from the lungs.

Body Systems

Herbivores generally have longer digestive systems than carnivores and omnivores. Many plant products, such as starches and fruits, are easy to digest. However, when a diet includes eating large amounts of leaves, large amounts of cellulose must be digested. Large molars start the digestive process by grinding the leaves into smaller pieces. Then the food moves slowly through the long digestive system where it is broken down.

While amphibians, reptiles, and birds all have red blood cells, those of mammals differ in that they don't have a nucleus in their mature state. This allows more room in the cells for hemoglobin to carry oxygen. The biconcave shape of mammalian red blood cells give them more surface area to absorb oxygen.

Types of Mammals

Mammals are thought to have evolved from a group of ancient reptiles called therapsids. These animals had both reptilian and mammalian characteristics.

---

chapter content resources

Internet Resources
For additional content background, visit
bookc.msscience.com to:
- access your book online
- find references to related articles in popular science magazines
- access Web links with related content background
- access current events with science journal topics

Print Resources
Animal Life, Copper Beech Books, 2002
A Field Guide to the Birds of Eastern and Central North America by Roger Tory Peterson, Houghton Mifflin Co; 5th edition, 2002
Building a Backyard Bird Habitat by Scott Shalaway, Satckpole Books, 2000
The Encyclopedia of Mammals by David W. MacDonald, Checkmark Books, 1995

Jeff Rotman/Stone

Chapter Vocabulary

contour feather, p. 108
down feather, p. 108
endotherm, p. 108
preening, p. 108
mammal, p. 114
mammary gland, p. 114
omnivore, p. 115
carnivore, p. 115
herbivore, p. 115
monotreme, p. 118
marsupial, p. 118
placental, p. 119
gestation period, p. 119
placenta, p. 119
umbilical cord, p. 119

Science Journal Student answers will vary. Similar—warm-blooded; live on every continent on Earth; give parental care. Different—birds have feathers; mammals have hair or fur; birds lay eggs and most mammals do not; most birds fly, most mammals do not

INTERACTIVE CHALKBOARD
with Image Bank

PowerPoint® Presentations

This CD-ROM is an editable Microsoft® PowerPoint® presentation that includes:
- a pre-made presentation for every chapter
- interactive graphics
- animations
- audio clips
- image bank
- all new section and chapter questions
- Standardized Test Practice
- transparencies
- pre-lab questions for all labs
- Foldables directions
- links to bookc.msscience.com

Birds and Mammals

chapter preview

sections

1 Birds

2 Mammals
  Lab Mammal Footprints
  Lab Bird Counts
  Virtual Lab How are birds adapted to their habitat?

More Alike than Not!

Birds and mammals have adaptations that allow them to live on every continent and in every ocean. Some of these animals have adapted to withstand the coldest or hottest conditions. These adaptations help to make these animal groups successful.

Science Journal List similar characteristics of a mammal and a bird. What characteristics are different?

Theme Connection

Stability and Change A discussion of the adaptations of birds to life in the air and on land reinforces the steps in the evolution of different species that have moved from water to land environments. The theme of stability and change is continued in the discussion of mammal characteristics and origins. Both birds and mammals have developed homeostatic mechanisms for living on land.

About the Photo

In Harmony Birds and mammals often live together in harmony and interact. Birds will often eat insects that are parasites on a mammal. In return, the mammal is parasite-free!

Start-Up Activities

Bird Gizzards

You may have observed a variety of animals in your neighborhood. Maybe you have watched birds at a bird feeder. Birds don't chew their food because they don't have teeth. Instead, many birds swallow small pebbles, bits of eggshells, and other hard materials that go into the gizzard—a muscular digestive organ. Inside the gizzard, they help grind up the seeds. The lab below models the action of a gizzard.

1. Place some cracked corn, sunflower seeds, nuts or other seeds, and some gravel in an old sock.

2. Roll the sock on a hard surface and tightly squeeze it.

3. Describe the appearance of the seeds after rolling.

4. **Think Critically** Describe in your Science Journal how a bird's gizzard helps digest the bird's food.

 **Science Online** Preview this chapter's content and activities at bookc.msscience.com

 FOLDABLES Study Organizer

Birds and Mammals Make the following Foldable to help you organize information about the behaviors of birds and mammals.

STEP 1 **Fold** one piece of paper widthwise into thirds.

STEP 2 **Fold** down 2.5 cm from the top. (Hint: From the tip of your index finger to your middle knuckle is about 2.5 cm.)

STEP 3 **Fold** the rest into fifths.

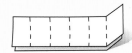

STEP 4 **Unfold**, lay the paper lengthwise, and draw lines along the folds. **Label** your table as shown.

	Birds	Mammals
Habitats		
Diet		
Movement		
Body Systems		
Young		

Make a Table As you read the chapter, complete the table describing the behaviors of birds and mammals.

1 Motivate

Bellringer

INTERACTIVE CHALKBOARD
PowerPoint® Presentations

Section Focus Transparencies also are available on the Interactive Chalkboard CD-ROM.

L2 ELL

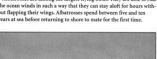

Tie to Prior Knowledge

Eggs Most students will have cracked open an egg or seen someone else do so. Have them describe what they see when they crack open an egg and infer what each part is or does. yellow yolk (nourishes the embryo until it is born), clear fluid (the vitelline membrane) Many students will have seen brown eggs at the grocery store or at home. Explain that brown and white eggs taste the same, and have the same nutritional value. The color of the egg shell is determined by hen's genetic make-up.

Text Question Answer

the presence of feathers

Birds

as you read

What You'll Learn

- **Identify** the characteristics of birds.
- **Identify** the adaptations birds have for flight.
- **Explain** how birds reproduce and develop.

Why It's Important

Most birds demonstrate structural and behavioral adaptations for flight.

Review Vocabulary
thrust: for an object moving through air, the horizontal force that pushes or pulls the object forward

New Vocabulary
- contour feather
- down feather
- endotherm
- preening

Figure 1 This robin's round nest is built of grasses and mud in a tree.

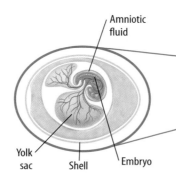

Amniotic fluid

Yolk sac   Shell   Embryo

Bird Characteristics

Birds are versatile animals. Geese have been observed flying at an altitude of 9,000 m, and penguins have been seen underwater at a depth of 543 m. An ostrich might weigh 155,000 g, while a hummingbird might weigh only 2 g. Some birds can live in the tropics and others can live in polar regions. Their diets vary and include meat, fish, insects, fruit, seeds, and nectar. Birds have feathers and scales and they lay eggs. Which of these characteristics is unique to birds?

Bird Eggs Birds lay amniotic (am nee AH tihk) eggs with hard shells, as shown in **Figure 1.** This type of egg provides a moist, protective environment for the developing embryo. The hard shell is made of calcium carbonate, the same chemical that makes up seashells, limestone, and marble. The egg is fertilized internally before the shell forms around it. The female bird lays one or more eggs usually in some type of nest, also shown in **Figure 1.** A group of eggs is called a clutch. One or both parents may keep the eggs warm, or incubate them, until they hatch. The length of time for incubation varies from species to species. The young are cared for by one or both parents.

106 ◆ C CHAPTER 4

Section 1 Resource Manager

Chapter FAST FILE Resources
Transparency Activity, pp. 40, 43–44
Directed Reading for Content Mastery, pp. 17, 18
Note-taking Worksheets, pp. 29–31
MiniLAB, p. 3
Lab Activity, pp. 9–10

Reinforcement, p. 25
Enrichment, p. 27
Home and Community Involvement, p. 27
Earth Science Critical Thinking/Problem Solving, p. 12

Figure 2 The hollow bones of birds are an adaptation for flight.
Infer *what advantages thin cross braces provide.*

Sternum The sternum has a structure called a keel, which is where flight muscles attach.

Tail A bird does not have a bony tail.

Leg bone

Hollow leg bone

Flight Adaptations

Flight Adaptations People have always been fascinated by the ability of birds to fly. Flight in birds is made possible by their almost hollow but strong skeleton, wings, feathers, strong flight muscles, and an efficient respiratory system. Well-developed senses, especially eyesight, and tremendous amounts of energy also are needed for flight.

Hollow Bones One adaptation that birds have for flight is a unique internal skeleton, as shown in **Figure 2.** Many bones of some birds are joined together. This provides more strength and more stability for flight. Most bones of birds that fly are almost hollow. These bones have thin cross braces inside that also strengthen the bones. The hollow spaces inside of the bones are filled with air.

Reading Check *What features strengthen a bird's bones?*

A large sternum, or breastbone, supports the powerful chest muscles needed for flight. The last bones of the spine support the tail feathers, which play an important part in steering and balancing during flight and landing.

INTEGRATE Astronomy

Star Navigation Many theories have been proposed about how birds navigate at night. Some scientists hypothesize that star positions help night-flying birds find their way. Research the location of the North Star. In your Science Journal, infer how the North Star might help birds fly at night.

Caption Answer
Figure 2 They give the bones strength and support.

Quick Demo
Bird Behavior
Materials live bird
Estimated Time 10 minutes
Procedure If someone in the class has a pet bird (canary, parakeet, parrot), ask that student to bring the bird to class so its characteristics and behavior may be observed. L1 IS **Visual-Spatial**

INTEGRATE Astronomy

Star Navigation The North Star is located very close to the northern celestial pole, making its position appear relatively fixed. It is one of the brightest stars in the night sky. Because of this, it can be used in navigation.

Reading Check

Answer Many bones are joined; cross braces within hollow bones add strength.

Activity

Flaps per Minute Organize the class into pairs. Have one student keep time and count while the other holds his or her arms straight out and flaps them up and down. See how many times a student can flap his or her arms in one minute and how long it takes for the student to tire. Explain that just as our leg muscles are well developed for walking, the chest muscles of most birds are well developed for flying. L1 IS **Kinesthetic**

Differentiated Instruction

Learning Disabled Ask students to draw or take pictures of different birds found around school or their homes. They should identify the birds and start a bird diary. Have them note the time of day they saw each bird, its location, and any other interesting observations. L2 IS **Visual-Spatial and Linguistic**

Fun Fact

Bird eggs come in a variety of sizes. Some hummingbird eggs are as small as a pea; some ostrich eggs are larger than softballs!

Mini LAB

Purpose to discover the function of down feathers [L2] [IS]
Kinesthetic

Materials two alcohol thermometers, polyester fiber or cotton, two plastic bags, container of cold water, Science Journal

Teaching Strategy Check that students thoroughly cover the bulb of the thermometer.

Analysis

1. the thermometer without fiber or cotton
2. down feathers

Assessment

Oral Ask students to infer if the amount of down feathers would be different for bird species in different environments. Use **Performance Assessment in the Science Classroom,** p. 89.

✓ Reading Check

Answer To help maintain a constant body temperature

Virtual Labs

Bird Adaptations *How are birds adapted to their habitat?*

Mini LAB

Modeling Feather Function

Procedure 🌊 🧤

1. Wrap **polyester fiber** or **cotton** around the bulb of an **alcohol thermometer.** Place it into a **plastic bag.** Record its temperature in your **Science Journal.**
2. Place a second **alcohol thermometer** into a **plastic bag** and record its temperature.
3. Simultaneously submerge the thermometers into a **container** of **cold water,** keeping the top of each bag above the water's surface.
4. After 2 min, record the temperature of each thermometer.

Analysis

1. Which thermometer had the greater change in temperature?
2. Infer the type of feather that the fiber or cotton models.

Feathers Birds are the only animals that have feathers. Their bodies are covered with two main types of feathers—contour feathers and down feathers. Strong, lightweight **contour feathers** give a bird its coloring and smooth shape. These are also the feathers that a bird uses when flying. The contour feathers on the wings and tail help the bird steer and keep it from spinning out of control.

Have you ever wondered how ducks can swim in a pond on a freezing cold day and keep warm? Soft, fluffy **down feathers** provide an insulating layer next to the skin of adult birds and cover the bodies of young birds. Birds are **endotherms,** meaning they maintain a constant body temperature. Feathers help birds maintain their body temperature, and grow in much the same way as your hair grows. Each feather grows from a microscopic pit in the skin called a follicle (FAH lih kul). When a feather falls out, a new one grows in its place. As shown in **Figure 3,** the shaft of a feather has many branches called barbs. Each barb has many branches called barbules that give the feather strength.

✓ Reading Check
Why are some young birds covered with down feathers?

A bird has an oil gland located just above the base of its tail. Using its bill or beak, a bird rubs oil from the gland over its feathers in a process called **preening.** The oil conditions the feathers and helps them last longer.

Figure 3 Down feathers help keep birds warm. Contour feathers are the feathers used for flight, and the feathers that cover the body.

Down feather

Contour feather

Shaft

Shaft

Barb

Barbule

Visual Learning

Figure 3 What differences do you see between down feathers and contour feathers? Contour feathers are larger, with a more rigid shaft, and the barbs are hooked together. Down feathers are smaller, fluffier, and softer. The hairlike filaments are not hooked together, and the shaft is very flexible.

✓ Active Reading

Reflective Journal Have students divide sheets of paper into several columns. Have them record their thoughts about an activity under headings such as *What I did, What I learned, What questions I have, What surprised me,* and *Overall response.* Have students write a Reflective Journal entry for the MiniLAB on this page. [L2]

Figure 4 Wings provide an upward force called lift for birds and airplanes.
Describe *how birds are able to fly.*

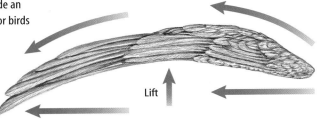

Lift

Bald eagles are able to soar for long periods of time because their wings have a large surface area to provide lift.

This glider gets lift from its wings the same way a bald eagle gets lift.

INTEGRATE Physics

Wings Although not all birds fly, most wings are adapted for flight. Wings are attached to powerful chest muscles. By flapping its wings, a bird attains thrust to go forward and lift to stay in the air. Its wings move up and down, as well as back and forth.

The shape of a bird's wings helps it fly. The wings are curved on top and flat or slightly curved on the bottom. Humans copied this shape to make airplane wings, as shown in **Figure 4.** When a bird flies, air moves more slowly across the bottom than across the top of its wings. Slow-moving air has greater pressure than fast-moving air, resulting in an upward push called lift. The amount of lift depends on the total surface area of the wing, the speed at which air moves over the wing, and the angle of the wing to the moving air. Once birds with large wings, such as vultures, reach high altitudes, they can soar and glide for a long time without having to beat their wings.

Wings also serve important functions for birds that don't fly. Penguins are birds that use their wings to swim underwater. Ostriches use their wings in courtship and to maintain their balance while running or walking.

INTEGRATE Social Studies

Bird Pests Some birds have become pests in urban areas. Research to learn what birds are considered pests in urban areas, what effect they have on the urban environment, and what measures are taken to reduce the problems they create. Build a bulletin board showing your results.

Bird Body Structure Use diagrams to show students the internal and external structures of a bird. Point out the digestive tract, oil gland, and air sacs. Have students make a list of the bird's internal and external characteristics. ⬜L2

🔲 **Visual-Spatial**

Fun Fact

Because birds use large amounts of energy to fly, the crop and the gizzard help birds obtain maximum energy from food. The crop continuously stores and releases food. The gizzard grinds the food so it can be digested faster.

Use Science Words

Word Origin Birds belong to the class Aves. *Avis* is the Latin word for bird and is the root of many bird-related words. Ask students to find words with this root and explain their meanings. *Aviator—pilot or member of an aircraft crew; avian—relating to birds; aviary—enclosure for breeding and rearing birds* ⬜L2

Discussion

Endothermic Disadvantages What is a disadvantage of being endothermic? *It takes more food to maintain body temperature.* ⬜L2

Fun Fact

The chest or pectoral muscles of birds are primarily responsible for the movement of the wings. These muscles are well developed in birds, accounting for as much as 25% of the entire mass of the bird.

Science Online

Topic: Homing Pigeons
Visit bookc.msscience.com for Web links to information about homing pigeons.

Activity Name two past uses for homing pigeons, and write an advertisement for a new use in the future.

Figure 5 A bird's blood is circulated quickly so enough oxygen-filled blood is carried to the bird's muscles.

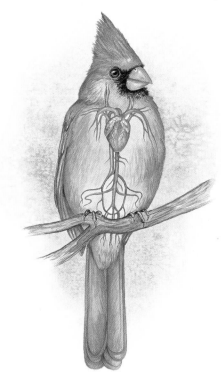

Body Systems

Whether they fly, swim, or run, most birds are extremely active. Their body systems are adapted for these activities.

Digestive System Because flying uses large amounts of energy, birds need large amounts of high energy foods, such as nuts, seeds, nectar, insects, and meat. Food is broken down quickly in the digestive system to supply this energy. In some birds, digestion can take less than an hour—for humans digestion can take more than a day.

From a bird's mouth, unchewed food passes into a digestive organ called the crop. The crop stores the food until it absorbs enough moisture to move on. The food enters the stomach where it is partially digested before it moves into the muscular gizzard. In the gizzard, food is ground and crushed by small stones and grit that the bird has swallowed. Digestion is completed in the intestine, and then the food's nutrients move into the bloodstream.

Respiratory System Body heat is generated when energy in food is combined with oxygen. A bird's respiratory system efficiently obtains oxygen, which is needed to power flight muscles and to convert food into energy. Birds have two lungs. Each lung is connected to balloonlike air sacs that reach into different parts of the body, including some of the bones. Most of the air inhaled by a bird passes into the air sacs behind the lungs. When a bird exhales, air with oxygen passes from these air sacs into the lungs. Air flows in only one direction through a bird's lungs. Unlike other vertebrates, birds receive air with oxygen when they inhale and when they exhale. This provides a constant supply of oxygen for the flight muscles.

Circulatory System A bird's circulatory system consists of a heart, arteries, capillaries, and veins, as shown in **Figure 5.** Their four-chambered heart is large compared to their body. On average, a sparrow's heart is 1.68 percent of its body weight. The average human heart is only 0.42 percent of the human's body weight. Oxygen-filled blood is kept separate from carbon dioxide-filled blood as both move through a bird's heart and blood vessels. A bird's heart beats rapidly—an active hummingbird's heart can beat more than 1,000 times per minute.

Owl

Hummingbird

The Importance of Birds

Birds play important roles in nature. Some are sources of food and raw materials, and others are kept as pets. Some birds, like the owl in **Figure 6,** help control pests, such as destructive rodents. Barn swallows and other birds help keep insect populations in check by eating them. Some birds, like the hummingbird in **Figure 6,** are pollinators for many flowers. As they feed on the flower's nectar, pollen collects on their feathers and is deposited on the next flower they visit. Other birds eat fruits, then their seeds are dispersed in the birds' droppings. Seed-eating birds help control weeds. Birds can be considered pests when their populations grow too large. In cities where large numbers of birds roost, their droppings can damage buildings. Some droppings also can contain microorganisms that can cause diseases in humans.

Uses of Birds Humans have hunted birds for food and fancy feathers for centuries. Eventually, wild birds such as chickens and turkeys were domesticated and their meat and eggs became a valuable part of human diets. Feathers are used in mattresses and pillows because of their softness and ability to be fluffed over and over. Down feathers are good insulators. Even bird droppings, called guano (GWAH noh), are collected from seabird colonies and used as fertilizer.

Parakeets, parrots, and canaries often are kept as pets because many sing or can be taught to imitate sounds and human voices. Most birds sold as pets are bred in captivity, but some wild birds still are collected illegally, which threatens many species.

Figure 6 In nature, some birds, like the owl on the left, help control pests. Others, like the hummingbird above, pollinate flowers. **Identify** *other important uses of birds.*

Inquiry Lab

Building a Bird House or Feeder

Purpose to explore bird characteristics and behavior, which will aid in designing a house or feeder that birds could safely use L1

Possible Materials wood, 2-liter bottle, string, nails, hammer, birdseed, nesting materials, pinecones, suet, peanut butter, grapevine wreaths

Estimated Time one class section

Teaching Strategies
• Have students brainstorm materials that they could use and designs they might create.
• Discard any plans and materials that would be dangerous to the birds or the students. Keep in mind that birds like to use their beaks to peel and peck. Avoid using anything with lead, or may be contain a lead-based paint. Avoid sharp edges.
• As an extension, you can install these at various areas around the school, or students can take them home and report on the activity. Keep a tally of bird visitors, time of visits, etc.
• Allow students to explore other questions as they arise.

For additional inquiry activities, see *Science Inquiry Labs.*

Curriculum Connection

History Over 4,000 years ago, humans used pigeons as messengers. The first recorded use of messenger pigeons was in 1200 B.C. by Ramses III, who sent four birds out in different directions with the message that he had taken the throne. Have students research how homing pigeons find their way home. Two hypotheses are that they use an odor map or navigate by Earth's magnetic field. L2

Cultural Diversity

Earliest Bird Sankar Chatterjee is best known for his 1986 discovery of *Protoavis*, a 225-million-year-old fossil that may turn out to be the earliest bird known. Have students research the work of Chatterjee. L2

Visualizing Birds

Have students examine the pictures and read the captions. Then ask the following questions:

How does the shape of the heron's beak help it catch food in its environment? The beak is long and helps it scoop up fish.

Why do seed-eating birds need grasping claws? They need to be able to hook onto tree limbs or hold on to tree bark.

What other adaptation do you think birds of prey must have besides sharp beaks and grasping claws? They must be able to see well so they can spot and track prey, and to fly fast so they can catch prey.

Activity

Bird Statistics Have students research bird statistics, naming the birds with the following characteristics:

- Tallest and heaviest: ostrich
- Largest wingspan: Andean condor, albatross, marabou stork
- Earliest known: Archaeopteryx
- Smallest: hummingbird of Cuba
- Fastest: swift
- Fastest diver: peregrine falcon
- Fastest swimmer: penguin
- Largest eyes: ostrich

Have students list in a table or on the board other interesting statistics found. L2

Figure 7

There are almost 9,000 living species of birds. Birds are subdivided into smaller groups based on characteristics such as beak size and shape, foot structure, and diet. Birds belonging to several groups are shown here.

INSECT EATERS This nuthatch has a pointed beak that can pry up bark or bore into wood to find insects.

WATERBIRDS Wood ducks have webbed feet that propel them through the water.

FLIGHTLESS BIRDS The ostrich evolved in places where there were once few mammal predators. Though they cannot fly, some flightless birds are fast runners.

BIRDS OF PREY This osprey has large claws that grasp and a sharp beak that tears flesh.

WADING BIRDS The great blue heron's long legs allow it to walk in shallow water.

SEED EATERS This cardinal's thick, strong beak can crack seeds.

112 ◆ **C CHAPTER 4** Birds and Mammals

Differentiated Instruction

Challenge Have students consider birds adapted to extreme environments, such as penguins or roadrunners. Have students draw conclusions about the adaptations that allow these birds to survive, then confirm their conclusions with research. L3

Teacher FYI

Extinction More than 80 species of birds have become extinct in the last 300 years. Causes of extinction include habitat destruction; collecting bird parts such as feathers, beaks, and talons; illegal pet trade; competition from introduced species; and toxic effects of pesticides, oil spills, and chemical dumping.

Origin of Birds Birds, like those in **Figure 7,** have some characteristics of reptiles, including scales on their feet and legs. Scientists learn about the origins of most living things by studying their fossils; however, few fossils of birds have been found. Some scientists hypothesize that birds developed from reptiles millions of years ago.

Archaeopteryx (ar kee AHP tuh rihks)—a birdlike fossil—is about 150 million years old. Although it is not known that *Archaeopteryx* was a direct ancestor of modern birds, evidence shows that it had feathers and wings similar to modern birds. However, it had solid bones, teeth, a long bony tail, and clawed front toes, like some reptiles.

In 1991 in Texas, scientists discovered a fossil that had hollow bones and a well-developed sternum with a keel. *Protoavis* (proh toh AY vihs) lived about 225 million years ago. No fossil feathers were found with *Protoavis*. Scientists do not know if it was an ancestor of modern birds or a type of ground-living dinosaur. **Figure 8** shows an artist's idea of what *Archaeopteryx* and *Protoavis* may have looked like.

Figure 8 The first *Archaeopteryx* fossil was found more than 100 years ago. *Archaeopteryx,* to the left, is considered a link between reptiles and birds. *Protoavis,* below, may be an ancestor of birds.

section 1 review

Summary

Bird Characteristics

- Birds are feathered vertebrates. Females lay hard-shelled amniotic eggs, which hatch after an incubation period.
- Most birds are capable of flight, due to a hollow strong skeleton, wings, feathers, strong flight muscles, and efficient body systems.

Body Systems

- Birds have no teeth, but grind food in their gizzard.
- Birds take in oxygen while inhaling and exhaling, which provides more oxygen for flight.

Importance of Birds

- Birds pollinate plants, are a food source, keep pest populations low, and are used commercially.

Self Check

1. **Describe** the type of feather that helps birds maintain their body temperature.
2. **Sequence** Make a network-tree concept map about birds using the following terms: *birds, beaks, hollow bones, wings, eggs, adaptations for flight, feathers,* and *air sacs.*
3. **Think Critically** Hypothesize why most birds eat nuts, berries, insects, nectar, or meat, but not grass and leaves.

Applying Skills

4. **Venn Diagram** Draw a Venn diagram to compare and contrast the characteristics of birds that fly and birds that do not fly.
5. **Communicate** Many expressions mention birds, such as "proud as a peacock" and "wise as an owl." Make a list of several of these expressions and then decide which are accurate.

Bird Fossils Why are fewer bird fossils found in the fossil record than those of reptiles and mammals? Their small, lightweight bones often disintegrate or are crushed before they can become fossils.

3 Assess

DAILY INTERVENTION

Check for Understanding

Visual-Spatial Have students work together to develop a plan showing how the area near your school can be made into a more favorable habitat for a specific species of bird. L1 COOP LEARN IS

Reteach

Bird Survival How does the diversity of birds help them survive? Because birds have different adaptations for different environments, they can live all over the world. If they all lived in one place, there would not be enough food or shelter. L2 IS **Logical-Mathematical**

☑ Assessment

Performance Assess students' abilities to compare and contrast birds native to your area by having them examine pictures that show the birds' beaks and feet. Students can make a model of a hypothetical bird's feet, and describe their bird's lifestyle. Use **Performance Assessment in the Science Classroom,** p.123. L2 P

section 1 review

1. Down feathers provide insulation that helps a bird maintain its body temperature.
2. The network-tree should begin with birds, then adaptations for flight (include lightweight bones, feathers, air sacs). Eggs, beaks, and wings should be level with adaptations for flight.
3. Because birds need so much energy, they eat high-energy foods such as nuts and berries.
4. Have students work in pairs to compare diagrams and check answers.
5. Possible answers: "Water off a duck's back" and "eagle eyes" are accurate. Others such as "eats like a bird," "wise as an owl," "happy as a lark," and "crazy as a loon" are inaccurate.

Characteristics of Mammals

You probably can name dozens of mammals, but can you list
a few of their common characteristics? **Mammals** are endothermic vertebrates that have hair and produce milk to feed their
young, as shown in **Figure 9.** Like birds, mammals care for their
young. Mammals can be found almost everywhere on Earth.
Each mammal species is adapted to its unique way of life.

Skin and Glands Skin covers and protects the bodies of all
mammals. A mammal's skin is an organ that produces hair and
in some species, horns, claws, nails, or hooves. The skin also
contains different kinds of glands. One type of gland found in
all mammals is the mammary gland. Female mammals have
mammary glands that produce milk for feeding their young.
Oil glands produce oil that lubricates and conditions the hair
and skin. Sweat glands in some species remove wastes and help
keep them cool. Many mammals have scent glands that secrete
substances that can mark their territory, attract a mate, or be a
form of defense.

Figure 9 Mammals, such as
this moose, care for their young
after they are born.
Explain *how mammals feed their
young.*

Figure 10 Mammals have teeth that are shaped specifically for the food they eat.

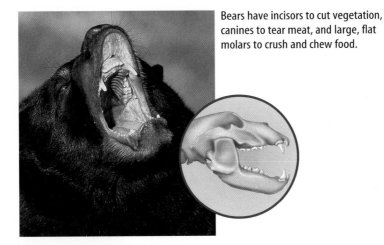

Bears have incisors to cut vegetation, canines to tear meat, and large, flat molars to crush and chew food.

A tiger easily can tear away the flesh of an animal because of large, sharp canine teeth and strong jaw muscles.

A horse's back teeth, called molars, are large. **Infer** *how a horse chews.*

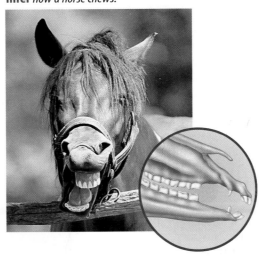

Teeth Notice that each mammal in **Figure 10** has different kinds of teeth. Almost all mammals have specialized teeth. Scientists can determine a mammal's diet by examining its teeth. Front teeth, called incisors, bite and cut. Sometimes the teeth next to the incisors, called canine teeth, are well developed to grip and tear. Premolars and molars at the back of the mouth shred, grind, and crush. Animals, like the bear in **Figure 10,** and humans, have all four kinds of teeth. They eat plants and other animals, so they are called **omnivores.** A **carnivore,** like the tiger in **Figure 10,** has large canine teeth and eats only the flesh of other animals. **Herbivores,** such as the horse in **Figure 10,** eat only plants. Their large premolars and molars grind the tough fibers in plants.

Differentiated Instruction

Learning Disabled Display a wall map of the world. Ask students to affix drawings and magazine pictures of mammals to the map to show where each mammal is commonly found. Students can visit a local zoo to take pictures of mammals to add to the map. L1 LS **Visual-Spatial**

Teacher FYI

Mutualism Some birds and mammals have developed unique mutualistic relationships. Ostriches and gazelles feed near each other. Both watch for predators and can alert each other to an approaching predator. Their visual abilities differ, so each benefits from the other species' watchfulness.

Caption Answer
Figure 10 Horses use molars for grinding grasses.

Quick Demo

Mammal Behavior

Materials live mammal pet, such as a gerbil, hamster, or guinea pig

Estimated Time 10 minutes

Procedure If someone in your class has a pet gerbil, hamster, or guinea pig, have that student bring the pet to class for a day. Have students observe its characteristics and behavior and record their observations. L1 LS **Visual-Spatial**

Activity

Animal Teeth Obtain models or pictures that show the teeth of mammals that eat different foods. A veterinarian might be a source of these models. Have students identify the incisors, canines, premolars, and molars on each model. L2 LS **Visual-Spatial**

IDENTIFYING Misconceptions

Humans as Mammals Students may not think of themselves as mammals. To help them realize that humans are classified as mammals, list the specific characteristics of mammals on the chalkboard. Include *endothermic, hair, mammary glands, oil glands, sweat glands, specialized teeth,* and *well-developed body systems* in the list. Invite volunteers to circle each characteristic possessed by humans.

Mini LAB

Purpose Students model how fat insulates an animal. L1

ELL **IS** **Kinesthetic**

Materials two self-sealing plastic bags, vegetable shortening, bowl of ice water

Teaching Strategy Have students hold the hand in the blubber mitten under the ice water, and time how long it takes for the cold to penetrate. Point out that real blubber insulates from cold indefinitely.

Analysis

1. the hand that is bare
2. Blubber is an insulator—it traps air and protects against cold.

Assessment

Performance Ask students to design and carry out an experiment comparing the insulating properties of polyester batting and plastic foam peanuts. Use **Performance Assessment in the Science Classroom**, p. 95.

P

Try at Home

Caption Answer

Figure 11 Plants contain materials that are harder to digest than meats.

Mini LAB

Inferring How Blubber Insulates

Procedure

1. Fill a **self-sealing plastic bag** about one-third full with **vegetable shortening.**
2. Turn another self-sealing plastic bag inside out. Carefully place it inside the bag with the shortening so that you are able to seal one bag to the other. This is a blubber mitten.
3. Put your hand in the blubber mitten and place it in **ice water** for 5 s. Remove the blubber mitten when finished.
4. Put your bare hand in the same bowl of ice water for 5 s.

Analysis

1. Which hand seemed colder?
2. Infer how a layer of blubber provides protection against cold water.

Try at Home

Figure 11 Herbivores, like this elk, have four-chambered stomachs and long intestinal tracts that contain microorganisms, which help break down the plant material.
Explain why herbivores need a longer digestive system than carnivores.

Hair All adult mammals have hair on their bodies. It may be thick fur that covers all or part of the animal's body, or just a few hairs around the mouth. Fur traps air and helps keep the animal warm. Whiskers located near the mouth help many mammals sense their environments. Whales have almost no hair. They rely on a thick layer of fat under their skin, called blubber, to keep them warm. Porcupine quills and hedgehog spines are modified hairs that offer protection from predators.

Body Systems

The body systems of mammals are adapted to their activities and enable them to survive in many environments.

Mammals have four-chambered hearts that pump oxygen-filled blood directly throughout the body in blood vessels. Mammals have lungs made of millions of microscopic sacs. These sacs increase the lungs' surface area, allowing a greater exchange of carbon dioxide and oxygen.

A mammal's nervous system consists of a brain, spinal cord, and nerves. In mammals, the part of the brain involved in learning, problem solving, and remembering is larger than in other animals. Another large part of the mammal brain controls its muscle coordination.

The digestive systems of mammals vary according to the kinds of food they eat. Herbivores, like the one shown in **Figure 11,** have long digestive tracts compared to carnivores because plants take longer to digest than meat.

Stomach Small intestine Large intestine

LAB DEMONSTRATION

Purpose to compare mammal hair

Materials samples of mammal hair (from humans, dogs, cats, gerbils, horses, and so on); glycerin, projecting microscope, microscope slides, cover slips

Preparation Place a drop of glycerin on each slide, add the animal hair, then the coverslip.

Procedure Project the hairs under low and high power. Students should draw what they see and write brief descriptions.

Expected Outcome Students observe differences in the hair of different mammals.

Assessment

How are the hairs of various mammals alike? All mammal hairs have layers and are covered by lines, blocks, or surface scales. How are they different? The layers have different thicknesses and different shaped lines cutting through, or no lines at all.

Reproduction and Caring for Young All mammals reproduce sexually. Most mammals give birth to live young after a period of development inside the female reproductive organ called the uterus. Many mammals are nearly helpless, and sometimes even blind, when they are born. They can't care for themselves for the first several days or even years. If you've seen newborn kittens or human babies, you know they just eat, sleep, grow, and develop. However, the young of some mammals, such as antelope, deer, and elephants, are well developed at birth and are able to travel with their constantly moving parents. These young mammals usually can stand by the time they are a few minutes old. Marine mammals, such as the whales, shown in **Figure 12,** can swim as soon as they are born.

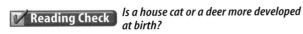
Reading Check *Is a house cat or a deer more developed at birth?*

During the time that young mammals are dependent on their female parent's milk, they learn many of the skills needed for their survival. Defensive skills are learned while playing with other young of their own kind. Other skills are learned by imitating adults. In many mammal species only females raise the young. Males of some species, such as wolves and humans, help provide shelter, food, and protection for their young.

Figure 12 When a whale is born, the female whale must quickly push the newborn whale to the water's surface to breathe. Otherwise, the newborn whale will drown.

Reading Check

Answer A deer is more developed, enabling it to travel with its constantly-moving parents.

Applying Science

Teaching Strategies
Have students make a bar graph of the information in the table, to more easily see the relationships. L2

Answers
1. The greater the heart rate, the shorter the life span.
2. No; humans have advanced technology and medical procedures that extend their lifespan.

Use an Analogy
Endothermic Energy Mammals are endotherms. In the case of animals, respiration and oxidation of food are similar to the burning of fuel in a furnace to produce energy. Have students breathe onto their hands and observe that their breath is warm. L1

Applying Science

Does a mammal's heart rate determine how long it will live?

Some mammals live long lives, but other mammals live for only a few years. Do you think that a mammal's life span might be related to how fast its heart beats? Use your ability to interpret a data table to answer this question.

Identifying the Problem
The table on the right lists the average heart rates and life spans of several different mammals. Heart rate is recorded as the number of heartbeats per minute, and life span is recorded as the average maximum years. When you examine the data, look for a relationship between the two variables.

Mammal Heart Rates and Life Spans

Mammal	Heart Rate (beats/min)	Life Span (years)
Mouse	400	2
Large dog	80	15
Bear	40	15–20
Elephant	25	75

Solving the Problem
1. Infer how heart rate and life span are related in mammals.
2. Humans have heart rates of about 70 beats per minute. Some humans may live for more than 100 years. Is this consistent with the data in the table? Explain.

SECTION 2 Mammals **C ◆ 117**

Science Journal

Mammal Communication Have each student choose a different mammal and investigate how the mammal communicates. Encourage students to write reports in their Science Journals that include information on both auditory signals and body language used by the mammal. L2 IS **Linguistic**

Teacher FYI

Monotreme Eggs Monotreme eggs are flexible and leathery, like the eggs of reptiles, not hard and smooth like bird eggs. Female monotremes incubate their eggs. Platypuses often curl up around their eggs. Echidnas carry their eggs around with them in a pouch that develops only during breeding season.

Caption Answer

Figure 13 It has mammary glands.

Discussion

Marsupial Advantages What advantages do the developing young marsupials have compared with the developing young monotremes? The developing young marsupials are protected in the female parent's pouch. The young monotremes are left alone while the parents seek food, making them more vulnerable to predators.

Figure 13 A duck-billed platypus is a mammal, yet it lays eggs. *Explain why the duck-billed platypus is classified as a mammal.*

Figure 14 Opossums are the only marsupials found in North America. A joey, or young kangaroo, returns to its mother's pouch when danger is near.

Types of Mammals

Mammals are classified into three groups based on how their young develop. The three mammal groups are monotremes (MAH nuh treemz), marsupials (mar SEW pee ulz), and placentals (pluh SEN tulz).

Monotremes The duck-billed platypus, shown in **Figure 13,** is a monotreme. **Monotremes** are mammals that lay eggs with leathery shells. The female incubates the eggs for about ten days. After the young hatch, they nurse by licking the female's skin and hair where milk oozes from the mammary glands. Monotreme mammary glands do not have nipples.

Marsupials Many of the mammals that are classified as marsupials live in Australia, New Guinea, or South America. Only one type of marsupial, the opossum, lives in North America. **Marsupials** give birth to immature young that usually crawl into an external pouch on the female's abdomen. However, not all marsupials have pouches. Whether an immature marsupial is in a pouch or not, it instinctively crawls to a nipple. It stays attached to the nipple and feeds until it is developed. In pouched marsupials, the developed young return to the pouch for feeding and protection. Examples of marsupials are kangaroos and opossums, as shown in **Figure 14,** wallabies, koalas, bandicoots, and Tasmanian devils.

A joey with its mother

Opossums

Differentiated Instruction

English-Language Learners Place illustrations of the three types of mammals in the room for students to observe. Caption illustrations with simple, definitive sentences such as *monotremes lay eggs, most marsupials have pouches, and placentals give birth to developed young.* L1 IS **Visual-Spatial**

Curriculum Connection

Language Arts Asian elephants, apes, pandas, manatees, dolphins, and rhinos are a few mammals that are likely to become extinct within 50 years due to poaching and destruction of habitat. Have students bring articles from recent newspapers and science magazines about the exploitation of mammals and the conservation efforts to save them. They can make a presentation of their findings to the class. L2

Placentals In **placentals,** embryos completely develop inside the female's uterus. The time during which the embryo develops in the uterus is called the **gestation period.** Gestation periods range from 16 days in hamsters to 650 days in elephants. Placentals are named for the **placenta,** an organ that develops from tissues of the embryo and tissues that line the inside of the uterus. The placenta absorbs oxygen and food from the mother's blood. An umbilical cord connects the embryo to the placenta, as shown in **Figure 15.** Several blood vessels make up the umbilical cord. Blood in the **umbilical cord** transports food and oxygen from the placenta to the embryo and removes waste products from the embryo. The female parent's blood doesn't mix with the embryo's blood. Examples of placentals are shown in **Table 1** on the following two pages.

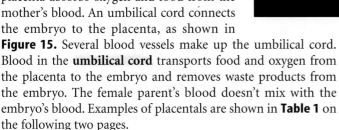

Figure 15 An unborn mammal receives nutrients and oxygen through the umbilical cord. **Compare and contrast** *placental, marsupial, and monotreme development.*

✓ Reading Check *How does an embryo receive the things it needs to grow?*

Some placental groups include unusual animals such as the manatee shown in **Figure 16.** Dugongs and manatees are aquatic mammals. They have no back legs, and their front legs are modified into flippers. Another group includes small, rabbit-like animals called hyraxes that have hooves and molars for grinding vegetation. The aardvark is the only member of its group. Aardvarks have tubelike teeth and dig termites for food. Many Southeast Asian islands are home to members of a group that includes gliding lemurs. Pangolins, another group of placentals, look like anteaters covered with scales.

Figure 16 A manatee swims slowly below the surface of the water.

Science Online

Topic: Manatee Habitats
Visit bookc.msscience.com for Web links to recent news or magazine articles about manatees and their habitats.

Activity Create a pamphlet about the manatees' habitat, their threats, and what people can do to help them.

✓ Reading Check

Answer The umbilical cord transports food and oxygen from the placenta to the embryo.

Discussion

Mammal Gestation Is there a connection between the size of mammals and their gestation periods? Generally, the gestation periods of larger species are longer than those of smaller species. An exception to this rule are tigers, lions, and other large cats, who have average gestation period of 3.5 months, shorter than that of a domestic sheep.

Caption Answer

Figure 15 Placentals develop inside the uterus of the mother; marsupials develop a short time in the uterus, followed by development in a pouch; monotremes develop inside an egg.

Curriculum Connection

Geography Mammals first appeared during the Jurassic period and diversified during the Cenozoic Era. Monotremes and marsupials developed in Australia and South America; placentals dominated North America. When North and South America joined, placentals spread southward. Australia remained separate and has a diverse population of monotremes and marsupials. Have students locate these areas on a world map. L1

Differentiated Instruction

Challenge Have students research and report on gestation periods of mammals and the average number of offspring born to different species. Some gestation periods are: opossum—12 days; hamster—16 to 37 days; mouse—20 to 30 days; rabbit—30 days; dog—53 to 71 days; cat—52 days; guinea pig—63 days; human—266 days; cow—238 days; horse—340 days; giraffe—453 to 464 days; and Asian elephant—609 to 760 days. L3

Make a Model

Placentals Mobile Have students make a mobile that shows the orders of placentals they have studied. L1 ELL IS **Kinesthetic**

Activity

Listing Placentals Have students keep records of every placental they see for a period of three days. Then have them classify the mammals according to order. L2 IS **Logical-Mathematical**

Discussion

Retractable Claws In what ways do retractable claws help lions and other cats to survive? They use their claws to climb trees and hold prey. The claws can be retracted, enabling the animals to walk and run faster.

IDENTIFYING Misconceptions

Camel Humps Students may think that camels store water in their humps. In reality, the humps contain fat, which provides energy and, when oxidized, can manufacture water. This fat helps camels survive in the desert where food and water are scarce.

Table 1 Placentals

Order	Examples		Major Characteristics
Rodentia (roh DEN chuh)	beavers, mice, rats, squirrels		one pair of chisel-like front teeth adapted for gnawing; incisors grow throughout life; herbivores
Chiroptera (ki RAHP tuh ruh)	bats		front limbs adapted for flying; active at night; different species feed on fruit, insects, fish, or other bats
Insectivora (ihn sek TIH vuh ruh)	moles, shrews, hedgehogs		small; feed on insects, earthworms, and other small animals; most have long skulls and narrow snouts; high metabolic rate
Carnivora (kar NIH vuh ruh)	cats, dogs, bears, foxes, raccoons		long, sharp canine teeth for tearing flesh; most are predators, some are omnivores
Primates (PRI maytz)	apes, monkeys, humans		arms with grasping hands and opposable thumbs; eyes are forward facing; large brains; omnivores
Artiodactyla (ar tee oh DAHK tih luh)	deer, moose, pigs, camels, giraffes, cows		hooves with an even number of toes; most are herbivores with large, flat molars; complex stomachs and intestines

Differentiated Instruction

Challenge Have students discuss the definition of "intelligence." Then explain that dolphins are surpassed in cerebrum-to-body mass ratio only by humans and chimpanzees. Have students research current studies investigating the intelligence of dolphins and share their findings in an oral report to the class. They should include a definition of intelligence in their reports. L3

Teacher FYI

Hibernating Animals Examples of hibernating mammals include certain bats, echidnas, chipmunks, and woodchucks. Most scientists do not consider bears to be true hibernators because their body temperature drops only slightly. Bears go into a state called *torpor*.

Order	Examples		Major Characteristics
Cetacea (sih TAY shuh)	whales, dolphins, porpoises		one or two blowholes on top of the head for breathing; forelimbs are modified into flippers; teeth or baleen
Lagomorpha (la guh MOR fuh)	rabbits, hares, pikas		some with long hind legs adapted for jumping and running; one pair of large, upper incisors; one pair of small, peglike incisors
Pinnipedia (pih nih PEE dee uh)	sea lions, seals, walruses		marine carnivores; limbs modified for swimming
Edentata (ee dehn TAH tuh)	anteaters, sloths, armadillos		eat insects and other small animals; most are toothless or have tiny, peglike teeth
Perissodactyla (puh ris oh DAHK tih luh)	horses, zebras, tapirs, rhinoceroses		hooves with an odd number of toes; skeletons adapted for running; herbivores with large, grinding molars
Proboscidea (proh boh SIH dee uh)	elephants		a long nose called a trunk; herbivores; upper incisor teeth grow to form tusks; thick, leathery skin

SECTION 2 Mammals **C ◆ 121**

Fun Fact

Armadillos are the only members of the order Edentata that live in the United States. The armadillo's most distinguishing feature is its hardened skin, which is arranged in a pattern of bands around its body. The tough bands act like an armor to protect the animal from predators.

IDENTIFYING Misconceptions

Elephants v. Whales Some students may think that elephants are the largest animals living today. It is true that elephants are the largest *land* animals. However, many whale species are much larger than the largest elephants. The largest elephants weigh 6,000 kg (13,000 pounds). The largest whales weigh 135,000 kg (300,000 pounds). Blue whales are the largest whales and in fact are the largest animal to have ever lived—much larger than dinosaurs, a misconception some students may have.

Visual Learning

Table 1 Look at this table and name each animal's order. Which mammals are plant-eaters with legs adapted for running and jumping? *Lagomorpha* Which order has hooves with one or three toes and skeletons adapted for running? *Perissodactyla* Which order has blowholes for breathing? *Cetacea* Which mammals have front limbs adapted for flying and are most active at night? *Chiroptera* Which mammals have long, sharp canine teeth for tearing flesh? *Carnivora* L2

Importance of Mammals

Mammals, like other organisms, are important in maintaining a balance in the environment. Carnivores, such as lions, help control populations of other animals. Bats help pollinate flowers and control insects. Other mammals pick up plant seeds in their fur and distribute them. However, mammals and other animals are in trouble today. As millions of wildlife habitats are destroyed for shopping centers, recreational areas, housing, and roads, many mammals are left without food, shelter, and space to survive. Because humans have the ability to reason, they have a responsibility to learn that their survival is related closely to the survival of all mammals. What can you do to protect the mammals in your community?

Figure 17 The *Dvinia* was an ancestor of ancient mammals.

Origin of Mammals About 65 million years ago, dinosaurs and many other organisms became extinct. This opened up new habitats for mammals, and they began to branch out into many different species. Some of these species gave rise to modern mammals. Today, more than 4,000 species of mammals have evolved from animals similar to the one in **Figure 17,** which lived about 200 million years ago.

section 2 review

Summary

Characteristics of Mammals

● Mammals have mammary glands, hair covering all or part of the body, and teeth specialized to the foods they eat.

● A mammal's body systems are well-adapted to the environment it lives in.

Types of Mammals

● There are three types of mammals: monotremes, which lay eggs; marsupials, which give birth to immature young that are nursed until developed, usually in a pouch; and placentals, which completely develop inside the female.

Importance of Mammals

● Mammals help maintain a balance in the environment. They are a food source, pollinators, and used commercially.

Self Check

1. **Describe** five characteristics of mammals and explain how they allow mammals to survive in different environments.

2. **Compare and contrast** birds and mammals.

3. **Describe** the differences between herbivores, carnivores, and omnivores.

4. **Classify** the following animals into the three mammal groups: whales, koalas, horses, elephants, opossums, kangaroos, rabbits, bats, bears, platypuses, and monkeys.

5. **Think Critically** How have humans contributed to the decrease in many wildlife populations?

Applying Math

6. **Solve One-Step Equations** The tallest land mammal is the giraffe at 5.6 m. Calculate your height in meters, and determine how many of you it would take to be as tall as the giraffe.

 Science online bookc.msscience.com/self_check_quiz

section 2 review

LAB

Mammal F**oo**tprints

BENCH TESTED

Have you ever seen an animal footprint in the snow or soft soil? In this lab, you will observe pictures of mammal footprints and identify the mammal that made the footprint.

Real-World Question

How do mammal footprints differ?

Goals
- **Identify** mammal footprints.
- **Predict** where mammals live based on their footprints.

Materials
diagram of footprints

Procedure

1. Copy the following data table in your Science Journal.

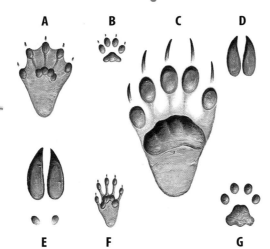

A   B   C   D

E   F   G

Identifying Mammal Footprints

Animal	Letter of Footprint	Traits of Footprint
Bear	C	
Beaver	A	
Cougar	G	
Coyote	B	Answers will vary.
Deer	D	
Moose	E	
Raccoon	F	

2. Compare and contrast the different mammal footprints in the above diagram.

3. Based on your observations, match each footprint to an animal listed in the first column of the data table.

4. **Write** your answers in the column labeled *Letter of Footprint*. Complete the data table.

Conclude and Apply

1. Which mammals have hoofed feet?
2. Which mammals have clawed toes?
3. Which mammals have webbed feet?
4. **Explain** how the different feet are adapted to the areas in which these different mammals live.
5. What are the differences between track **B** and track **E**? How does that help you identify the track?

Communicating Your Data

Compare your conclusions with those of other students in your class. **For more help, refer to the** Science Skill Handbook.

Real-World Question

Purpose Students observe how mammal footprints differ. L2
COOP LEARN **IS** **Naturalist**

Process Skills observe, predict, compare and contrast, infer

Time Required 50 minutes

Procedure

Teaching Strategy Have students use reference materials to help them identify the footprints. Students may think that cougars do not have claws because claws don't show in the footprint. Point out that cougars have retractable claws that they use for capturing prey and climbing. Use this as an opportunity to talk about how making a simple visual observation may be misleading and that collecting further data is sometimes necessary to reach the right conclusion.

Conclude and Apply

1. deer, moose
2. coyote, bear, raccoon, beaver
3. beaver
4. Beavers use their webbed feet to swim. Deer and moose live in open, flat areas where hooves help them run. Coyotes, bears, and raccoons use their claws to dig; bears and raccoons climb trees.
5. B is an animal with paw pads and claws. E is an animal with split hooves. The size and shape of the prints help you identify the animal that left them.

✔ Assessment

Performance Have students choose another characteristic of mammals, such as their teeth, and describe how these adaptations help them to survive. Use **Performance Assessment in the Science Classroom,** p. 89 L2

Communicating Your Data

Students should discuss why their conclusions did or did not agree. They can cite their references to support their arguments.

Real-World Question

Purpose

Internet Students use Internet sites that can be accessed through bookc.msscience.com/internet_lab.

Non-Internet Sources Collect materials about local birds from nature centers. Then they will observe birds in their neighborhoods.

Time Required one week to one month

Make a Plan

Preparation

Internet To run through the steps that the students will follow, visit bookc.msscience.com/internet_lab.

Non-Internet Collect field guides and other materials about birds found in your area.

Follow Your Plan

Teaching Strategies

- Have field quides handy for students to use near the place where they conduct their bird observations.
- Allow class time for students to build their feeders and make their observations.
- Have students devise a table for recording data.

Bird Counts

Real-World Question

What is the most common bird in your neighborhood? Think about the types of birds that you observe around your neighborhood. What types of food do they eat? Do all birds come to a bird feeder? Form a hypothesis about the type of bird that you think you will see most often at your bird feeder.

Cardinal

Make a Plan

1. **Research** general information about how to attract and identify birds. Determine where you will make your observations.
2. **Search** reference sources to find out how to build a bird feeder. Do all birds eat the same types of seeds?
3. **Select** the type of feeder you will build and the seed you will use based on your research.
4. What variables can you control in this lab? Do seasonal changes, length of time, or weather conditions affect your observations?
5. What will you do to identify the birds that you do not know?

Follow Your Plan

1. Make sure your teacher approves your plan before you start.
2. **Record** your data in your Science Journal each time you make an observation of the birds at your bird feeder.

Goals

- **Research** how to build a bird feeder and attract birds to it.
- **Observe** the types of birds that visit your feeder.
- **Identify** the types of birds that you observe at your bird feeder.
- **Graph** your results and then communicate them to other students.

Data Source

Visit bookc.msscience.com/ internet_lab for Web links to more information about how to build a bird feeder, hints on bird-watching, and data from other students who do this lab.

Safety Precautions

American Goldfinch

Alternative Inquiry Lab

Real-World Connection To make this Lab an Inquiry Lab, give the students more personal investment into the problem by connecting it to the real world. Tell the students that they are ornithologists, scientists who study birds, studying changes in the bird population in the local area. What kinds of birds are found in your area? Has the landscape changed and, if so, has that affected the bird population? It is important that they collect as much accurate information as possible. The data collected will help other scientists understand more about birds. Encourage them to research how ornithologists conduct their bird counts and to research and look for rare or endangered bird species from your area. L3

Analyze Your Data

1. **Write** a description of where you placed your feeder and when you made your bird observations.
2. **Record** the total number of birds you observed each day.
3. **Record** the total number of each type of bird species you observed each day.
4. **Graph** your data using a line graph, a circle graph, or a bar graph.

Black-capped Chickadee

Conclude and Apply

1. **Interpret Data** What type of bird was most common to your feeder?
2. **Explain** if all of your classmates' data agree with yours. Why or why not?
3. **Review** your classmates' data and determine if the location of bird observations affected the number of birds observed.
4. **Infer** if the time of day affected the number of birds observed. Explain.
5. **Infer** Many birds eat great numbers of insects. What might humans do to maintain a healthy environment for birds?

Birds at a feeder

Communicating Your Data

Find this lab using the link below. Post your data in the table provided. **Compare** your data to those of other students. Combine your data with those of other students and plot the combined data on a map to recognize patterns in bird populations.

Science Online

bookc.msscience.com/internet_lab

LAB C ◆ 125

Analyze Your Data

1. Students should include information about nearby structures, bushes, and trees.
2. Answers will vary.
3. Answers will vary.
4. Students may wish to make a bar graph summarizing the number of birds observed each day. Line graphs of individual species observed could also be devised. Circle graphs could be made to represent the percentage of each species observed over the course of the activity.

Conclude and Apply

1. Answers will vary. Have students describe birds' appearances in their journals.
2. Answers will vary. Data may vary because of the amount of time spent observing birds.
3. Location will likely affect the number of birds observed.
4. More birds may be observed during morning hours.
5. Possible answer: by reducing amounts of insecticides used

☑ Assessment

Portfolio Have students make a field guide for the birds they observed. In their guides, they should describe markings, beak shape, types of food eaten, and other unique characteristics of the observed birds. Use **Performance Assessment in the Science Classroom**, p. 165. **L2** **P**

Communicating Your Data

Have students prepare a written report that describes their findings. Include information such as days and times of observation, weather conditions, and numbers of birds counted. If they combine their data with other classes, have them add conclusions about the density and location of bird populations.

SCIENCE Stats

Content Background

Bird eggs have many adaptations that help them survive until they hatch. For example, the color of bird's eggs helps to camouflage the eggs to avoid predation. The shape of a particular species' eggs can give clues about where the nests are found. Eggs with a pointed end are common in birds that nest on ledges. These eggs tend to roll in circles when disturbed, keeping the eggs from rolling off the ledge. Other eggs have a texture that is adapted to the environment in which they are found. For example, certain species of ducks lay eggs with a greasy, water-repellent coating.

Discussion

Ostrich Eggs Why must ostrich eggs be able to support a weight equal to that of an adult human? Students should infer that the ostrich that sits on the eggs to incubate them weighs about the same amount as a human adult.

Activity

Incubation Periods Have students work in pairs to research the incubation period of the eggs of four different species of birds. Students should display their findings in a bar graph and share their graphs with the class. L2

Applying Math

Answer 4

SCIENCE Stats

Eggciting Facts

Did you know...

...The ostrich lays the biggest egg of all birds now living. Its egg is 15 cm to 20 cm long and 10 cm to 15 cm wide. The volume of the ostrich egg is about equal to 24 chicken eggs. It can have a mass from approximately 1 kg to a little more than 2 kg. The shell of an ostrich egg is 1.5 mm thick and can support the weight of an adult human.

...The bird that lays the smallest egg is the hummingbird. Hummingbird eggs are typically 1.3 cm long and 0.8 cm wide. The smallest hummingbird egg on record was less than 1 cm long and weighed 0.36 g.

Ostrich egg

Hummingbird egg and nest

Elephant Bird/Vouron Patra (Aepyornis maximus)

Ostrich egg

Elephant bird egg

...The elephant bird, extinct within the last 1,000 years, laid an egg that was seven times larger than an ostrich egg. These eggs weighed about 12 kg. They were 30 cm long and could hold up to 8.5 L of liquid. It could hold the equivalent of 12,000 hummingbird eggs.

Applying Math How many elephant bird eggs would it take to equal a dog weighing 48 kg?

Graph It

Go to bookc.msscience.com/science_stats and research the egg length of an American robin, a house sparrow, a bald eagle, and a Canada goose. Make a bar graph of this information.

Graph It

Have students use graph paper to make their graphs as accurate as possible. Have students research the size of these birds and make a graph of their relative sizes. Have the students determine if there is a correlation between the size of the bird and the size of the eggs it produces. L2

Reviewing Main Ideas

Section 1 Birds

1. Birds are endothermic animals that are covered with feathers and lay eggs.

2. Adaptations that enable most birds to fly include wings; feathers; a strong, light-weight skeleton; and efficient body systems.

3. Birds lay eggs enclosed in hard shells. All birds' eggs are incubated until they hatch.

Section 2 Mammals

1. Mammals are endothermic animals with fur or hair.

2. Mammary glands of female mammals can produce milk.

3. Mammals have teeth that are specialized for eating certain foods. Herbivores eat plants, carnivores eat meat, and omnivores eat plants and meat.

4. There are three groups of mammals. Monotremes lay eggs. Most marsupials have pouches for the development of their young. Placental offspring develop within a uterus and are nourished through a placenta.

5. Mammals are important in maintaining balance in the environment.

Visualizing Main Ideas

Copy and complete the following concept map on mammals.

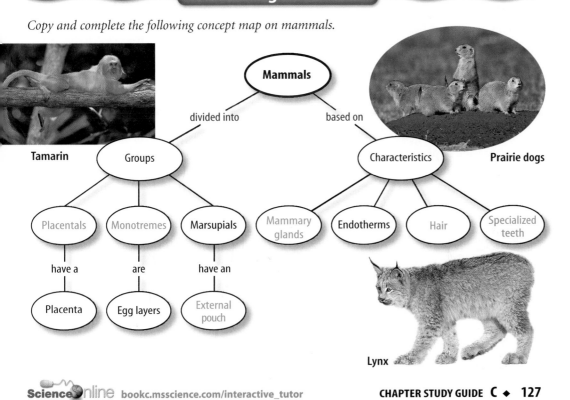

Tamarin

Prairie dogs

Lynx

Reviewing Main Ideas

Summary statements can be used by students to review the major concepts of the chapter.

Visualizing Main Ideas

See student page.

Science online

Visit bookc.msscience.com
/self_check_quiz
/interactive_tutor
/vocabulary_puzzlemaker
/chapter_review
/standardized_test

Assessment Transparency

For additional assessment questions, use the *Assessment Transparency* located in the transparency book.

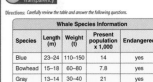

Assessment

Assessment Transparency **Birds and Mammals**

Directions: *Carefully review the table and answer the following questions.*

Whale Species Information

Species	Length (m)	Weight (t)	Present population x 1,000	Endangered
Blue	23–24	110–150	14	yes
Bowhead	15–18	60–80	7.8	yes
Gray	13–14	30–40	21	yes
Minke	9–11	20–30	N/A	no
Killer	7–9	4–6	N/A	no
Sei	12–17	20–30	54	yes
Sperm	16–18	15–20	1,950	yes

1. According to the information in the table, which whale is the longest?
   A Minke
   B Bowhead
   C Sperm
   D Blue

2. Based on the information in the table, which of the following statements about killer whales seems reasonable?
   F They don't swim as quickly as the bowhead.
   G They must be short and heavy.
   H They only eat sea plants.
   J They must be sleek and thin.

3. The two whales listed in the table that are the most different in size are the ___.
   A blue and minke
   B blue and killer
   C killer and minke
   D blue and bowhead

Birth and Mammals

chapter **4** **Review**

Using Vocabulary

1. Omnivores eat both plants and animals; carnivores eat other animals; herbivores eat plants.

2. Contour feathers are used for flight. Down feathers help insulate birds.

3. Monotremes lay eggs; marsupials give birth to immature offspring that develop in their mother's pouch.

4. The umbilical cord attaches the embryo to the placenta, a saclike organ that absorbs oxygen and food from the female's blood.

5. Endotherms maintain a constant body temperature. Mammals are endotherms.

6. Placentals are mammals in which the embryo develops inside the uterus of the female. Monotremes lay eggs.

7. A mammal is an endothermic vertebrate with hair and mammary glands that produce milk to feed its young.

8. A mammal that eats both plants and other animals is an omnivore.

9. Endotherms maintain a constant body temperature. Birds are endotherms that are covered with down feathers to conserve warmth.

10. Preening is an activity that keeps the feathers in the correct place as well as conditioning them. Down feathers provide insulation.

Checking Concepts

11. A	16. A
12. D	17. C
13. C	18. A
14. C	19. C
15. C	20. B

Using Vocabulary

carnivore p.115	marsupial p.118
contour feather p.108	monotreme p.118
down feather p.108	omnivore p.115
endotherm p.108	placenta p.119
gestation period p.119	placental p.119
herbivore p.115	preening p.108
mammal p.114	umbilical cord p.119
mammary gland p.114	

Explain the difference between the vocabulary words in each of the following sets.

1. omnivore—carnivore—herbivore

2. contour feather—down feather

3. monotreme—marsupial

4. placenta—umbilical cord

5. endotherm—mammal

6. placental—monotreme

7. mammary gland—mammal

8. mammal—omnivore

9. endotherm—down feather

10. preening—down feather

Checking Concepts

Choose the word or phrase that best answers the question.

11. Which of the following birds has feet adapted for moving on water?
    A) duck   C) owl
    B) oriole   D) rhea

12. Birds do NOT use their wings for which of the following activities?
    A) flying   C) balancing
    B) swimming   D) eating

13. Which of these mammals lay eggs?
    A) carnivores C) monotremes
    B) marsupials D) placentals

14. Birds use which of the following organs to crush and grind their food?
    A) crop   C) gizzard
    B) stomach   D) small intestine

15. Which of the following mammals is classified as a marsupial?
    A) cat   C) kangaroo
    B) human   D) camel

Use the photo below to answer question 16.

16. What are mammals with pouches, like the koala pictured above, called?
    A) marsupials C) placentals
    B) monotremes D) chiropterans

17. Which of the following have mammary glands without nipples?
    A) marsupials C) monotremes
    B) placentals D) omnivores

18. Teeth that are used for tearing food are called what?
    A) canines   C) molars
    B) incisors   D) premolars

19. Bird eggs do NOT have which of the following structures?
    A) hard shells C) placentas
    B) yolks   D) membranes

20. Which of the following animals eat only plant materials?
    A) carnivores C) omnivores
    B) herbivores D) endotherms

 Science Online bookc.msscience.com/vocabulary_puzzlemaker

Use the ExamView® Pro Testmaker CD-ROM to:

• create multiple versions of tests
• create modified tests with one mouse click for inclusion students
• edit existing questions and add your own questions
• build tests aligned with state standards using built-in State Curriculum Tags
• change English tests to Spanish with one mouse click and vice versa

Thinking Critically

21. Compare and contrast bird and mammal reproduction.

22. Classify You are a paleontologist studying fossils. One fossil appears to have hollow bones, a keeled breastbone, and a short, bony tail. How would you classify it?

23. Explain which type of bird, a duck or an ostrich, would have lighter bones.

24. List the features of birds that allow them to be fully adapted to life on land.

25. Concept Map Copy and complete this concept map about birds.

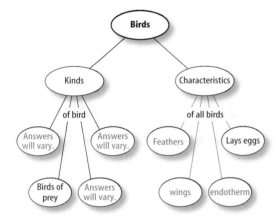

26. Describe A mammal's teeth are similar in size and include all four types of teeth. What kind of mammal has teeth like this?

27. Classify You discover three new species of placentals, with the following traits. Using **Table 1** in this chapter, place each placental into the correct order.
Placental 1 swims and eats meat.
Placental 2 flies and eats fruit.
Placental 3 runs on four legs and hunts.

28. Classify Group the following mammals as herbivore, carnivore, or omnivore: bear, tiger, opossum, raccoon, mouse, rabbit, seal, and ape.

29. Compare and contrast the teeth of herbivores, carnivores, and omnivores. How are their types of teeth adapted to their diets?

Performance Activities

30. Song with Lyrics Create a song about bird adaptations for flight by changing the words to a song that you know. Include in your song as many adaptations as possible.

Applying Math

Use the graph below to answer questions 31 and 32.

Record of Canada Geese	
Year	Number of Geese
1996	550
1997	600
1998	575
1999	750
2000	825

31. Number of Geese This table is a record of the approximate number of Canada geese that wintered at a midwestern wetland area over a five-year time period. Construct a line graph from these data.

32. Population Increase What percent increase occurred in the Canada goose population between 1996 and 2000? What percent increase occurred each year?

 Science Online bookc.msscience.com/chapter_review

CHAPTER REVIEW C ◆ **129**

Thinking Critically

21. Both reproduce sexually; birds lay and incubate eggs; most mammals give birth to live young after a period of development in the uterus.

22. as a bird

23. Ducks have lighter bones than ostriches; ostriches do not fly but ducks do.

24. The amniotic egg and specialized beaks, feet, and wings allow birds to live on land.

25. See student page.

26. an omnivore

27. Mammal 1: *Pinnipedia;* Mammal 2: *Chiroptera;* Mammal 3: *Carnivora*

28. herbivores: rabbit, mouse; carnivores: tiger, seal; omnivores: raccoon, ape, bear, opossum

29. herbivores: large incisors for cutting off blades of grass, molars to grind plants; carnivores: small incisors, large canine teeth to grip and tear food; omnivores: canines, incisors, and molars to feed on both plants and animals

Performance Activities

30. Songs may be simple as long as the lyrics discuss bird adaptations for flight. Use **Performance Assessment in the Science Classroom,** p.151.

Applying Math

National Math Standards
1, 5, 9

31. Graphs should show a slight increase, then slight decrease, followed by a steady, sharp increase.

32. Between 1996 and 2000 there was a 50% increase. 1996 to 1997 there was a 9% increase, 1997 to 1998 there was a 4% decrease, 1998 to 1999 there was a 30% increase, and 1999 to 2000 there was a 10% increase.

✔ Assessment   Resources

📁 **Reproducible Masters**
Chapter *Fast File* Resources
Chapter Review, pp. 33–34
Chapter Tests, pp. 35–38
Assessment Transparency Activity, p. 45
Glencoe Science Web site
Chapter Review Test
Standardized Test Practice

Glencoe Technology
🔊 Assessment Transparency
⬤ Exam*View*® Pro Testmaker
📺 MindJogger Videoquiz
⬤ Interactive Chalkboard

Part 1 | Multiple Choice

1. A
2. B
3. B
4. D
5. D
6. C
7. C
8. A
9. B

Part 1 | Multiple Choice

Record your answers on the answer sheet provided by your teacher or on a sheet of paper.

Use the illustration below to answer questions 1–2.

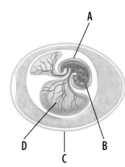

1. Which letter represents amniotic fluid?
  A. A   **C.** C
  B. B   **D.** D

2. Which letter represents a developing embryo?
  A. A   **C.** C
  B. B   **D.** D

3. Which of the following features is an adaptation that allows birds to fly?
  A. a gizzard
  B. bones that are almost hollow
  C. a crop
  D. a four-chambered heart

4. Which of the following is a monotreme?
  A. a penguin   **C.** a kangaroo
  B. an eagle   **D.** a platypus

5. What is a characteristic that sets mammals apart from birds?
  A. They help pollinate flowers.
  B. They have a four-chambered heart.
  C. They have special glands that produce milk for feeding their young.
  D. They have a special skeleton that is lightweight but strong.

Use the illustration below to answer questions 6–7.

6. What part of the mammal's body is indicated by 1–4 in the diagram?
  A. small intestine   **C.** stomach
  B. large intestine   **D.** gizzard

7. Which animals have this type of digestive system?
  A. carnivorous birds
  B. carnivorous mammals
  C. herbivorous mammals
  D. birds that eat only nuts and seeds

8. What is the significance of *Archaeopteryx*?
  A. It was the first birdlike fossil found.
  B. It represents the direct ancestor of birds.
  C. It was probably a ground-living dinosaur with wings.
  D. It is the oldest birdlike fossil.

9. What is the unique characteristic of a marsupial?
  A. They all live in Australia.
  B. Their young develop in a pouch.
  C. They lay eggs.
  D. They provide milk for their young.

130 ◆ C STANDARDIZED TEST PRACTICE

Part 2 | Short Response/Grid In

10. keel, feathers, bones that are almost hollow

11. the animal maintains a nearly constant body temperature

12. flight, shape, color

13. insulation

14. the crop stores food while it absorbs moisture; the gizzard grinds up food

15. Birds are able to receive oxygen when they inhale and when they exhale.

16. horns, nails, hooves, hair

17. monotremes—platypus; marsupial—opossum; placental—humans

Part 2 | Short Response/Grid In

Record your answers on the answer sheet provided by your teacher or on a sheet of paper.

10. What are two examples of body features that enable birds to fly?

11. What does it mean if an animal is an endotherm?

Use the photos below to answer questions 12 and 13.

12. What is the purpose of feather B?

13. What is the purpose of feather A?

14. In a bird's digestive system, what purpose do the crop and gizzard serve?

15. What adaptation in birds provides a constant supply of oxygen for the flight muscles?

16. Give two examples of special structures produced by the skin of mammals.

17. Give the names of the three groups of mammals based on how their young develop. Give an example of each one.

Test-Taking Tip

Essay Organization For essay questions, spend a few minutes listing and organizing the main points that you plan to discuss. Make sure to do all of this work on your scratch paper, not on the answer sheet.

Question 18 List the characteristics that you want to discuss in one column, and the advantage in flight in another column.

Part 3 | Open Ended

Record your answers on a sheet of paper.

18. Describe the physical characteristics of birds' bones that make flight possible.

19. Compare the barbs of a contour feather with those of a down feather.

20. Describe the function of wings in flightless birds such as penguins and ostriches.

21. Explain how feathers help a bird fly.

Use the illustration below to answer questions 22 and 23.

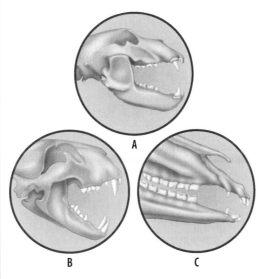

22. How can you tell that diagram C does NOT represent a carnivore? What can you tell about the diet of the animal that would have the type of teeth shown in diagram C?

23. What can you say about the diets of the animals represented by the teeth shown in diagrams A and B?

Rubrics

The following rubrics are sample scoring devices for short response and open-ended questions.

Short Response

Points	Description
2	The student demonstrates a thorough understanding of the science of the task. The response may contain minor flaws that do not detract from the demonstration of a thorough understanding.
1	The student has provided a response that is only partially correct.
0	The student has provided a completely incorrect solution or no response at all.

Open Ended

Points	Description
4	The student demonstrates a thorough understanding of the science of the task. The response may contain minor flaws that do not detract from the demonstration of a thorough understanding.
3	The student demonstrates an understanding of the science of the task. The response is essentially correct and demonstrates an essential but less than thorough understanding of the science.
2	The student demonstrates only a partial understanding of the science of the task. Although the student may have used the correct approach to a solution or may have provided a correct solution, the work lacks an essential understanding of the underlying science concepts.
1	The student demonstrates a very limited understanding of the science of the task. The response is incomplete and exhibits many flaws.
0	The student provides a completely incorrect solution or no response at all.

Part 3 | Open Ended

18. Birds' bones are almost hollow and have cross braces that add strength.

19. The barbs of down feathers are soft and have very few barbules. Contour feathers have many barbules to keep the barbs aligned and thus, give the feather strength.

20. penguins—swimming; ostriches—courtship and maintaining balance when walking or running

21. Air moves more slowly across the bottom than across the top of the wings creating more pressure lifting upward.

22. There are no large, sharp canines. The size and number of molars indicate that the animal is an herbivore.

23. The animal in diagram B eats more meat, and the animal in diagram A probably eats both meat and vegetation.

Section/Objectives	Standards		Labs/Features
	National	**State/Local**	
Chapter Opener	See pp. 16T–17T for a Key to Standards.		**Launch Lab:** How do animals communicate?, p. 133 **Foldables**, p. 133
Section 1 Types of Behavior ⏰ 2 sessions 📦 1 block 1. **Identify** the differences between innate and learned behavior. 2. **Explain** how reflexes and instincts help organisms survive. 3. **Identify** examples of imprinting and conditioning.	National Content Standards: UCP.1–UCP.4, A.1, A.2, C.3, C.5		**Integrate Health,** p. 135 **Science Online,** p. 137 **MiniLAB:** Observing Conditioning, p. 138
Section 2 Behavioral Interactions ⏰ 3 sessions 📦 1.5 blocks 4. **Explain** why behavioral adaptations are important. 5. **Describe** how courtship behavior increases reproductive success. 6. **Explain** the importance of social behavior and cyclic behavior.	National Content Standards: UCP.1–UCP.4, A.1, A.2, C.2, C.4, C.5, G.3		**MiniLAB:** Demonstrating Chemical Communication, p. 143 **Integrate History,** p. 144 **Visualizing Bioluminescence,** p. 145 **Science Online,** p. 146 **Applying Science:** How can you determine which animals hibernate?, p. 147 **Lab:** Observing Earthworm Behavior, p. 149 **Lab:** Animal Habitats, p. 150 **Oops! Accidents in Science:** Going to the Dogs, p. 152

Lab Materials	Reproducible Resources	Section Assessment	Technology
Launch Lab: Science Journal, various objects	**Chapter FAST FILE Resources** Foldables Worksheet, p. 15 Directed Reading Overview, p. 17 Note-taking Worksheets, pp. 29–31	GLENCOE'S **ASSESSMENT** ADVANTAGE	**Teacher Works** includes: • Interactive Teacher Edition • Lesson Planner with calendar • Access to all program blacklines • Correlations to standards • Web links
MiniLAB: photos of different foods and landscapes *Need materials?* Contact Science Kit at 1-800-828-7777 or www.sciencekit.com on the Internet.	**Chapter FAST FILE Resources** Transparency Activity, p. 40 MiniLAB, p. 3 Enrichment, p. 27 Reinforcement, p. 25 Directed Reading, p. 18 Lab Activity, pp. 9–11 Transparency Activity, pp. 43–44 **Home and Community Involvement,** p. 44	**Portfolio** Reteach, p. 139 **Performance** MiniLAB, p. 138 Applying Skills, p. 139 **Content** Section Review, p. 139	Section Focus Transparency Teaching Transparency Virtual Labs CD-ROM Guided Reading Audio Program Interactive Chalkboard CD-ROM
MiniLAB: sample of perfume, air freshener, or flavoring oil **Lab:** scissors, shoe box with lid, flashlight, tape, paper, moist paper towels, earthworms, timer **Lab:** poster board, markers or colored pencils, materials to make a scale model	**Chapter FAST FILE Resources** Transparency Activity, p. 41 MiniLAB, p. 4 Enrichment, p. 28 Reinforcement, p. 26 Directed Reading, pp. 19, 20 Lab Worksheet, pp. 5–6, 7–8 Lab Activity, pp. 13–14 **Reading and Writing Skill Activities,** p. 5 **Lab Management and Safety,** p. 43	**Portfolio** Cultural Diversity, p. 145 Curriculum Connection, p. 146 **Performance** MiniLAB, p. 143 Applying Science, p. 147 **Content** Applying Math, p. 148 Section Review, p. 148	Section Focus Transparency Virtual Labs CD-ROM Guided Reading Audio Program Interactive Chalkboard CD-ROM Video Lab

End of Chapter Assessment

GLENCOE'S **ASSESSMENT** ADVANTAGE

Blackline Masters	Technology	Professional Series
Chapter FAST FILE Resources Chapter Review, pp. 33–34 Chapter Tests, pp. 35–38 **Standardized Test Practice,** pp. 23–26	MindJogger Videoquiz Virtual Labs CD-ROM ExamView® Pro Testmaker TeacherWorks CD-ROM Interactive Chalkboard CD-ROM	**Performance Assessment in the Science Classroom (PASC)**

Transparencies

Section Focus

1. Section Focus Transparency — **What Cold Front?**

Adults of many species know how to care for and protect their young without being taught. Animals are born knowing some behaviors, but they learn many others.

1. How do the adult penguins know how to warm a chick?
2. Name some behaviors you have learned. Name one behavior you were born with.

L2

2. Section Focus Transparency — **Jump Back!**

The snow leopard, which is sometimes called an ounce, is on the endangered species list. Found mainly in the mountains of Asia, the snow leopard tends to live alone. Though snow leopards are solitary animals, they still must interact with other snow leopards as well as with other species.

1. How would you describe this animal's behavior?
2. What are some ways the snow leopard might interact with other animals?

L2

This is a representation of key blackline masters available in the Teacher Classroom Resources. See Resource Manager boxes within the chapter for additional information.

Key to Teaching Strategies

The following designations will help you decide which activities are appropriate for your students.

| L1 | Level 1 activities should be appropriate for students with learning difficulties. |

| L2 | Level 2 activities should be within the ability range of all students. |

| L3 | Level 3 activities are designed for above-average students. |

| ELL | ELL activities should be within the ability range of English-Language Learners. |

| COOP LEARN | Cooperative Learning activities are designed for small group work. |

| LS | Multiple Learning Styles logos, as described on page 12T, are used throughout to indicate strategies that address different learning styles. |

| P | These strategies represent student products that can be placed into a best-work portfolio. |

| PBL | Problem-Based Learning activities apply real-world situations to learning. |

Assessment

Assessment Transparency — **Animal Behavior**

Directions: Carefully review the table and answer the following questions.

Fall Bird Migration–Long Island (New York)		
Bird	Approximate arrival date	Approximate departure date
Oldsquaw	November 1	April 1
Sanderling	August 1	October 1
White-winged scoter	September 1	May 1
Yellow-crowned night heron	July 1	November 1

1. Which two birds have the greatest chance of not encountering one another in the Long Island Sound area?
   A Sanderling and white-winged scoter
   B Sanderling and yellow-crowned night heron
   C Oldsquaw and white-winged scoter
   D Oldsquaw and yellow-crowned night heron
2. The bird that remains in the Long Island Sound area for the shortest period of time is the ___.
   F white-winged scoter
   G oldsquaw
   H sanderling
   J yellow-crowned night heron
3. The bird that remains in the Long Island Sound area for the longest period of time is the ___.
   A white-winged scoter   C sanderling
   B oldsquaw   D yellow-crowned night heron

L2

Teaching

Teaching Transparency — **Problem Solving**

L2

Hands-on Activities

Student Text Lab Worksheet

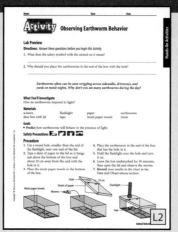

Name ___ Date ___ Class ___

Activity — Observing Earthworm Behavior

Lab Preview
Directions: Answer these questions before you begin this Activity.

1. What does the safety symbol with the animal in it mean?

2. Why should you place the earthworms in the end of the box with the hole?

Earthworms often can be seen wriggling across sidewalks, driveways, and yards on moist nights. Why don't you see many earthworms during the day?

What You'll Investigate
How do earthworms respond to light?

Materials
scissors   flashlight   paper   earthworms
shoe box with lid   tape   moist paper towels   timer

Goals
• Predict how earthworms will behave in the presence of light.

Safety Precautions

Procedure
1. Cut a round hole, smaller than the end of the flashlight, near one end of the lid.
2. Tape a sheet of paper to the lid so it hangs just above the bottom of the box and about 10 cm away from the end with the hole in it.
3. Place the moist paper towels in the bottom of the box.
4. Place the earthworms in the end of the box that has the hole in it.
5. Hold the flashlight over the hole and turn it on.
6. Leave the box undisturbed for 30 minutes, then open the lid and observe the worms.
7. **Record** your results in the chart in the Data and Observations section.

L2

Laboratory Activities

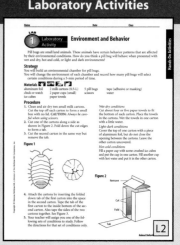

Name ___ Date ___ Class ___

Laboratory Activity — Environment and Behavior

Pill bugs are small land animals. These animals have certain behavior patterns that are affected by their environmental conditions. How do you think a pill bug will behave when presented with wet and dry, hot and cold, or light and dark environments?

Strategy
You will build an environmental chamber for pill bugs.
You will change the environment of each chamber and record how many pill bugs will select certain conditions during a 5-min period of time.

Materials
aluminum foil   2 milk cartons (0.5-L)   5 pill bugs   tape (adhesive or masking)
clock or watch   2 paper cups (small)   scissors   water
ice cubes   paper towels

Procedure
1. Clean and air dry two small milk cartons. Cut the top of each carton to form a small box with no lid. CAUTION: Always be careful when using scissors.
2. Cut one of the cartons along a side as shown in Figure 2. Fold down the cut edges to form a tab.
3. Cut the second carton in the same way but remove the tab.

Figure 1

Wet-dry conditions
Cut about four or five paper towels to fit the bottom of each carton. Place the towels in the cartons. Wet the towels in one carton with a little water.

Light-dark conditions
Cover the top of one carton with a piece of aluminum foil, but do not close the opening between the cartons. Leave the other carton uncovered.

Hot-cold conditions
Fill a paper cup with some crushed ice cubes and put the cup in one carton. Fill another cup with hot water and put it in the other carton.

Figure 2

4. Attach the cartons by inserting the folded down tab of the first carton into the space in the second carton. Tape the tab of the first carton to the inside bottom of the second carton. Also tape the sides of the two cartons together. See Figure 3.
5. Your teacher will assign you one of the following sets of conditions to study. Follow the directions for that set of conditions only.

L2

Meeting Different Ability Levels

Content Outline

Note-taking Worksheet — Animal Behavior

L2

Reinforcement

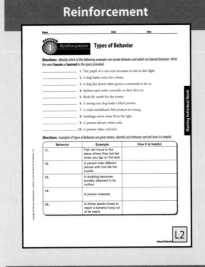

Reinforcement — Types of Behavior

L2

Enrichment

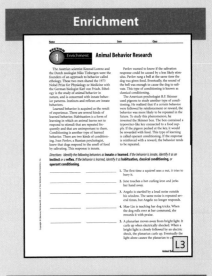

Enrichment — Animal Behavior Research

L3

Directed Reading (English/Spanish)

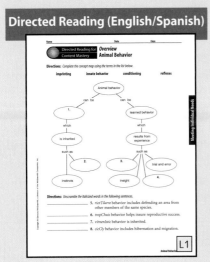

Directed Reading for Content Mastery — Overview: Animal Behavior

L1

Study Guide

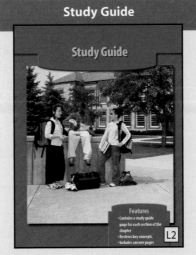

Study Guide

Features
- Contains a study guide page for each section of the chapter
- Reviews key concepts
- Includes answer pages

L2

Reading Essentials

Reading Essentials for Glencoe Science — An Interactive Student Workbook

Features
- Condensed core content
- Actively involves students in reading
- Reinforces key vocabulary

L1

Assessment

Test Practice Workbook

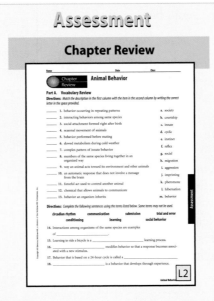

Chapter 10 Animal Behavior — Standardized Test Practice

L2

Chapter Review

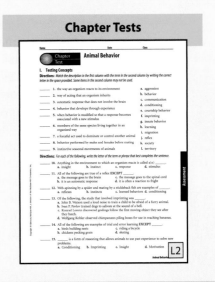

Chapter Review — Animal Behavior

L2

Chapter Tests

Chapter Test — Animal Behavior

L2

Science Content Background

section 1 — Types of Behavior

Ethology

The scientific study of animal behavior in an organism's natural environment is called ethology. Konrad Z. Lorenz, a founder of ethology, studied the behavior of birds and developed a theory of animal behavior that stressed its inherited aspects. Lorenz and two other ethologists—Karl von Frisch of Austria, who studied bee communication, and Nikolaas Tinbergen of the Netherlands, who studied gull and fish behavior—received the 1973 Nobel prize for their work.

Early ethologists thought that most behaviors were instinctual. In contrast, psychologists thought that the environment modified instinctual behavior and that learning was more important. Today, ideas from both groups are combined in studies of animal behavior.

Innate Behavior

Innate behavior often also is called instinctive behavior. It is triggered by a specific environmental stimulus that causes a behavior called a fixed action pattern. Although innate behaviors are inherited, the environment plays a role in the development of them. For example, young toads instinctively flick their tongues at all dark objects, a fixed action pattern. If it catches a bee and is stung, it learns to avoid bees.

Learned Behavior

It is sometimes difficult to distinguish between innate behavior and learned behavior. Learned behaviors and innate behaviors involve neural and often hormonal mechanisms. The complexity of an animal's brain and nervous system is genetically determined. Animals with more complex brains receive more input from experience and exhibit learned behavior. Though learning is not instinctive, it can be automatic. For example, people learn how to use eating utensils. After a while, this action does not require conscious thought.

Habituation is learning to tune out unimportant stimuli. When animals ignore unimportant stimuli they conserve energy to deal with relevant stimuli. A person may ignore constant noises, such as traffic outside a window.

Imprinting

Goats, sheep, and the Alaskan fur seals are imprinted during the first few minutes after the birth of their offspring to recognize the offspring by their odor. The mother will accept any young that they smell during this critical period and reject any young that they did not smell.

Trial and Error

Trial-and-error learning also is called operant conditioning. Animals repeat behaviors that result in positive stimuli and avoid behaviors that result in negative stimuli. For example, bears soon learn by trial and error that they will catch a fish by remaining quiet rather than splashing about in the water. The toad that learned to avoid bees learned by trial and error.

Teacher to Teacher

Jeff Remington
Palmyra Middle School
Palmyra, Pennsylvania

"As a follow-up to the pupil dilation activity, I ask students if each of their eyes is independent in regard to that reflex. Students are unsure. To investigate, students partner again in a darkened room. Students get a penlight and an index card. One student holds an index card between their eyes while the other student shines the pen light on only one eye. Students find that both eyes respond even though only one is stimulated."

Jeff Remington

---

section 2
Social Behavior
Animal Societies

Some animal societies are organized into dominance hierarchies, such as a pecking order within a society of chickens. Animals with a high rank in the hierarchy usually have access to more food and thus have more reproductive success. The young of these dominant animals will have some of the same characteristics that helped their parents survive. If food is scarce, animals lower in the hierarchy die and the population is reduced to a number the habitat can support.

In many animal societies, reproduction occurs at the same time within the group. Having many young in a population at once ensures that some will survive to adulthood. Ethologists think that this type of behavior is more common when members of a group are related.

A group of animals is more likely to be successful in finding food than an individual alone. Some animals, like wolves and hyenas, hunt in groups so they can more easily corner prey.

Territorial Behavior

Dominant individuals are usually more successful in defending a territory. Because only individuals with territories mate, genes of the best-adapted individuals are likely to pass on to the next generation. Some territories are only large enough for mating. Other larger territories help ensure an adequate food supply for offspring.

Sound Communication

Whales "sing," and dolphins emit clicking noises that can travel more than 100 kilometers underwater. Elephants emit low-frequency sounds called infrasound. These sounds are in the same sound range as earthquakes and cannot be heard by humans. Elephants emit these sounds as warnings and female elephants "sing" at this frequency to attract mates.

Migration

Animals use a variety of navigational devices to find their way. Honeybees use polarized light. Birds use the Sun during the day or the stars at night, much as humans use a compass and map.

Brandon D. Cole/Corbis

chapter content resources

Internet Resources
For additional content background, visit
bookc.msscience.com to:
- access your book online
- find references to related articles in popular science magazines
- access Web links with related content background
- access current events with science journal topics

Print Resources
Guide to Bird Behavior, by Donald Stokes, Little Brown and Company, 2002
Measuring Behavior, by Paul Martin and Patrick Bateson, Cambridge University Press, 1993

chapter 5

Chapter Vocabulary

behavior, p. 134
innate behavior, p. 135
reflex, p. 135
instinct, p. 136
imprinting, p. 137
conditioning, p. 138
insight, p. 139
social behavior, p. 140
society, p. 141
aggression, p. 142
courtship behavior, p. 143
pheromone, p. 143
cyclic behavior, p. 146
hibernation, p. 147
migration, p. 148

Science Journal Animals may call, sing, leave scent marks, or display to other animals to indicate the territory is occupied.

INTERACTIVE CHALKBOARD
with Image Bank

PowerPoint® Presentations

This CD-ROM is an editable Microsoft® PowerPoint® presentation that includes:

• a pre-made presentation for every chapter
• interactive graphics
• animations
• audio clips
• image bank
• all new section and chapter questions
• Standardized Test Practice
• transparencies
• pre-lab questions for all labs
• Foldables directions
• links to bookc.msscience.com

chapter 5

Animal Behavior

chapter preview

sections

1 Types of Behavior

2 Behavioral Interactions
Lab Observing Earthworm Behavior
Lab Animal Habitats
Virtual Lab How do mealworms behave in response to various stimuli?

Why do animals fight?

Animals often defend territories from other members of the same species. Fighting is usually a last resort to protect a territory that contains food, shelter, and potential mates.

Science Journal What other behaviors might an animal use to signal that a territory is occupied?

132 ◆ C

Theme Connection

Stability and Change Survival of a species is dependent upon the ability of its members to respond to changes in the environment by changing either themselves or their behaviors. Complex patterns of behavior have evolved in animals to help them successfully compete in a variety of environments.

About the Photo

Wolf Packs These wolves were photographed in Montana. Wolves are social animals that live in packs. Sometimes, fights break out when wolves from one pack cross into the territory of another pack, or when a wolf is trying to improve its rank in the pack.

Start-Up Activities

How do animals communicate?

One way humans communicate is by speaking. Other animals communicate without the use of sound. For example, a gull chick pecks at its parent's beak to get food. Try the lab below to see if you can communicate without speaking.

1. Form groups of students. One at a time, have each student choose an object and describe that object using gestures.

2. The other students observe and try to identify the object that is being described.

3. **Think Critically** In your Science Journal, describe how you and the other students were able to communicate without speaking to one another.

 **Preview this chapter's content and activities at** bookc.msscience.com

---

FOLDABLES
Study Organizer

Behavior As you study behaviors, make the following Foldable to help you find the similarities and differences between the behaviors of two animals.

STEP 1 Fold a vertical sheet of paper in half from top to bottom.

STEP 2 Fold in half from side to side with the fold at the top.

STEP 3 Unfold the paper once. Cut only the fold of the top flap to make two tabs.

STEP 4 Turn the paper vertically and label the front tabs as shown.

| Observed Behaviors of Animal 1 |
| Observed Behaviors of Animal 2 |

Read and Write Before you read the chapter, choose two animals to compare. As you read the chapter, list the behaviors you learn about Animal 1 and Animal 2 under the appropriate tab.

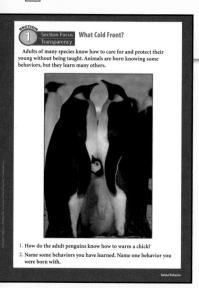
as you read

What You'll Learn

- **Identify** the differences between innate and learned behavior.
- **Explain** how reflexes and instincts help organisms survive.
- **Identify** examples of imprinting and conditioning.

Why It's Important

Innate behavior helps you survive on your own.

Review Vocabulary

salivate: to secrete saliva in anticipation of food

New Vocabulary

- behavior
- innate behavior
- reflex
- instinct
- imprinting
- conditioning
- insight

Behavior

When you come home from school, does your dog run to meet you? Your dog barks and wags its tail as you scratch behind its ears. Sitting at your feet, it watches every move you make. Why do dogs do these things? In nature, dogs are pack animals that generally follow a leader. They have been living with people for about 12,000 years. Domesticated dogs treat people as part of their own pack, as shown in **Figure 1.**

Animals are different from one another in their behavior. They are born with certain behaviors, and they learn others. **Behavior** is the way an organism interacts with other organisms and its environment. Anything in the environment that causes a reaction is called a stimulus. A stimulus can be external, such as a rival male entering another male's territory; or internal, such as hunger or thirst. You are the stimulus that causes your dog to bark and wag its tail. Your dog's reaction to you is a response.

Figure 1 Dogs are pack animals by nature. A pack of wild dogs must work together to survive. This domesticated dog (right) has accepted a human as its leader.

Cliff swallows build nests out of mud.

Hummingbirds build delicate cup-shaped nests on branches of trees.

Figure 2 Bird nests come in different sizes and shapes. This male weaverbird is knotting the ends of leaves together to secure the nest.

Innate Behavior

A behavior that an organism is born with is called an **innate behavior.** These types of behaviors are inherited. They don't have to be learned.

Innate behavior patterns occur the first time an animal responds to a particular internal or external stimulus. For birds like the swallows and the hummingbird in **Figure 2** building a nest is innate behavior. When it's time for the female weaverbird to lay eggs, the male weaverbird builds an elaborate nest, also shown in **Figure 2.** Although a young male's first attempt may be messy, the nest is constructed correctly.

The behavior of animals that have short life spans is mostly innate behavior. Most insects do not learn from their parents. In many cases, the parents have died or moved on by the time the young hatch. Yet every insect reacts innately to its environment. A moth will fly toward a light, and a cockroach will run away from it. They don't learn this behavior. Innate behavior allows animals to respond instantly. This quick response often means the difference between life and death.

Reflexes The simplest innate behaviors are reflex actions. A **reflex** is an automatic response that does not involve a message from the brain. Sneezing, shivering, yawning, jerking your hand away from a hot surface, and blinking your eyes when something is thrown toward you are all reflex actions.

In humans a reflex message passes almost instantly from a sense organ along the nerve to the spinal cord and back to the muscles. The message does not go to the brain. You are aware of the reaction only after it has happened. Your body reacts on its own. A reflex is not the result of conscious thinking.

INTEGRATE
Health

Reflex A tap on a tendon in your knee causes your leg to straighten. This is known as the knee-jerk reflex. Abnormalities in this reflex tell doctors of a possible problem in the central nervous system. Research other types of reflexes and write a report about them in your Science Journal.

Activity

Animal Communication Play an audiotape of animal communication sounds—whales, wolves, birds, or pet sounds. Why do animals need to communicate with one another? Possible answers: to warn, to locate food, to court Can you identify the message sent by any of these sounds? Students may distinguish some repeated sounds. How could you determine the message? Observe the animals in their natural habitats and note what other animals do upon hearing each sound. L2

Discussion

Ancient Survival How was the survival of ancient people dependent on their knowledge of animal behavior? They had to know the habits and behavior of animals in order to hunt and fish for food and to train animals to do work.

Fun Fact

Behaviors are more likely to be innate in animals that develop without parental care.

INTEGRATE
Health

Reflex Many vital body processes, such as breathing, heartbeat, diameter of blood vessels, and sweat gland secretions, are reflex actions.

Research Have students investigate how else behavior can influence their health.

Differentiated Instruction

Visually and Hearing Impaired Chirping is an innate behavior of crickets. Place crickets in an aquarium with moist soil and lettuce. Have hearing-impaired students observe the crickets through magnifying lenses to note how chirping is produced. Visually impaired students can listen to the chirps and estimate the room's temperature (°F) using this method: Count the number of chirps in 14 s, add 40. L2 **LS Auditory-Musical**

Challenge Many students will find animal communication interesting. Have them research and design a project that involves tape-recording and analyzing animal sounds. L3 **LS Auditory-Musical**

Figure 3 Spiders, like this orb weaver spider, know how to spin webs as soon as they hatch.

Instincts An **instinct** is a complex pattern of innate behavior. Spinning a web like the one in **Figure 3** is complicated, yet spiders spin webs correctly on the first try. Unlike reflexes, instinctive behaviors can take weeks to complete. Instinctive behavior begins when the animal recognizes a stimulus and continues until all parts of the behavior have been performed.

✓ Reading Check
What is the difference between a reflex and an instinct?

Learned Behavior

All animals have innate and learned behaviors. Learned behavior develops during an animal's lifetime. Animals with more complex brains exhibit more behaviors that are the result of learning. However, the behavior of insects, spiders, and other arthropods is mostly instinctive behavior. Fish, reptiles, amphibians, birds, and mammals all learn. Learning is the result of experience or practice.

Learning is important for animals because it allows them to respond to changing situations. In changing environments, animals that have the ability to learn a new behavior are more likely to survive. This is especially important for animals with long life spans. The longer an animal lives, the more likely it is that the environment in which it lives will change.

Learning also can modify instincts. For example, grouse and quail chicks, shown in **Figure 4,** leave their nests the day they hatch. They can run and find food, but they can't fly. When something moves above them, they instantly crouch and keep perfectly still until the danger has passed. They will crouch without moving even if the falling object is only a leaf. Older birds have learned that leaves will not harm them, but they freeze when a hawk moves overhead.

Figure 4 As they grow older, these quail chicks will learn which organisms to avoid.
Describe *why it is important for young quail to react the same toward all organisms.*

136 ◆ C

 LAB DEMONSTRATION

Imprinting Learned behavior includes imprinting, trial and error, conditioning, and insight. Have you ever seen young ducks following their mother? This is an important behavior because the adult bird has had more experience in finding food, escaping predators, and getting along in the world. **Imprinting** occurs when an animal forms a social attachment, like the condor in **Figure 5,** to another organism within a specific time period after birth or hatching.

Konrad Lorenz, an Austrian naturalist, developed the concept of imprinting. Working with geese, he discovered that a gosling follows the first moving object it sees after hatching. The moving object, whatever it is, is imprinted as its parent. This behavior works well when the first moving object a gosling sees is an adult female goose. But goslings hatched in an incubator might see a human first and become imprinted on that human. Animals that become imprinted toward animals of another species have difficulty recognizing members of their own species.

Trial and Error Can you remember when you learned to ride a bicycle? You probably fell many times before you learned how to balance on the bicycle. After a while you could ride without having to think about it. You have many skills that you learned through trial and error, such as feeding yourself and tying your shoes, as shown in **Figure 6.**

Behavior that is modified by experience is called trial-and-error learning. Many animals learn by trial and error. When baby chicks first try to feed themselves, they peck at many stones before they get any food. As a result of trial and error, they learn to peck only at food particles.

Science Online

Topic: Captive Breeding
Visit bookc.msscience.com for Web links to information about captive breeding.

Activity Identify and describe techniques used to raise captive species and introduce them into the wild.

Figure 6 Were you able to tie your shoes on the first attempt? **List** other things you do every day that require learning.

Differentiated Instruction

English-Language Learners Have students draw symbols on one side of a card and a vocabulary word on the other side. Pair students up and have them show the symbol and vocabulary word to their partner. Have students guess the vocabulary word from the symbol. This is an example of trial-and-error learning.

Visual Learning

Figure 5 The use of puppets of adult condors ensures that expected imprinting occurs. Predict what would likely occur if puppets of adult geese had been used to feed the condor chicks. Because of imprinting, the chicks would form a social attachment to adult geese instead of to adult condors. L2

LS Logical-Mathematical

Purpose to observe the affects of conditioning [L1] [ELL]

[IS] **Visual-Spatial**

Materials photos of food and landscapes

Teaching Strategy Have students show their partners several different types of food.

Analysis

1. Usually, staring at pictures of food causes a person to feel hungry.
2. Generally, landscape pictures remind people of places, but they do not stimulate a response or feeling. At times, landscapes can evoke feelings of nostalgia.
3. Large pictures of appetizing foods condition consumers to feel hungry and crave the food product.

Assessment

Performance Ask students to design another experiment in which they test for conditioning. Use **Performance Assessment in the Science Classroom,** p. 95.

✔ **Reading Check**

Answer Conditioning causes a response to one stimulus to become associated with a different stimulus.

Mini LAB

Observing Conditioning

Procedure

1. Obtain several **photos of different foods and landscapes** from your teacher.
2. Show each picture to a classmate for 20 s.
3. Record how each photo made your partner feel.

Analysis

1. How did your partner feel after looking at the photos of food?
2. What effect did the landscape pictures have on your partner?
3. Infer how advertising might condition consumers to buy specific food products.

Figure 7 In Pavlov's experiment, a dog was conditioned to salivate when a bell was rung. It associated the bell with food.

Conditioning Do you have an aquarium in your school or home? If you put your hand above the tank, the fish probably will swim to the top of the tank, expecting to be fed. They have learned that a hand shape above them means food. What would happen if you tapped on the glass right before you fed them? Soon the fish probably will swim to the top of the tank if you just tap on the glass. Because they are used to being fed after you tap on the glass, they associate the tap with food.

Animals often learn new behaviors by conditioning. In **conditioning,** behavior is modified so that a response to one stimulus becomes associated with a different stimulus. There are two types of conditioning. One type introduces a new stimulus before the usual stimulus. Russian scientist Ivan P. Pavlov performed experiments using this type of conditioning. He knew that the sight and smell of food made hungry dogs secrete saliva. Pavlov added another stimulus. He rang a bell before he fed the dogs. The dogs began to connect the sound of the bell with food. Then Pavlov rang the bell without giving the dogs food. They salivated when the bell was rung even though he did not give them food. The dogs, like the one in **Figure 7,** were conditioned to respond to the bell.

In the second type of conditioning, the new stimulus is given after the affected behavior. Getting an allowance for doing chores is an example of this type of conditioning. You do your chores because you want to receive your allowance. You have been conditioned to perform an activity that you may not have done if you had not been offered a reward.

✔ **Reading Check** *How does conditioning modify behavior?*

Cultural Diversity

Hunting The lifestyle and survival of hunting cultures revolved around the responses of hunted animals. Have students select a Native American nation and read about its relationship with the animals it depended upon. Ask students to report on animal behaviors that were important to the cultures, such as when salmon swam upriver to spawn (Northwestern nations) or patterns of bison herd movement (Plains nations).

Teacher FYI

Conditioning Conditioning is very common in the animal kingdom. For example, birds learn to avoid certain brightly colored caterpillars that have a bad taste. Birds associate the color pattern with the bad taste. Other species of caterpillars who mimic the appearance of the bad-tasting organisms also benefit from this conditioning, as birds will avoid them also.

Insight How does learned behavior help an animal deal with a new situation? Suppose you have a new math problem to solve. Do you begin by acting as though you've never seen it before, or do you use what you have learned previously in math to solve the problem? If you use what you have learned, then you have used a kind of learned behavior called insight. **Insight** is a form of reasoning that allows animals to use past experiences to solve new problems. In experiments with chimpanzees, as shown in **Figure 8,** bananas were placed out of the chimpanzees' reach. Instead of giving up, they piled up boxes found in the room, climbed them, and reached the bananas. At some time in their lives, the chimpanzees must have solved a similar problem. The chimpanzees demonstrated insight during the experiment. Much of adult human learning is based on insight. When you were a baby, you learned by trial and error. As you grow older, you will rely more on insight.

Figure 8 This illustration shows how chimpanzees may use insight to solve problems.

section 1 review

Summary

Behavior
- Animals are born with certain behaviors, while other behaviors are learned.
- A stimulus is anything in the environment that causes a reaction.

Innate and Learned Behaviors
- Innate behaviors are those behaviors an organism inherits, such as reflexes and instincts.
- Learned behavior allows animals to respond to changing situations.
- Imprinting, trial and error, conditioning, and insight are examples of learned behavior.

Self Check

1. **Compare and contrast** a reflex and an instinct.
2. **Compare and contrast** imprinting and conditioning.
3. **Think Critically** Use what you know about conditioning to explain how the term *mouthwatering food* might have come about.

Applying Skills

4. **Use a Spreadsheet** Make a spreadsheet of the behaviors in this section. Sort the behaviors according to whether they are innate or learned behaviors. Then identify the type of innate or learned behavior.

 Science nline bookc.msscience.com/self_check_quiz

section 1 review

1. reflex: automatic response, doesn't involve brain; instinct: complex pattern of innate behavior
2. Imprinting occurs when an animal forms a social attachment to another organism within a specific time period after birth or hatching. Conditioning occurs when a response to one stimulus becomes associated with a different stimulus.
3. The response to the stimulus of food is the production of saliva. Upon conditioning, the sight, smell, or thought of food can cause the production of saliva.
4. innate: reflexes and instincts; learned: imprinting, trial and error, conditioning, and insight; An example should be provided for each.

Teacher **FYI**

Insight Much of human learning is based on insight. Babies first learn by trial and error. As they grow older, they rely on insight. Solving problems is an example of using insight.

3 Assess

DAILY INTERVENTION

Check for Understanding

Logical-Mathematical Place the words *Innate Behavior* on one side of the board and *Learned Behavior* on the other side. Have students write secondary headings of reflex, instinct, imprint, trial-and-error, conditioning, and insight under the appropriate heading. Ask students to give an example of each behavior.

Reteach

Vocabulary Concept Map Have students make a concept map using all vocabulary terms in this section. L2 **LS** **Visual-Spatial** P

Assessment

Portfolio Have students write a paragraph in their Science Journals describing the type of learning that occurs when crows in a farmer's field do not react to a scarecrow that has been in place for a month. Use **Performance Assessment in the Science Classroom**, p. 99. L2

as you read

What You'll Learn

- **Explain** why behavioral adaptations are important.
- **Describe** how courtship behavior increases reproductive success.
- **Explain** the importance of social behavior and cyclic behavior.

Why It's Important

Organisms must be able to communicate with each other to survive.

🔍 Review Vocabulary

nectar: a sweet liquid produced in a plant's flower that is the main raw material of honey

New Vocabulary

- social behavior
- society
- aggression
- courtship behavior
- pheromone
- cyclic behavior
- hibernation
- migration

Instinctive Behavior Patterns

Complex interactions of innate behaviors between organisms result in many types of animal behavior. For example, courtship and mating within most animal groups are instinctive ritual behaviors that help animals recognize possible mates. Animals also protect themselves and their food sources by defending their territories. Instinctive behavior, just like natural hair color, is inherited.

Social Behavior

Animals often live in groups. One reason, shown in **Figure 9,** is that large numbers provide safety. A lion is less likely to attack a herd of zebras than a lone zebra. Sometimes animals in large groups help keep each other warm. Also, migrating animal groups are less likely to get lost than animals that travel alone.

Interactions among organisms of the same species are examples of **social behavior.** Social behaviors include courtship and mating, caring for the young, claiming territories, protecting each other, and getting food. These inherited behaviors provide advantages that promote survival of the species.

✔ Reading Check *Why is social behavior important?*

Figure 9 When several zebras are close together, their stripes make it difficult for predators to pick out one individual.

140 ◆ C

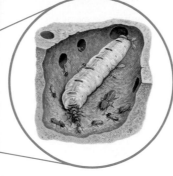

Figure 10 Termites built this large mound in Australia. The mound has a network of tunnels and chambers for the queen termite to deposit eggs into.

Societies Insects such as ants, bees, and the termites shown in **Figure 10,** live together in societies. A **society** is a group of animals of the same species living and working together in an organized way. Each member has a certain role. Usually a specific female lays eggs, and a male fertilizes them. Workers do all the other jobs in the society.

Some societies are organized by dominance. Wolves usually live together in packs. A wolf pack has a dominant female. The top female controls the mating of the other females. If plenty of food is available, she mates and then allows the others to do so. If food is scarce, she allows less mating. During such times, she is usually the only one to mate.

Territorial Behavior

Many animals set up territories for feeding, mating, and raising young. A territory is an area that an animal defends from other members of the same species. Ownership of a territory occurs in different ways. Songbirds sing, sea lions bellow, and squirrels chatter to claim territories. Other animals leave scent marks. Some animals, like the tiger in **Figure 11,** patrol an area and attack other animals of the same species who enter their territory. Why do animals defend their territories? Territories contain food, shelter, and potential mates. If an animal has a territory, it will be able to mate and produce offspring. Defending territories is an instinctive behavior. It improves the survival rate of an animal's offspring.

Figure 11 A tiger's territory may cover several miles. It will confront any other tiger who enters it. **Explain** *what may be happening in this photo.*

SECTION 2 Behavioral Interactions **C ◆ 141**

Visual Learning

Figure 11 What other animals defend their territories? Possible answers: songbirds, sea lions, squirrels

2 Teach

Make a Model

Social Animals Have students work in groups of three to make a model of animals with social behavior, such as honeybees, hornets, ants, beavers, or wolves. Ask them to identify the members of the group modeled and explain their roles. L2

Discussion

Roaring Some male lions roar to compete for mates. Roaring takes a lot of strength. How might roaring prevent a fight between two males? The roar's intensity illustrates the strength of a male. A weaker male will likely leave the area rather than fight.

Caption Answer

Figure 11 One tiger may have entered into the other tiger's territory.

Inquiry Lab

Observing Territory Behavior

Purpose To explore territory behavior, have students design an experiment to elicit a response from an animal in a territory.

Possible Materials tape player and bird song tape

Estimated Time 1 class session

Teaching Strategies

• Students can play a song of a resident bird during the spring to elicit a response from the bird.

• Students could place two territorial fish of the same species in an aquarium, place food on one end and observe their behavior.

• Be cautious of which animals are experimented on since some animals such as dogs could attack, some species may not be territorial, and some species may be territorial at certain times of the year.

• Allow students to explore other questions that arise. L2

For additional inquiry activities, see *Science Inquiry Labs.*

IDENTIFYING Misconceptions

Describing Animal Behavior Students may typically describe animal behavior in human terms using such words as *pain*, *emotions*, and *desire*. There is a tendency to relate all animal behavior in terms of human reactions. Caution students not to think of animal behavior in terms of their own behavior.

Use Science Words

Word Origin The term *anthropomorphism* is derived from the Greek terms *anthropos*, meaning "man," and *morphe*, meaning "form." Have students use a dictionary to find the meaning of *anthropomorphism* and use the word in a sentence. It is the application of human characteristics to anything not human.

Discussion

Fish Schools How do fish benefit from forming schools? When swimming in a school, a fish is less vulnerable to attack by a predator.

Use an Analogy

Offensive Defense Discuss the meaning of the expression: *The best defense is a good offense.* Explain that some animals that travel together will mount an attack against predators as a means of protection. For example, some monkeys will throw sticks at an approaching leopard.

Figure 12 Young wolves roll over and make themselves as small as possible to show their submission to adult wolves.

Figure 13 During the waggle dance, if the food source is far from the hive, the dance takes the form of a figure eight. The angle of the waggle is equal to the angle from the hive between the Sun and nectar source.

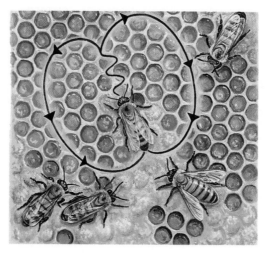

Aggression Have you ever watched as one dog approached another dog that was eating a bone? What happened to the appearance of the dog with the bone? Did its hair on its back stick up? Did it curl its lips and make growling noises? This behavior is called aggression. **Aggression** is a forceful behavior used to dominate or control another animal. Fighting and threatening are aggressive behaviors animals use to defend their territories, protect their young, or to get food.

Many animals demonstrate aggression. Some birds let their wings droop below their tail feathers. It may take another bird's perch and thrust its head forward in a pecking motion as a sign of aggression. Cats lay their ears flat, arch their backs, and hiss.

Submission Animals of the same species seldom fight to the death. Teeth, beaks, claws, and horns are used for killing prey or for defending against members of a different species.

To avoid being attacked and injured by an individual of its own species, an animal shows submission. Postures that make an animal appear smaller often are used to communicate surrender. In some animal groups, one individual is usually dominant. Members of the group show submissive behavior toward the dominant individual. This stops further aggressive behavior by the dominant animal. Young animals also display submissive behaviors toward parents or dominant animals, as shown in **Figure 12.**

Communication

In all social behavior, communication is important. Communication is an action by a sender that influences the behavior of a receiver. How do you communicate with the people around you? You may talk, make noises, or gesture like you did in this chapter's Launch Lab. Honeybees perform a dance, as shown in **Figure 13,** to communicate to other bees in the hive the location of a food source. Animals in a group communicate with sounds, scents, and actions. Alarm calls, chemicals, speech, courtship behavior, and aggression are forms of communication.

142 ◆ C CHAPTER 5 Animal Behavior

Differentiated Instruction

Learning Disabled Write all the letters of the alphabet in random order on a sheet of paper. Provide each student three copies of the sheet and have them mark the copies 1, 2, and 3. Give students 10 seconds to find the letters and draw a line to connect them in alphabetical order. Time the students for three trials. L1 IN **Kinesthetic**

Curriculum Connection

Health Studies show that the health of hospitalized and institutionalized people often improves when they develop a relationship with an animal. Have students research capuchin monkeys or guide dogs and write reports explaining how the interaction of animals and people is thought to promote better health.

Figure 14 This male Emperor of Germany bird of paradise attracts mates by posturing and fanning its tail.
List *other behaviors animals use to attract mates.*

Courtship Behavior

A male bird of paradise, shown in **Figure 14,** spreads its tail feathers and struts. A male sage grouse fans its tail, fluffs its feathers, and blows up its two red air sacs. These are examples of behavior that animals perform before mating. This type of behavior is called **courtship behavior.** Courtship behaviors allow male and female members of a species to recognize each other. These behaviors also stimulate males and females so they are ready to mate at the same time. This helps ensure reproductive success.

In most species the males are more colorful and perform courtship displays to attract a mate. Some courtship behaviors allow males and females to find each other across distances.

INTEGRATE Chemistry **Chemical Communication** Ants are sometimes seen moving single file toward a piece of food. Male dogs frequently urinate on objects and plants. Both behaviors are based on chemical communication. The ants have laid down chemical trails that others of their species can follow. The dog is letting other dogs know he has been there. In these behaviors, the animals are using chemicals called pheromones (FER uh mohnz) to communicate. A chemical that is produced by one animal to influence the behavior of another animal of the same species is called a **pheromone.** They are powerful chemicals needed only in small amounts. They remain in the environment so that the sender and the receiver can communicate without being in the same place at the same time. They can advertise the presence of an animal to predators, as well as to the intended receiver of the message.

Males and females use pheromones to establish territories, warn of danger, and attract mates. Certain ants, mice, and snails release alarm pheromones when injured or threatened.

Mini LAB

Demonstrating Chemical Communication

Procedure
1. Obtain a **sample of perfume or air freshener.**
2. Spray it into the air to leave a scent trail as you move around the house or apartment to a hiding place.
3. Have someone try to discover where you are by following the scent of the substance.

Analysis
1. What was the difference between the first and last room you were in?
2. Would this be an efficient way for humans to communicate? Explain.

Try at Home

Caption Answer

Figure 14 Examples include fireflies that use bioluminescence to attract mates, birds that sing, and many species that release pheromones.

Teacher FYI

Woodpeckers' Courtship Courtship patterns are complex innate behaviors. The ranges of two types of woodpeckers overlap in a narrow region of Texas. Despite similarities in appearance and behavior, they do not interbreed because they use different cues in recognizing mates.

Mini LAB

Purpose to observe a method of chemical communication

Materials perfume, air freshener, or flavoring oil

Teaching Strategy Have students choose a strong scent with a pleasant odor. Be certain students are not allergic to the scent.

Analysis
1. The scent would be stronger in the last room.
2. Yes; a person could be located by the scent.

Assessment

Oral How do law enforcement officers help trained dogs pick up the scent of a missing person? They have the dog smell an object that belonged to the missing person. L2

Try at Home

Teacher FYI

Pheromones Ants make a "pheromone trail" from their nest to food sources for other ants to follow. Some female insects give off pheromones that attract males. Scientists have developed artificial pheromones for use in pest control. Traps contain the female pheromones, which attract the males.

Behavioral Warnings Some animals are very sensitive to changes in the environment that precede violent natural events, such as earthquakes, hurricanes, typhoons, and other storms. In China, people have learned that unusual panicky behavior by certain animals may signal an imminent earthquake. Have students research this behavior and how it can benefit people. L2

IDENTIFYING Misconceptions

Adaptive Traits Some students may think individual organisms evolve a structure or behavior in order to respond to their environments. In reality, traits pre-exist that may help an animal adapt. The animals that survive pass the traits to offspring. For example, if a population of flies is sprayed with a deadly chemical, some may already have a genetic makeup that causes them to be resistant to the chemical. As a result, they survive and pass the trait on to their offspring.

INTEGRATE History

Morse Code Another ship must be in the line of sight to decode the message, improving the security of the message. It allows ships to maintain radio silence to avoid detection.

Figure 15 Many animals use sound to communicate.

Frogs often croak loud enough to be heard far away.

Pileated woodpecker calls often can be heard above everything else in the forest.

Howler monkeys got their name because of the sounds they make.

INTEGRATE History

Morse Code Samuel B. Morse created a code in 1838 using numbers to represent letters. His early work led to Morse code. Naval ships today still use Morse code to communicate with each other using huge flashlights mounted on the ships' decks. In your Science Journal, write what reasons you believe that Morse code is still used by the Navy.

144 ◆ **C CHAPTER 5** Animal Behavior

Sound Communication Male crickets rub one forewing against the other forewing. This produces chirping sounds that attract females. Each cricket species produces several calls that are different from other cricket species. These calls are used by researchers to identify different species. Male mosquitoes have hairs on their antennae that sense buzzing sounds produced by females of their same species. The tiny hairs vibrate only to the frequency emitted by a female of the same species.

Vertebrates use a number of different forms of sound communication. Rabbits thump the ground, gorillas pound their chests, beavers slap the water with their flat tails, and frogs, like the one in **Figure 15,** croak. Do you think that sound communication in noisy environments is useful? Seabirds that live where waves pound the shore rather than in some quieter place must rely on visual signals, not sound, for communication.

Light Communication Certain kinds of flies, marine organisms, and beetles have a special form of communication called bioluminescence. Bioluminescence, shown in **Figure 16,** is the ability of certain living things to give off light. This light is produced through a series of chemical reactions in the organism's body. Probably the most familiar bioluminescent organisms in North America are fireflies. These insects are not flies, but beetles. The flash of light that is produced on the underside of the last abdominal segments is used to locate a prospective mate. Each species has its own characteristic flashing. Males fly close to the ground and emit flashes of light. Females must flash an answer at exactly the correct time to attract males.

Differentiated Instruction

Challenge Have students use encyclopedias and other resources to find out what environmental factors might trigger an animal's urge to hibernate. Examples include decreasing temperature, shorter day length, and weather conditions. L3

Science Journal

Animal Entertainers Animals often perform in circus acts. Have students research and write reports on animals as entertainers. Have students consider whether the behaviors of animals such as dolphins, birds, and elephants should be modified for entertainment.

Figure 16

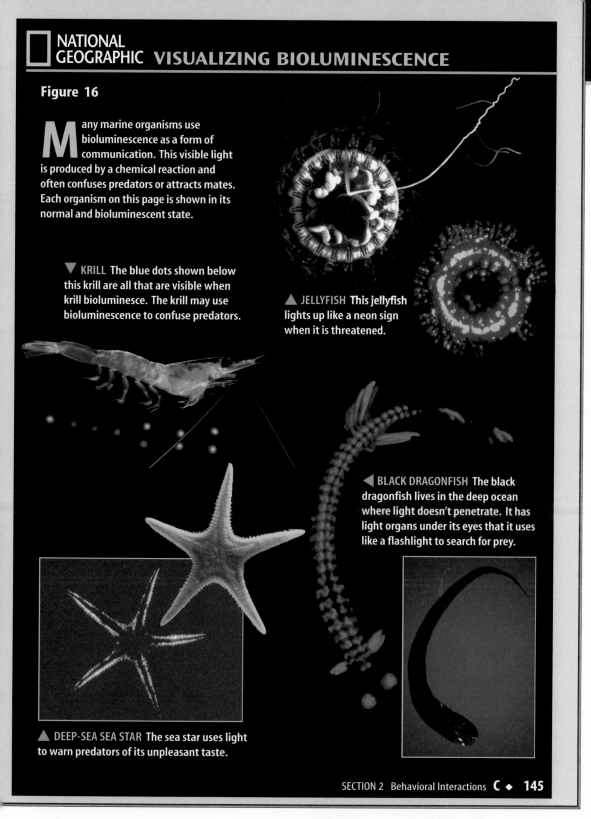

Many marine organisms use bioluminescence as a form of communication. This visible light is produced by a chemical reaction and often confuses predators or attracts mates. Each organism on this page is shown in its normal and bioluminescent state.

▼ **KRILL** The blue dots shown below this krill are all that are visible when krill bioluminesce. The krill may use bioluminescence to confuse predators.

▲ **JELLYFISH** This jellyfish lights up like a neon sign when it is threatened.

◄ **BLACK DRAGONFISH** The black dragonfish lives in the deep ocean where light doesn't penetrate. It has light organs under its eyes that it uses like a flashlight to search for prey.

▲ **DEEP-SEA SEA STAR** The sea star uses light to warn predators of its unpleasant taste.

SECTION 2 Behavioral Interactions **C ◆ 145**

Visualizing Bioluminescence

Have students examine the pictures and read the captions. Then ask the following questions.

During which times are organisms bioluminescent? Possible answers: Organisms that live near the surface are bioluminescent at night. Organisms that live in the deep sea, where there is no light, can use bioluminescence all the time.

Explain how bioluminescence can be used to attract prey. Possible answer: Prey organisms are attracted to the light, which is often coming from the mouthparts or a fleshy lure of the predator. As the unsuspecting prey approaches to investigate, it nears the mouth and is gobbled up.

Activity

Bioluminescent Animals Have students find examples of land animals that are bioluminescent and record where in the world they can be found living. Students can make a simple map of the world and draw in the representative bioluminescent animals found in different locations. Possible answers: fireflies are found east of the continental divide in the U.S., a type of beetle larvae called railroad worms is found in Central and South America, glowworms, which are fly larvae, can be found in caves in New Zealand, and land snails in Malaysia. Other bioluminescent land animals include some types of earthworms, centipedes, and millipedes. L2

Cultural Diversity

Adapting to the Environment People who live in desert areas often wear loose-fitting, light-weight, light-colored garments that reflect sunlight and heat. They may live in tents that enable them to take advantage of the smallest breezes. A tundra, rain forest, or deciduous forest would call for different cultural adaptations. Students can make posters that show the food, shelter, and clothing of different cultures. L2 **LS Kinesthetic** P

Differentiated Instruction

Challenge Have students investigate why there are almost no bioluminescent animals found in freshwater. Possible answer: Scientists hypothesize that the different chemical composition of freshwater may account for the lack of bioluminescence. Some essential chemical may be missing in the freshwater that will not allow the reaction to proceed. L3

Use Science Words

Word Origin The term *circadian* comes from the Latin word *circum*, meaning "around," and *dies*, meaning "day." Have students make a list of additional words derived from the Latin word *circum*. Possible answers: circuit, circulate, circumference, circumvent L2 LS **Linguistic**

Answer when an animal is active during the day

Caption Answer

Figure 17 cyclic behavior called nocturnal behavior

Quick Demo

Communication

Purpose to demonstrate forms of nonverbal communication

Materials none

Estimated Time 1 minute

Procedure Shake a student's hand. Ask what message was communicated by the action. Have class members identify other actions that send messages.

Topic: Owl Behavior

Visit bookc.msscience.com for Web links to information about owl behavior.

Activity List five different types of owl behavior and describe how each behavior helps the owl survive.

Figure 17 Barn owls usually sleep during the day and hunt at night.
Identify *the type of behavior the owl is exhibiting.*

146 ◆ C

Uses of Bioluminescence Many bioluminescent animals are found deep in oceans where sunlight does not reach. The ability to produce light may serve several functions. One species of fish dangles a special luminescent organ in front of its mouth. This lures prey close enough to be caught and eaten. Deep-sea shrimp secrete clouds of a luminescent substance when disturbed. This helps them escape their predators. Patterns of luminescence on an animal's body may serve as marks of recognition similar to the color patterns of animals that live in sunlit areas.

Cyclic Behavior

Why do most songbirds rest at night while some species of owls rest during the day? Some animals like the owl in **Figure 17** show regularly repeated behaviors such as sleeping in the day and feeding at night.

A **cyclic behavior** is innate behavior that occurs in a repeating pattern. It often is repeated in response to changes in the environment. Behavior that is based on a 24-hour cycle is called a circadian rhythm. Most animals come close to this 24-hour cycle of sleeping and wakefulness. Experiments show that even if animals can't tell whether it is night or day, they continue to behave in a 24-hour cycle.

Animals that are active during the day are diurnal (dy UR nul). Animals that are active at night are nocturnal. Owls are nocturnal. They have round heads, big eyes, and flat faces. Their flat faces reflect sound and help them navigate at night. Owls also have soft feathers that make them almost silent while flying.

Reading Check *What is a diurnal behavior?*

Curriculum Connection

Health Point out that people function according to a circadian rhythm. The most familiar aspect of this is the sleep-wake cycle. Have students research what body changes occur during sleep and how people behave when they are deprived of sleep for several days. Sleep deprivation can cause fatigue, inability to concentrate, and visual or tactile illusions and hallucinations. L3 P

Science Journal

Problems in Studying Behavior Have students list some of the problems of using animals, including humans, in behavioral studies. Possible answers: Animals other than humans cannot communicate in words. Equating animal responses with those of humans may not always work.

Hibernation Some cyclic behaviors also occur over long periods of time. **Hibernation** is a cyclic response to cold temperatures and limited food supplies. During hibernation, an animal's body temperature drops to near that of its surroundings, and its breathing rate is greatly reduced. Animals in hibernation, such as the bats in **Figure 18,** survive on stored body fat. The animal remains inactive until the weather becomes warm in the spring. Some mammals and many amphibians and reptiles hibernate.

Figure 18 Many bats find a frost-free place like this abandoned coal mine to hibernate for the winter when food supplies are low.

Animals that live in desertlike environments also go into a state of reduced activity. This period of inactivity is called estivation. Desert animals sometimes estivate due to extreme heat, lack of food, or periods of drought.

Applying Science

How can you determine which animals hibernate?

Many animals hibernate in the winter. During this period of inactivity, they survive on stored body fat. While they are hibernating, they undergo several physical changes. Heart rate slows down and body temperature decreases. The degree to which the body temperature decreases varies among animals. Scientists disagree about whether some animals truly hibernate or if they just reduce their activity and go into a light sleep. Usually, a true hibernator's body temperature will decrease significantly while it is hibernating.

Identifying the Problem

The table on the right shows the difference between the normal body temperature and the hibernating body temperature of several animals. What similarities do you notice?

Average Body Temperatures of Hibernating Animals		
Animal	**Normal Body Temperature (°C)**	**Hibernating Body Temperature (°C)**
Woodchuck	37	3
Squirrel	32	4
Grizzly bear	32–37	27–32
Whippoorwill	40	18
Hoary marmot	37	10

Solving the Problem

1. Which animals would you classify as true hibernators and which would you classify as light sleepers? Explain.
2. Some animals such as snakes and frogs also hibernate. Why would it be difficult to record their normal body temperature?

SECTION 2 Behavioral Interactions **C** ◆ **147**

Figure 19 Many monarch butterflies travel from the United States to Mexico for the winter.

Migration Instead of hibernating, many animals move to new locations when the seasons change. This instinctive seasonal movement of animals is called **migration.** Most animals migrate to find food or to reproduce in environments that are more favorable for the survival of offspring. Many bird species fly for hours or days without stopping. The blackpoll warbler flies more than 4,000 km, nearly 90 hours nonstop from North America to its winter home in South America. Monarch butterflies, shown in **Figure 19,** can migrate as far as 2,900 km. Gray whales swim from arctic waters to the waters off the coast of northern Mexico. After the young are born, they make the return trip.

section 2 review

Summary

Instinctive Behavior Patterns

- Instinctive behavior patterns are inherited.
- Courtship and mating are instinctive for most animal groups.

Social and Territorial Behaviors

- Interactions among organisms of a group are examples of social behavior.
- Many animals protect a territory for feeding, mating, and raising young.

Communication and Cyclic Behavior

- Species can communicate with each other using behavior, chemicals, sound, or bioluminescence.
- Cyclic behaviors occur in response to environmental changes.

Self Check

1. **Describe** some examples of courtship behavior and how this behavior helps organisms survive.
2. **Identify** and **explain** two reasons that animals migrate.
3. **Compare and contrast** hibernation and migration.
4. **Think Critically** Suppose a species of frog lives close to a loud waterfall. It often waves a bright blue foot in the air. What might the frog be doing?

Applying Math

5. **Solve One-Step Equations** Some cicadas emerge from the ground every 17 years. The population of one type of caterpillar peaks every five years. If the peak cycle of the caterpillars and the emergence of cicadas coincided in 1990, in what year will they coincide again?

148 ◆ **C CHAPTER 5** Animal Behavior

 Science Online bookc.msscience.com/self_check_quiz

section 2 review

1. Answers will vary. These behaviors help ensure reproductive success.
2. to find food and to reproduce in a favorable environment for offspring
3. An animal that hibernates stays in the same place and becomes inactive until environmental conditions become favorable. An animal that migrates moves to a location with favorable conditions.
4. Possible answer: signalling other frogs, either to attract a mate or to defend its territory
5. Since 17 and 5 are prime numbers, the cycles will again coincide in 17 × 5, or 85 years from 1990; 1990 + 85 = 2075.

Observing Earthworm Behavior

Earthworms can be seen at night wriggling across wet sidewalks and driveways. Why don't you see many earthworms during the day?

▶ Real-World Question

How do earthworms respond to light?

Goals

■ **Predict** how earthworms will behave in the presence of light.

Materials

scissors	paper
shoe box with lid	moist paper towels
flashlight	earthworms
tape	timer

Safety Precautions

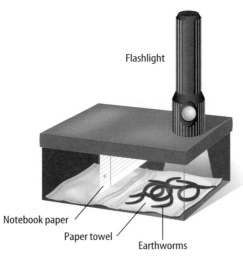

Flashlight

Notebook paper
Paper towel
Earthworms

▶ Procedure

1. Cut a round hole, smaller than the end of the flashlight, near one end of the lid.

2. Tape a sheet of paper to the lid so it hangs just above the bottom of the box and about 10 cm away from the end with the hole in it.

3. Place the moist paper towels in the bottom of the box.

4. Place the earthworms in the end of the box that has the hole in it.

5. Hold the flashlight over the hole and turn it on.

6. Leave the box undisturbed for 30 minutes, then open the lid and observe the worms.

7. **Record** the results of your experiment in your Science Journal.

▶ Conclude and Apply

1. **Identify** which direction the earthworms moved when the light was turned on.

2. **Infer** Based on your observations, what can you infer about earthworms?

3. **Explain** what type of behavior the earthworms exhibited.

4. **Predict** where you would need to go to find earthworms during the day.

Communicating Your Data

Write a story that describes a day in the life of an earthworm. List activities, dangers, and problems an earthworm might face. Include a description of its habitat. **For more help, refer to the** Science Skill Handbook.

▶ Real-World Question

Purpose Students observe earthworm responses to light. L2 LS **Kinesthetic**

Process Skills observe and infer, recognize cause and effect

Time Required 45 minutes

Safety Precautions Caution students to wash their hands after handling earthworms.

▶ Procedure

Teaching Strategy Have students keep their hands moist while handling earthworms. Remind them to handle worms gently.

▶ Conclude and Apply

1. away from the light
2. Earthworms prefer darkness to light.
3. Innate behavior; the earthworms instinctively move away from the light and toward the darkened area.
4. in the soil

✓ Assessment

Process Have students use their observations to list what they think an earthworm needs to survive. soil, darkness, moisture Use **Performance Assessment in the Science Classroom**, p. 89. L2

Communicating Your Data

Students should base their story on their knowledge of earthworms and their habitat.

Model and Invent

Real-World Question

Purpose Students research information about animals in their natural habitats, and then design and build a model of a habitat that supports the survival of that animal. L2 LS
Logical-Mathematical

Process Skills make models, research information, predict, collect data, measure in SI, recognize cause and effect, interpret data, communicate, use proportions

Time Required one to two weeks

Possible Materials Provide basic materials for making models such as modeling clay, scrap paper, scissors, and glue. Encourage reusing and recycling by having students bring in scrap materials from home.

Safety Precautions Discuss the dangers of any materials being used, such as sharp scissors or glue with strong fumes.

Make a Model

Possible Procedures Direct students to think about the types of animals with which they are familiar. What types of food do they eat? What kind of environment do they need to survive? Have students discuss and research other types of animals that could live in the same environments. Provide reference materials or allow students to use library resources and the Internet.

Goals
- **Research** the natural habitat and basic needs of one animal.
- **Design** and model an appropriate zoo, animal park, or aquarium environment for this animal. Working cooperatively with your classmates, design an entire zoo or animal park.

Possible Materials
poster board
markers or colored pencils
materials that can be used to make a scale model

Animal Habitats

Real-World Question

Zoos, animal parks, and aquariums are safe places for wild animals. Years ago, captive animals were kept in small cages or behind glass windows. Almost no attempt was made to provide natural habitats for the animals. People who came to see the animals could not observe the animal's normal behavior. Now, most captive animals are kept in exhibit areas that closely resemble their natural habitats. These areas provide suitable environments for the animals so that they can interact with members of their same species and have healthier, longer lives. What types of environments are best suited for raising animals in captivity? How can the habitats provided at an animal park affect the behavior of animals?

Make a Model

1. Choose an animal to research. Find out where this animal is found in nature. What does it eat? What are its natural predators? Does it exhibit unique territorial, courtship, or other types of behavior? How is this animal adapted to its natural environment?

150 ◆ **C**

2. **Design** a model of a proposed habitat in which this animal can live successfully. Don't forget to include all of the things, such as shelter, food, and water, that your animal will need to survive. Will there be any other organisms in the habitat?

3. **Research** how zoos, animal parks, or aquariums provide habitats for animals. Information may be obtained by contacting scientists who work at zoos, animal parks, and aquariums.

4. **Present** your design to your class in the form of a poster, slide show, or video. Compare your proposed habitat with that of the animal's natural environment. Make sure you include a picture of your animal in its natural environment.

⊙ Test Your Model

1. Using all of the information you have gathered, create a model exhibit area for your animal.

2. Indicate what other plants and animals may be present in the exhibit area.

⊙ Analyze Your Data

1. **Decide** whether all of the animals studied in this lab can coexist in the same zoo or wildlife preserve.

2. **Analyze** problems that might exist in your design. Suggest some ways you might want to improve your design.

⊙ Conclude and Apply

1. **Interpret Data** Using the information provided by the rest of your classmates, design an entire zoo or aquarium that could include the majority of animals studied.

2. **Predict** which animals could be grouped together in exhibit areas.

3. **Determine** how large your zoo or wildlife preserve needs to be. Which animals require a large habitat?

ℭommunicating Your Data

Give an oral presentation to another class on the importance of providing natural habitats for captive animals. **For more help, refer to the Science Skill Handbook.**

Teaching Strategies

- Distribute lists of zoo Web sites.
- Encourage students to make a checklist of items they need to include in their models.

⊙ Test Your Model

Expected Outcome Students should build a model that is appropriate for their chosen animal. Areas of concern might include sufficient land and water area and climate control.

⊙ Analyze Your Data

Direct students to record and then discuss the answers to these questions in small groups. Decisions to combine different animals in one habitat should be based on environmental concerns such as land and water requirements and climate considerations, including temperature and amount of precipitation. In the event of unfavorable conditions, adequate shelter must be available. Animals that have predator-prey relationships must also be separated geographically. L2

⊙ Conclude and Apply

Answers will vary. Have students discuss these answers in small groups.

ℭommunicating Your Data

Show students how to outline their presentations as a way of organizing their ideas. Suggest that they practice several times before giving the presentation.

✓ Assessment

Performance Have students make pamphlets encouraging the public to visit the model animal habitats they have devised. Use **Performance Assessment in the Science Classroom,** p. 129. L2

Oops! Accidents in SCIENCE

SOMETIMES GREAT DISCOVERIES HAPPEN BY ACCIDENT!

Going to the Dogs

A simple and surprising stroll showed that dogs really are humans' best friends

You've probably seen visually impaired people walking with their trusted "seeing-eye" dogs. Over 85 years ago, a doctor and his patient discovered this canine ability entirely by accident!

Near the end of World War I in Germany, Dr. Gerhard Stalling and his dog strolled with a patient—a German soldier who had been blinded—around hospital grounds.

A dog safely guides its owner across a street.

While they were walking, the doctor was called away. A few moments later, the doctor returned but the dog and the soldier were gone! Searching the paths frantically, Dr. Stalling made an astonishing discovery. His pet had led the soldier safely around the hospital grounds. Inspired by what his dog could do, Dr. Stalling set up the first school in the world dedicated to training dogs as guides.

German shepherds make excellent guide dogs.

German shepherds, golden retrievers, and Labrador retrievers seem to make the best guide dogs. They learn hand gestures and simple commands to lead visually impaired people safely across streets and around obstacles. This is what scientists call "learned behavior." Animals gain learned behavior through experience. But, a guide dog doesn't just learn to respond to special commands; it also must learn when *not* to obey. If its human owner urges the dog to cross the street and the dog sees that a car is approaching, the dog refuses because it has learned to disobey the command. This trait, called "intelligent disobedience," ensures the safety of the owner and the dog—a sure sign that dogs are still humans' best friends.

Write Lead a blindfolded partner around the classroom. Help your partner avoid obstacles. Then trade places. Write in your Science Journal about your experience leading and being led.

Science Online
For more information, visit bookc.msscience.com/oops

Resources for Teachers and Students

Dogs With Jobs, by Merrily Weisbord and Kim Kachanoff, Pocket Books, 2000

Working Dogs: Tales from Animal Planet's K-9 to 5 World, by Colleen Needles and Kit Carlson, Discovery Books, 2000

A Dog's Gotta Do What A Dog's Gotta Do: Dogs at Work, by Marilyn Singer, Henry Holt and Company, Inc., 2000

Reviewing Main Ideas

Section 1 Types of Behavior

1. Behavior that an animal has when it's born is innate behavior. Other animal behaviors are learned through experience.

2. Reflexes are simple innate behaviors. An instinct is a complex pattern of innate behavior.

3. Learned behavior includes imprinting, in which an animal forms a social attachment immediately after birth.

4. Behavior modified by experience is learning by trial and error.

5. Conditioning occurs when the response to one stimulus becomes associated with another. Insight is the ability to use past experiences to solve new problems.

Section 2 Behavioral Interactions

1. Behavioral adaptations such as defense of territory, courtship behavior, and social behavior help species of animals survive and reproduce.

2. Courtship behaviors allow males and females to recognize each other and prepare to mate.

3. Interactions among members of the same species are social behaviors.

4. Communication among organisms occurs in several forms, including chemical, sound, and light.

5. Cyclic behaviors are behaviors that occur in repeating patterns. Animals that are active during the day are diurnal. Animals that are active at night are nocturnal.

Visualizing Main Ideas

Copy and complete the following concept map on types of behavior.

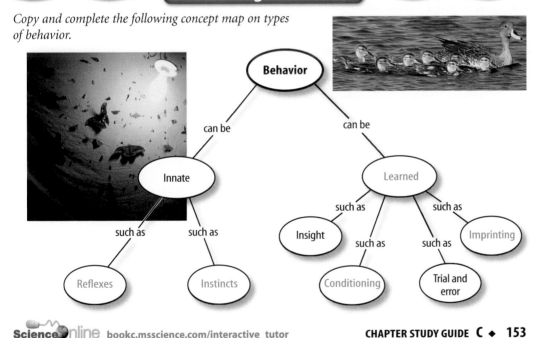

Reviewing Main Ideas

Summary statements can be used by students to review the major concepts of the chapter.

Visualizing Main Ideas

See student page.

Visit bookc.msscience.com
/self_check_quiz
/interactive_tutor
/vocabulary_puzzlemaker
/chapter_review
/standardized_test

Assessment Transparency

For additional assessment questions, use the *Assessment Transparency* located in the transparency book.

Using Vocabulary

1. Conditioning is the modification of established behaviors. Imprinting is the formation of a new behavior. Both are learned behaviors.

2. Not all innate behaviors are social behaviors, but all social behaviors are innate behaviors.

3. Instinct is an innate behavior, and insight is a learned behavior. Both can be complex patterns of behavior.

4. Social behavior is an innate behavior. The social behaviors within an animal population form a society.

5. Instinct: complex pattern of innate behavior; reflex: simple innate behavior.

6. Hibernation is a period of inactive behavior, and migration is the seasonal movement of an animal or animal populations. Both are cyclic behaviors.

7. Courtship behavior is a social behavior between males and females of a species. Chemicals called pheromones usually stimulate courtship behavior.

8. All migrations are cyclic behaviors, but not all cyclic behaviors are migrations.

9. Aggression is just one of the many types of social behaviors.

10. Behavior is the interaction of one organism with another organism. Some behaviors are learned and others are instinctive. Reflex is the simplest innate behavior.

Checking Concepts

11. A	16. C
12. B	17. A
13. C	18. C
14. D	19. A
15. C	

Using Vocabulary

aggression p. 142	insight p. 139
behavior p. 134	instinct p. 136
conditioning p. 138	migration p. 148
courtship behavior p. 143	pheromone p. 143
cyclic behavior p. 146	reflex p. 135
hibernation p. 147	social behavior p. 140
imprinting p. 137	society p. 141
innate behavior p. 135	

Explain the differences between the pairs of vocabulary words given below. Then explain how the words are related.

1. conditioning—imprinting

2. innate behavior—social behavior

3. insight—instinct

4. social behavior—society

5. instinct—reflex

6. hibernation—migration

7. courtship behavior—pheromone

8. cyclic behavior—migration

9. aggression—social behavior

10. behavior—reflex

Checking Concepts

Choose the word or phrase that best answers the question.

11. What is an instinct an example of?
    A) innate behavior
    B) learned behavior
    C) imprinting
    D) conditioning

12. What is an area that an animal defends from other members of the same species called?
    A) society   C) migration
    B) territory   D) aggression

13. Which animals depend least on instinct and most on learning?
    A) birds   C) mammals
    B) fish   D) amphibians

14. What is a spider spinning a web an example of?
    A) conditioning   C) learned behavior
    B) imprinting   D) an instinct

15. What is a forceful act used to dominate or control another called?
    A) courtship   C) aggression
    B) reflex   D) hibernation

16. What is an organized group of animals doing specific jobs called?
    A) community   C) society
    B) territory   D) circadian rhythm

17. What is the response of inactivity and slowed metabolism that occurs during cold conditions?
    A) hibernation   C) migration
    B) imprinting   D) circadian rhythm

18. Which of the following is a reflex?
    A) writing   C) sneezing
    B) talking   D) riding a bicycle

Use the photo below to answer question 19.

19. The photo above is an example of what type of communication?
    A) light communication
    B) sound communication
    C) chemical communication
    D) cyclic behavior

 Science Online bookc.msscience.com/vocabulary_puzzlemaker

Use the Exam*View*® Pro Testmaker CD-ROM to:
- create multiple versions of tests
- create modified tests with one mouse click for inclusion students
- edit existing questions and add your own questions
- build tests aligned with state standards using built-in State Curriculum Tags
- change English tests to Spanish with one mouse click and vice versa

Thinking Critically

20. Explain the type of behavior involved when the bell rings at the end of class.

21. Describe the advantages and disadvantages of migration as a means of survival.

22. Explain how a habit, such as tying your shoes, is different from a reflex.

23. Explain how behavior increases an animal's chance for survival using one example.

24. Infer Hens lay more eggs in the spring when the number of daylight hours increases. How can farmers use this knowledge of behavior to their advantage?

25. Record Observations Make observations of a dog, cat, or bird for a week. Record what you see. How did the animal communicate with other animals and with you?

26. Classify Make a list of 25 things that you do regularly. Classify each as an innate or learned behavior. Which behaviors do you have more of?

27. Concept Map Copy and complete the following concept map about communication. Use these words: *sound, chirping, biolumi-nescence,* and *buzzing.*

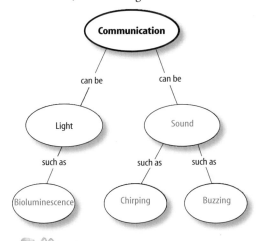

Performance Activities

28. Poster Draw a map showing the migration route of monarch butterflies, gray whales, or blackpoll warblers.

Applying Math

Use the graphs below to answer question 29.

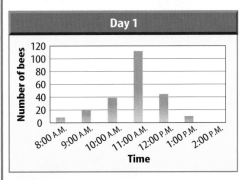
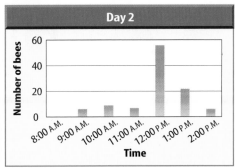

29. Bee Foraging Bees were trained to forage from 1:00 P.M. to 2:30 P.M. in New York and then were flown to California. The graphs above show the number of bees looking for food during the first two days in California. What was the difference in peak activity from day 1 to day 2? Was there a difference in the proportion of bees active during peak hours?

30. Bird Flight A blackpoll warbler flies 4,000 km nonstop from North America to South America in about 90 hours. What is its rate of speed?

 bookc.msscience.com/chapter_review

CHAPTER REVIEW C ◆ 155

Thinking Critically

20. Leaving the room when the bell rings is a conditioned learned response.

21. Migration allows organisms to survive changes in weather. Some organisms may not survive the long, stressful journey.

22. A habit is a learned behavior that has become automatic. A reflex is an innate behavior.

23. Behaviors that help obtain food, are protective, or are defensive help organisms survive.

24. A farmer can artificially lengthen the amount of "daylight" hens are exposed to by using lights, which stimulate the hens to lay more eggs.

25. Answers will be determined by the animal the student observes.

26. Possible answers may include: innate—sneezing, yawning, hiccups, jerking your hand away from something hot; learned—tying shoes, reading, writing, solving problems, riding a bike. Learned behaviors are probably more numerous.

27. See student page.

Performance Activities

28. Maps should indicate both spring and fall migration routes. Use **Performance Assessment in the Science Classroom,** p. 145.

Applying Math

National Math Standards
1, 5, 9

29. Peak activity occurred one hour later on day 2. Day 1 equals 48% and day 2 equals 53%.

30. 44.4 km/h

✔ Assessment   Resources

Reproducible Masters
Chapter *Fast File* Resources
Chapter Review, pp. 33–34
Chapter Tests, pp. 35–38
Assessment Transparency Activity, p. 45
Glencoe Science Web site
Chapter Review Test
Standardized Test Practice

Glencoe Technology
- Assessment Transparency
- Exam*View*® Pro Testmaker
- MindJogger Videoquiz
- Interactive Chalkboard

S A M P L E

Part 1 | Multiple Choice

1. D
2. B
3. A
4. D
5. C
6. B
7. A

Part 1 | Multiple Choice

Record your answers on the answer sheet provided by your teacher or on a sheet of paper.

1. Which of the following is true about innate behaviors?
   A. They are learned behaviors.
   B. They are observed in only some animals.
   C. They are the result of conscious thought.
   D. They include reflexes.

2. A spider spinning its web is an example of a(n)
   A. reflex.   C. imprinting.
   B. instinct.   D. conditioning.

Use the illustration below to answer questions 3 and 4.

3. The illustration above describes what kind of learned behavior?
   A. conditioning
   B. trial and error
   C. imprinting
   D. insight

4. Which of the following best describes this learned behavior?
   A. The dog learns to salivate when presented with food.
   B. The dog learns to eat only if the bell is rung.
   C. The dog is conditioned to stop salivating when a bell is rung.
   D. The dog is conditioned to salivate when a bell is rung.

5. Which of the following is an example of territorial behavior?
   A. A honeybee performs a waggle dance when it returns to the hive.
   B. A peacock fans his tail while approaching a peahen.
   C. A mountain goat charges and attacks an unfamiliar mountain goat.
   D. A group of bats remain in hibernation for the winter.

Use the photo below to answer questions 6 and 7.

6. The male wolf lying on its back is displaying what kind of behavior to the other male wolf?
   A. aggressive behavior
   B. submissive behavior
   C. cyclic behavior
   D. courtship behavior

7. Which of the following statements best describes the behavior of the wolf that is standing?
   A. The wolf is displaying its dominance over the wolf on the ground.
   B. The wolf is displaying courtship behavior to the other wolf.
   C. The wolf is using bioluminescence to communicate with the other wolf.
   D. The wolf is watching the other wolf perform the waggle dance.

156 ◆ C STANDARDIZED TEST PRACTICE

Part 2 | Short Response/Grid In

8. Possible answer: An innate behavior in hummingbirds could be its attraction to certain flowers.

9. Reflexes are simpler and more automatic.

10. insight learning

11. past experience in solving a similar problem

12. Young children learn mostly by trial-and-error, not insight, because they have limited experiences.

13. Possible answers: getting food, caring for young, defending territory, protecting others, mating

14. to avoid being attacked or hurt by an animal of its own species

Part 2 | Short Response/Grid In

Record your answers on the answer sheet provided by your teacher or on a sheet of paper.

8. Give an example of an innate behavior in a hummingbird.

9. Which is simpler and more automatic, instincts or reflexes?

Use the illustration below to answer questions 10 and 11.

10. What type of learning is shown above?

11. What is required in order for an animal to use this type of learning to solve a problem?

12. Could a young child solve a problem using insight? Why or why not?

13. Give three examples of social behaviors.

14. Why might an animal be submissive to another animal?

Test-Taking Tip

Compare and Contrast Make sure each part of the question is answered when listing discussion points. For example, if the question asks you to compare and contrast, make sure you list both similarities and differences.

Part 3 | Open Ended

Record your answers on a sheet of paper.

15. Compare and contrast the innate behaviors of animals with short life spans and animals with long life spans.

16. Give three examples of ways bioluminescence is used for communication.

17. Explain the difference between a diurnal animal and a nocturnal animal. Give an example of each.

18. Compare and contrast hibernation and estivation.

Use the photo below to answer questions 19 and 20.

19. Explain the type of behavior that is shown above.

20. How is this behavior related to why zoos feed newborn condors with hand puppets that look like adult condors?

21. A male antelope approaches a female antelope during the breeding season. Is the male antelope responding to an external stimulus, an internal stimulus, or both? Explain.

19. The picture is showing imprinting in birds. After hatching, newborn ducklings will follow the first moving object they see.

20. Since newborn condors imprint on the first moving object they see after hatching, it is important that a condor not a human hand feed condor chicks hatched in zoos.

21. The male antelope is responding to both: an internal stimulus—the need to breed; and an external stimulus—the female antelope.

Rubrics

For more help evaluating open-ended assessment questions, see the rubric on p. 10T.

Part 3 | Open Ended

15. Animals with short life spans show mostly innate behavior. Because their lives are short, they do not have time to learn from their parents or other animals like them. Animals with long life spans have innate and learned behaviors. The learned behaviors develop over the animal's lifetime.

16. Answers might include fireflies flash their undersides to attract a mate; jellyfish use bioluminescence to protect themselves when threatened; fish that live in the deep ocean use bioluminescence to find prey.

17. A diurnal animal is active during the day. A nocturnal animal is active during the night. Most owls are nocturnal animals. Butterflies are diurnal.

18. Hibernation is a response to cold temperatures and limited food supplies. Estivation is a response to dry or hot conditions, and limited food supplies.

Student Resources

CONTENTS

Scientific Methods

Scientists use an orderly approach called the scientific method to solve problems. This includes organizing and recording data so others can understand them. Scientists use many variations in this method when they solve problems.

Identify a Question

The first step in a scientific investigation or experiment is to identify a question to be answered or a problem to be solved. For example, you might ask which gasoline is the most efficient.

Gather and Organize Information

After you have identified your question, begin gathering and organizing information. There are many ways to gather information, such as researching in a library, interviewing those knowledgeable about the subject, testing and working in the laboratory and field. Fieldwork is investigations and observations done outside of a laboratory.

Researching Information Before moving in a new direction, it is important to gather the information that already is known about the subject. Start by asking yourself questions to determine exactly what you need to know. Then you will look for the information in various reference sources, like the student is doing in **Figure 1.** Some sources may include textbooks, encyclopedias, government documents, professional journals, science magazines, and the Internet. Always list the sources of your information.

Figure 1 The Internet can be a valuable research tool.

Evaluate Sources of Information Not all sources of information are reliable. You should evaluate all of your sources of information, and use only those you know to be dependable. For example, if you are researching ways to make homes more energy efficient, a site written by the U.S. Department of Energy would be more reliable than a site written by a company that is trying to sell a new type of weatherproofing material. Also, remember that research always is changing. Consult the most current resources available to you. For example, a 1985 resource about saving energy would not reflect the most recent findings.

Sometimes scientists use data that they did not collect themselves, or conclusions drawn by other researchers. This data must be evaluated carefully. Ask questions about how the data were obtained, if the investigation was carried out properly, and if it has been duplicated exactly with the same results. Would you reach the same conclusion from the data? Only when you have confidence in the data can you believe it is true and feel comfortable using it.

Interpret Scientific Illustrations As you research a topic in science, you will see drawings, diagrams, and photographs to help you understand what you read. Some illustrations are included to help you understand an idea that you can't see easily by yourself, like the tiny particles in an atom in **Figure 2.** A drawing helps many people to remember details more easily and provides examples that clarify difficult concepts or give additional information about the topic you are studying. Most illustrations have labels or a caption to identify or to provide more information.

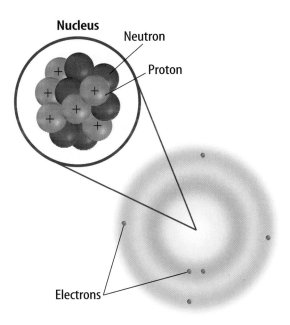

Figure 2 This drawing shows an atom of carbon with its six protons, six neutrons, and six electrons.

Concept Maps One way to organize data is to draw a diagram that shows relationships among ideas (or concepts). A concept map can help make the meanings of ideas and terms more clear, and help you understand and remember what you are studying. Concept maps are useful for breaking large concepts down into smaller parts, making learning easier.

Network Tree A type of concept map that not only shows a relationship, but how the concepts are related is a network tree, shown in **Figure 3.** In a network tree, the words are written in the ovals, while the description of the type of relationship is written across the connecting lines.

When constructing a network tree, write down the topic and all major topics on separate pieces of paper or notecards. Then arrange them in order from general to specific. Branch the related concepts from the major concept and describe the relationship on the connecting line. Continue to more specific concepts until finished.

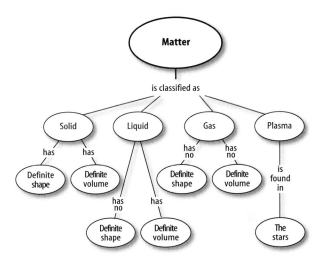

Figure 3 A network tree shows how concepts or objects are related.

Events Chain Another type of concept map is an events chain. Sometimes called a flow chart, it models the order or sequence of items. An events chain can be used to describe a sequence of events, the steps in a procedure, or the stages of a process.

When making an events chain, first find the one event that starts the chain. This event is called the initiating event. Then, find the next event and continue until the outcome is reached, as shown in **Figure 4.**

Initiating Event

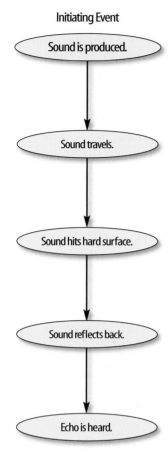

Figure 4 Events-chain concept maps show the order of steps in a process or event. This concept map shows how a sound makes an echo.

Cycle Map A specific type of events chain is a cycle map. It is used when the series of events do not produce a final outcome, but instead relate back to the beginning event, such as in **Figure 5.** Therefore, the cycle repeats itself.

To make a cycle map, first decide what event is the beginning event. This is also called the initiating event. Then list the next events in the order that they occur, with the last event relating back to the initiating event. Words can be written between the events that describe what happens from one event to the next. The number of events in a cycle map can vary, but usually contain three or more events.

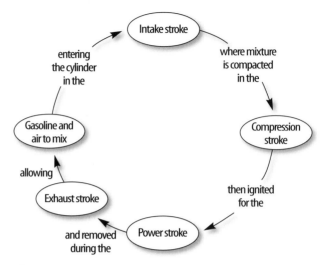

Figure 5 A cycle map shows events that occur in a cycle.

Spider Map A type of concept map that you can use for brainstorming is the spider map. When you have a central idea, you might find that you have a jumble of ideas that relate to it but are not necessarily clearly related to each other. The spider map on sound in **Figure 6** shows that if you write these ideas outside the main concept, then you can begin to separate and group unrelated terms so they become more useful.

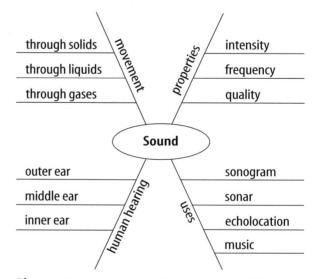

Figure 6 A spider map allows you to list ideas that relate to a central topic but not necessarily to one another.

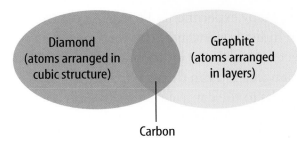

Figure 7 This Venn diagram compares and contrasts two substances made from carbon.

Venn Diagram To illustrate how two subjects compare and contrast you can use a Venn diagram. You can see the characteristics that the subjects have in common and those that they do not, shown in **Figure 7.**

To create a Venn diagram, draw two overlapping ovals that that are big enough to write in. List the characteristics unique to one subject in one oval, and the characteristics of the other subject in the other oval. The characteristics in common are listed in the overlapping section.

Make and Use Tables One way to organize information so it is easier to understand is to use a table. Tables can contain numbers, words, or both.

To make a table, list the items to be compared in the first column and the characteristics to be compared in the first row. The title should clearly indicate the content of the table, and the column or row heads should be clear. Notice that in **Table 1** the units are included.

Table 1 Recyclables Collected During Week			
Day of Week	**Paper (kg)**	**Aluminum (kg)**	**Glass (kg)**
Monday	5.0	4.0	12.0
Wednesday	4.0	1.0	10.0
Friday	2.5	2.0	10.0

Make a Model One way to help you better understand the parts of a structure, the way a process works, or to show things too large or small for viewing is to make a model. For example, an atomic model made of a plastic-ball nucleus and pipe-cleaner electron shells can help you visualize how the parts of an atom relate to each other. Other types of models can by devised on a computer or represented by equations.

Form a Hypothesis

A possible explanation based on previous knowledge and observations is called a hypothesis. After researching gasoline types and recalling previous experiences in your family's car you form a hypothesis—our car runs more efficiently because we use premium gasoline. To be valid, a hypothesis has to be something you can test by using an investigation.

Predict When you apply a hypothesis to a specific situation, you predict something about that situation. A prediction makes a statement in advance, based on prior observation, experience, or scientific reasoning. People use predictions to make everyday decisions. Scientists test predictions by performing investigations. Based on previous observations and experiences, you might form a prediction that cars are more efficient with premium gasoline. The prediction can be tested in an investigation.

Design an Experiment A scientist needs to make many decisions before beginning an investigation. Some of these include: how to carry out the investigation, what steps to follow, how to record the data, and how the investigation will answer the question. It also is important to address any safety concerns.

Test the Hypothesis

Now that you have formed your hypothesis, you need to test it. Using an investigation, you will make observations and collect data, or information. This data might either support or not support your hypothesis. Scientists collect and organize data as numbers and descriptions.

Follow a Procedure In order to know what materials to use, as well as how and in what order to use them, you must follow a procedure. **Figure 8** shows a procedure you might follow to test your hypothesis.

Procedure
1. Use regular gasoline for two weeks.
2. Record the number of kilometers between fill-ups and the amount of gasoline used.
3. Switch to premium gasoline for two weeks.
4. Record the number of kilometers between fill-ups and the amount of gasoline used.

Figure 8 A procedure tells you what to do step by step.

Identify and Manipulate Variables and Controls In any experiment, it is important to keep everything the same except for the item you are testing. The one factor you change is called the independent variable. The change that results is the dependent variable. Make sure you have only one independent variable, to assure yourself of the cause of the changes you observe in the dependent variable. For example, in your gasoline experiment the type of fuel is the independent variable. The dependent variable is the efficiency.

Many experiments also have a control—an individual instance or experimental subject for which the independent variable is not changed. You can then compare the test results to the control results. To design a control you can have two cars of the same type. The control car uses regular gasoline for four weeks. After you are done with the test, you can compare the experimental results to the control results.

Collect Data

Whether you are carrying out an investigation or a short observational experiment, you will collect data, as shown in **Figure 9.** Scientists collect data as numbers and descriptions and organize it in specific ways.

Observe Scientists observe items and events, then record what they see. When they use only words to describe an observation, it is called qualitative data. Scientists' observations also can describe how much there is of something. These observations use numbers, as well as words, in the description and are called quantitative data. For example, if a sample of the element gold is described as being "shiny and very dense" the data are qualitative. Quantitative data on this sample of gold might include "a mass of 30 g and a density of 19.3 g/cm^3."

Figure 9 Collecting data is one way to gather information directly.

Figure 10 Record data neatly and clearly so it is easy to understand.

When you make observations you should examine the entire object or situation first, and then look carefully for details. It is important to record observations accurately and completely. Always record your notes immediately as you make them, so you do not miss details or make a mistake when recording results from memory. Never put unidentified observations on scraps of paper. Instead they should be recorded in a notebook, like the one in **Figure 10.** Write your data neatly so you can easily read it later. At each point in the experiment, record your observations and label them. That way, you will not have to determine what the figures mean when you look at your notes later. Set up any tables that you will need to use ahead of time, so you can record any observations right away. Remember to avoid bias when collecting data by not including personal thoughts when you record observations. Record only what you observe.

Estimate Scientific work also involves estimating. To estimate is to make a judgment about the size or the number of something without measuring or counting. This is important when the number or size of an object or population is too large or too difficult to accurately count or measure.

Sample Scientists may use a sample or a portion of the total number as a type of estimation. To sample is to take a small, representative portion of the objects or organisms of a population for research. By making careful observations or manipulating variables within that portion of the group, information is discovered and conclusions are drawn that might apply to the whole population. A poorly chosen sample can be unrepresentative of the whole. If you were trying to determine the rainfall in an area, it would not be best to take a rainfall sample from under a tree.

Measure You use measurements everyday. Scientists also take measurements when collecting data. When taking measurements, it is important to know how to use measuring tools properly. Accuracy also is important.

Length To measure length, the distance between two points, scientists use meters. Smaller measurements might be measured in centimeters or millimeters.

Length is measured using a metric ruler or meter stick. When using a metric ruler, line up the 0-cm mark with the end of the object being measured and read the number of the unit where the object ends. Look at the metric ruler shown in **Figure 11.** The centimeter lines are the long, numbered lines, and the shorter lines are millimeter lines. In this instance, the length would be 4.50 cm.

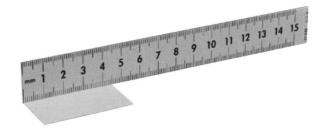

Figure 11 This metric ruler has centimeter and millimeter divisions.

Mass The SI unit for mass is the kilogram (kg). Scientists can measure mass using units formed by adding metric prefixes to the unit gram (g), such as milligram (mg). To measure mass, you might use a triple-beam balance similar to the one shown in **Figure 12.** The balance has a pan on one side and a set of beams on the other side. Each beam has a rider that slides on the beam.

When using a triple-beam balance, place an object on the pan. Slide the largest rider along its beam until the pointer drops below zero. Then move it back one notch. Repeat the process for each rider proceeding from the larger to smaller until the pointer swings an equal distance above and below the zero point. Sum the masses on each beam to find the mass of the object. Move all riders back to zero when finished.

Instead of putting materials directly on the balance, scientists often take a tare of a container. A tare is the mass of a container into which objects or substances are placed for measuring their masses. To mass objects or substances, find the mass of a clean container. Remove the container from the pan, and place the object or substances in the container. Find the mass of the container with the materials in it. Subtract the mass of the empty container from the mass of the filled container to find the mass of the materials you are using.

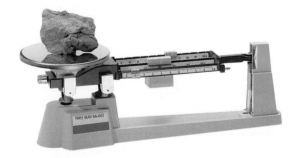

Figure 12 A triple-beam balance is used to determine the mass of an object.

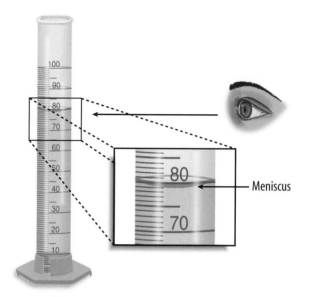

Meniscus

Figure 13 Graduated cylinders measure liquid volume.

Liquid Volume To measure liquids, the unit used is the liter. When a smaller unit is needed, scientists might use a milliliter. Because a milliliter takes up the volume of a cube measuring 1 cm on each side it also can be called a cubic centimeter ($cm^3 = cm \times cm \times cm$).

You can use beakers and graduated cylinders to measure liquid volume. A graduated cylinder, shown in **Figure 13,** is marked from bottom to top in milliliters. In lab, you might use a 10-mL graduated cylinder or a 100-mL graduated cylinder. When measuring liquids, notice that the liquid has a curved surface. Look at the surface at eye level, and measure the bottom of the curve. This is called the meniscus. The graduated cylinder in **Figure 13** contains 79.0 mL, or 79.0 cm^3, of a liquid.

Temperature Scientists often measure temperature using the Celsius scale. Pure water has a freezing point of 0°C and boiling point of 100°C. The unit of measurement is degrees Celsius. Two other scales often used are the Fahrenheit and Kelvin scales.

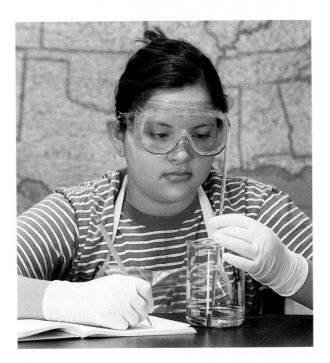

Figure 14 A thermometer measures the temperature of an object.

Scientists use a thermometer to measure temperature. Most thermometers in a laboratory are glass tubes with a bulb at the bottom end containing a liquid such as colored alcohol. The liquid rises or falls with a change in temperature. To read a glass thermometer like the thermometer in **Figure 14,** rotate it slowly until a red line appears. Read the temperature where the red line ends.

Form Operational Definitions An operational definition defines an object by how it functions, works, or behaves. For example, when you are playing hide and seek and a tree is home base, you have created an operational definition for a tree.

Objects can have more than one operational definition. For example, a ruler can be defined as a tool that measures the length of an object (how it is used). It can also be a tool with a series of marks used as a standard when measuring (how it works).

Analyze the Data

To determine the meaning of your observations and investigation results, you will need to look for patterns in the data. Then you must think critically to determine what the data mean. Scientists use several approaches when they analyze the data they have collected and recorded. Each approach is useful for identifying specific patterns.

Interpret Data The word *interpret* means "to explain the meaning of something." When analyzing data from an experiment, try to find out what the data show. Identify the control group and the test group to see whether or not changes in the independent variable have had an effect. Look for differences in the dependent variable between the control and test groups.

Classify Sorting objects or events into groups based on common features is called classifying. When classifying, first observe the objects or events to be classified. Then select one feature that is shared by some members in the group, but not by all. Place those members that share that feature in a subgroup. You can classify members into smaller and smaller subgroups based on characteristics. Remember that when you classify, you are grouping objects or events for a purpose. Keep your purpose in mind as you select the features to form groups and subgroups.

Compare and Contrast Observations can be analyzed by noting the similarities and differences between two more objects or events that you observe. When you look at objects or events to see how they are similar, you are comparing them. Contrasting is looking for differences in objects or events.

Recognize Cause and Effect A cause is a reason for an action or condition. The effect is that action or condition. When two events happen together, it is not necessarily true that one event caused the other. Scientists must design a controlled investigation to recognize the exact cause and effect.

Draw Conclusions

When scientists have analyzed the data they collected, they proceed to draw conclusions about the data. These conclusions are sometimes stated in words similar to the hypothesis that you formed earlier. They may confirm a hypothesis, or lead you to a new hypothesis.

Infer Scientists often make inferences based on their observations. An inference is an attempt to explain observations or to indicate a cause. An inference is not a fact, but a logical conclusion that needs further investigation. For example, you may infer that a fire has caused smoke. Until you investigate, however, you do not know for sure.

Apply When you draw a conclusion, you must apply those conclusions to determine whether the data supports the hypothesis. If your data do not support your hypothesis, it does not mean that the hypothesis is wrong. It means only that the result of the investigation did not support the hypothesis. Maybe the experiment needs to be redesigned, or some of the initial observations on which the hypothesis was based were incomplete or biased. Perhaps more observation or research is needed to refine your hypothesis. A successful investigation does not always come out the way you originally predicted.

Avoid Bias Sometimes a scientific investigation involves making judgments. When you make a judgment, you form an opinion. It is important to be honest and not to allow any expectations of results to bias your judgments. This is important throughout the entire investigation, from researching to collecting data to drawing conclusions.

Communicate

The communication of ideas is an important part of the work of scientists. A discovery that is not reported will not advance the scientific community's understanding or knowledge. Communication among scientists also is important as a way of improving their investigations.

Scientists communicate in many ways, from writing articles in journals and magazines that explain their investigations and experiments, to announcing important discoveries on television and radio. Scientists also share ideas with colleagues on the Internet or present them as lectures, like the student is doing in **Figure 15.**

Figure 15 A student communicates to his peers about his investigation.

Science Skill Handbook

SAFETY SYMBOLS

SAFETY SYMBOLS	HAZARD	EXAMPLES	PRECAUTION	REMEDY
DISPOSAL	Special disposal procedures need to be followed.	certain chemicals, living organisms	Do not dispose of these materials in the sink or trash can.	Dispose of wastes as directed by your teacher.
BIOLOGICAL	Organisms or other biological materials that might be harmful to humans	bacteria, fungi, blood, unpreserved tissues, plant materials	Avoid skin contact with these materials. Wear mask or gloves.	Notify your teacher if you suspect contact with material. Wash hands thoroughly.
EXTREME TEMPERATURE	Objects that can burn skin by being too cold or too hot	boiling liquids, hot plates, dry ice, liquid nitrogen	Use proper protection when handling.	Go to your teacher for first aid.
SHARP OBJECT	Use of tools or glassware that can easily puncture or slice skin	razor blades, pins, scalpels, pointed tools, dissecting probes, broken glass	Practice common-sense behavior and follow guidelines for use of the tool.	Go to your teacher for first aid.
FUME	Possible danger to respiratory tract from fumes	ammonia, acetone, nail polish remover, heated sulfur, moth balls	Make sure there is good ventilation. Never smell fumes directly. Wear a mask.	Leave foul area and notify your teacher immediately.
ELECTRICAL	Possible danger from electrical shock or burn	improper grounding, liquid spills, short circuits, exposed wires	Double-check setup with teacher. Check condition of wires and apparatus.	Do not attempt to fix electrical problems. Notify your teacher immediately.
IRRITANT	Substances that can irritate the skin or mucous membranes of the respiratory tract	pollen, moth balls, steel wool, fiberglass, potassium permanganate	Wear dust mask and gloves. Practice extra care when handling these materials.	Go to your teacher for first aid.
CHEMICAL	Chemicals can react with and destroy tissue and other materials	bleaches such as hydrogen peroxide; acids such as sulfuric acid, hydrochloric acid; bases such as ammonia, sodium hydroxide	Wear goggles, gloves, and an apron.	Immediately flush the affected area with water and notify your teacher.
TOXIC	Substance may be poisonous if touched, inhaled, or swallowed.	mercury, many metal compounds, iodine, poinsettia plant parts	Follow your teacher's instructions.	Always wash hands thoroughly after use. Go to your teacher for first aid.
FLAMMABLE	Flammable chemicals may be ignited by open flame, spark, or exposed heat.	alcohol, kerosene, potassium permanganate	Avoid open flames and heat when using flammable chemicals.	Notify your teacher immediately. Use fire safety equipment if applicable.
OPEN FLAME	Open flame in use, may cause fire.	hair, clothing, paper, synthetic materials	Tie back hair and loose clothing. Follow teacher's instruction on lighting and extinguishing flames.	Notify your teacher immediately. Use fire safety equipment if applicable.

 Eye Safety Proper eye protection should be worn at all times by anyone performing or observing science activities.

 Clothing Protection This symbol appears when substances could stain or burn clothing.

 Animal Safety This symbol appears when safety of animals and students must be ensured.

 Handwashing After the lab, wash hands with soap and water before removing goggles.

Safety in the Science Laboratory

The science laboratory is a safe place to work if you follow standard safety procedures. Being responsible for your own safety helps to make the entire laboratory a safer place for everyone. When performing any lab, read and apply the caution statements and safety symbol listed at the beginning of the lab.

General Safety Rules

1. Obtain your teacher's permission to begin all investigations and use laboratory equipment.

2. Study the procedure. Ask your teacher any questions. Be sure you understand safety symbols shown on the page.

3. Notify your teacher about allergies or other health conditions which can affect your participation in a lab.

4. Learn and follow use and safety procedures for your equipment. If unsure, ask your teacher.

5. Never eat, drink, chew gum, apply cosmetics, or do any personal grooming in the lab. Never use lab glassware as food or drink containers. Keep your hands away from your face and mouth.

6. Know the location and proper use of the safety shower, eye wash, fire blanket, and fire alarm.

Prevent Accidents

1. Use the safety equipment provided to you. Goggles and a safety apron should be worn during investigations.

2. Do NOT use hair spray, mousse, or other flammable hair products. Tie back long hair and tie down loose clothing.

3. Do NOT wear sandals or other open-toed shoes in the lab.

4. Remove jewelry on hands and wrists. Loose jewelry, such as chains and long necklaces, should be removed to prevent them from getting caught in equipment.

5. Do not taste any substances or draw any material into a tube with your mouth.

6. Proper behavior is expected in the lab. Practical jokes and fooling around can lead to accidents and injury.

7. Keep your work area uncluttered.

Laboratory Work

1. Collect and carry all equipment and materials to your work area before beginning a lab.

2. Remain in your own work area unless given permission by your teacher to leave it.

3. Always slant test tubes away from your-self and others when heating them, adding substances to them, or rinsing them.

4. If instructed to smell a substance in a container, hold the container a short distance away and fan vapors towards your nose.

5. Do NOT substitute other chemicals/substances for those in the materials list unless instructed to do so by your teacher.

6. Do NOT take any materials or chemicals outside of the laboratory.

7. Stay out of storage areas unless instructed to be there and supervised by your teacher.

Laboratory Cleanup

1. Turn off all burners, water, and gas, and disconnect all electrical devices.

2. Clean all pieces of equipment and return all materials to their proper places.

3. Dispose of chemicals and other materials as directed by your teacher. Place broken glass and solid substances in the proper containers. Never discard materials in the sink.

4. Clean your work area.

5. Wash your hands with soap and water thoroughly BEFORE removing your goggles.

Emergencies

1. Report any fire, electrical shock, glassware breakage, spill, or injury, no matter how small, to your teacher immediately. Follow his or her instructions.

2. If your clothing should catch fire, STOP, DROP, and ROLL. If possible, smother it with the fire blanket or get under a safety shower. NEVER RUN.

3. If a fire should occur, turn off all gas and leave the room according to established procedures.

4. In most instances, your teacher will clean up spills. Do NOT attempt to clean up spills unless you are given permission and instructions to do so.

5. If chemicals come into contact with your eyes or skin, notify your teacher immediately. Use the eyewash or flush your skin or eyes with large quantities of water.

6. The fire extinguisher and first-aid kit should only be used by your teacher unless it is an extreme emergency and you have been given permission.

7. If someone is injured or becomes ill, only a professional medical provider or someone certified in first aid should perform first-aid procedures.

1 A Sponge of Water

1 A Sponge of Water

Time Required 15 minutes

Materials

- Natural sponges will hold more water than artificial sponges.
- Do not purchase artificial sponges sold with soap already added to them.
- Have towels ready for students to use.

Safety Precautions

- Caution students to never drink water taken from their sponges.
- Consider conducting this lab outside to minimize the mess.

Teaching Strategy Discuss properties of natural and artificial sponges.

Conclude and Apply

1. A large, natural sponge can hold 500–1,000 mL depending on its size. An artificial sponge holds less.
2. Soldiers soaked up stream water with sponges and squeezed the water into their mouths.

EXTRA Labs

From Your Kitchen, Junk Drawer, or Yard

1 A Sponge of Water

Real-World Question
How much water does a sponge hold?

Possible Materials

- large natural sponge
- large artificial sponge (without soap)
- bucket
- shallow basin or pan
- water
- measuring cups (2)
- towel

Procedure
1. Submerge a large, natural sponge in a bucket of water for about 2 min so that it fills with water. Wait until bubbles stop rising up from the sponge.
2. Place the two measuring cups next to the bucket.

3. Carefully remove the sponge from the water and hold it over a measuring cup. Squeeze all the water out of the sponge into the measuring cup. If you reach the top mark on the measuring cup, use the second measuring cup.
4. Repeat steps 1–3 using the artificial sponge. Compare your results.

Conclude and Apply
1. How much water did each sponge hold?
2. Infer how Roman soldiers used sponges as canteens.

2 Invertebrate Groceries

Real-World Question
What types of invertebrates can you find in your local grocery store?

Possible Materials

- access to local grocery store
- guidebook to ocean invertebrates

Procedure
1. Go with an adult to the largest grocery store in your area.
2. Search the seafood section in the store for invertebrates sold as food.
3. Search the grocery aisles for invertebrate meat products.

4. Record all the invertebrate food you find in the store and identify each invertebrate as a mollusk, worm, arthropod, or echinoderm.
5. If you find more than one type of an organism such as crabs, ask a grocery store employee to identify the different types of animals for you.

Conclude and Apply
1. Identify the types of invertebrates you found.
2. What types of invertebrates were not in your grocery store?
3. Infer why we should be concerned about ocean pollution.

Adult supervision required for all labs.

These labs are available at bookc.msscience.com.

---

2 Invertebrate Groceries

Time Required 30 minutes

Materials Encourage students to visit a local outdoor farmer's market or ethnic grocery store to find more exotic invertebrates for sale.

Safety Precaution An adult should accompany students to the grocery store.

Teaching Strategy Purchase a variety of invertebrates from your local store and bring them in to show your class.

Conclude and Apply

1. Answers will vary but may include lobster, crabs, shrimp, crayfish, clams, mussels, oysters, and scallops.
2. Grocery stores probably will not sell insects, worms, or echinoderms.
3. Ocean pollution destroys or contaminates populations of marine invertebrates that are important food sources.

③ Frog Lives

▶ Real-World Question
What do the stages of frog metamorphosis look like?

Possible Materials 🔲 🔲 🔲 🔲 🔲
- gravel
- small aquarium or bucket
- water
- clean plastic milk jug
- *Anacharis* plants
- tadpole

▶ Procedure
1. Pour a 2-cm layer of aquarium gravel or small pebbles into a small aquarium.
2. Fill the aquarium with water and allow the water to sit for seven days.
3. Fill a clean, plastic milk jug with tap water and allow it to sit for seven days.
4. Plant several stalks of *Anacharis* plants in the gravel.
5. Purchase or catch a tadpole and place it in the aquarium along with some of the water from the place where you collected it.
6. Replace ten percent of the aquarium's water every other day with water from the milk jug.
7. Observe your tadpole each day for 2–3 weeks as it completes its metamorphosis into a frog.

▶ Conclude and Apply
1. Describe the metamorphosis of your frog.
2. Infer why you added the plant *Anacharis* to the aquarium.

④ Fly Like a Bird

▶ Real-World Question
How does a bird's wings keep it in the air?

Possible Materials 🔲
- tennis ball, racquetball, or softball
- plastic, throwable disc
- stopwatch or watch with second hand

▶ Procedure
1. Throw a ball in a straight line and parallel to the ground as hard as you can.
2. Have a partner use a stopwatch to time how long the ball stays in the air.
3. Throw the disc in a straight line and parallel to the ground so that it hovers.
4. Have a partner use a stopwatch to time how long the flying disc stays in the air.
5. Repeat steps 1–4 several times and record your times in your Science Journal.

▶ Conclude and Apply
1. Compare the maximum time the tennis ball stayed in the air to the longest time the flying disc stayed up.
2. Compare the shape of the flying disc when you hold it flat in front of you to the shape of a bird wing. How are they similar?
3. Infer how a bird's wings allow it to fly.

Adult supervision required for all labs.

---

③ Frog Lives

Time Required 40 minutes and short observation periods over two to three weeks

Materials Purchase extra tadpoles due to mortality rate.

Safety Precautions
- Students should thoroughly wash their hands after handling organisms.
- Students should obtain permission to collect animals on public property.
- Never release nonnative animals into local ecosystems.

Teaching Strategies
- Avoid placing the aquarium outside or in direct sunlight.
- Before the metamorphosis occurs, decide what you will do with the adult frogs.

Conclude and Apply
1. Students should provide both qualitative and quantitative descriptions.
2. to provide oxygen for the gill breathing tadpole

Extra Try at Home Labs

---

④ Fly Like a Bird

Time Required 30 minutes

Materials Brand name flying discs usually fly best.

Safety Precaution Caution students against throwing objects toward people, animals, cars, or buildings.

Teaching Strategies
- This lab works best when students can throw the ball and flying disc from atop a small hill.
- Choose a student who throws a flying disc well to demonstrate the lab for the entire class.

Conclude and Apply
1. Answers will vary, but the flying disc should stay aloft several seconds longer.
2. Both have the shape of an airfoil with a flat bottom and curved top surface.
3. Air moves across the top faster than the bottom. The slower air moving underneath has more pressure and provides lift to help keep the bird aloft.

5 Fighting Fish

Time Required 15 minutes

Materials Female Siamese fighting fish are usually sold in a community aquarium. Transfer them to small fish bowls.

Safety Precaution Students should wash their hands after handling fish or water.

Teaching Strategies
- Encourage students to hold the mirror up to the male fish for only a few seconds to avoid overly aggravating the fish.
- Explain that these fish developed these territorial behaviors because they live in small spaces in Asian rice paddies.

Conclude and Apply
1. The female won't react to the mirror. The male will display aggressive behavior such as facing the image, spreading his gill covering extensions and fins, and deepening the color of his scales.
2. territorial behavior
3. Males fight each other for nesting territory and mating rights with females.

5 Fighting Fish

Real-World Question
How will a Siamese fighting fish react to a mirror?

Possible Materials
- small fish bowls, glass bowls, or small jars (2)
- water (aquarium, purified)
- male Siamese fighting fish (*Betta splendens*) (1)
- female Siamese fighting fish (*Betta splendens*) (1)
- mirror

Procedure
1. Place a male Siamese fighting fish in a small fish bowl with water and a female Siamese fighting fish into a second bowl with water.
2. Hold the mirror up to the bowl with the male fish so that he sees his reflection and observe his reaction.
3. Hold the mirror up to the bowl with the female fish so that she sees her reflection and observe her reaction.

Conclude and Apply
1. Describe how the male and the female reacted to their reflections.
2. What type of behavior did the male Siamese fighting fish display?
3. Infer why the male fish displays this type of behavior.

Adult supervision required for all labs.

These labs are available at bookc.msscience.com.

Computer Skills

People who study science rely on computers, like the one in **Figure 16,** to record and store data and to analyze results from investigations. Whether you work in a laboratory or just need to write a lab report with tables, good computer skills are a necessity.

Using the computer comes with responsibility. Issues of ownership, security, and privacy can arise. Remember, if you did not author the information you are using, you must provide a source for your information. Also, anything on a computer can be accessed by others. Do not put anything on the computer that you would not want everyone to know. To add more security to your work, use a password.

Use a Word Processing Program

A computer program that allows you to type your information, change it as many times as you need to, and then print it out is called a word processing program. Word processing programs also can be used to make tables.

Figure 16 A computer will make reports neater and more professional looking.

Learn the Skill To start your word processing program, a blank document, sometimes called "Document 1," appears on the screen. To begin, start typing. To create a new document, click the *New* button on the standard tool bar. These tips will help you format the document.

- The program will automatically move to the next line; press *Enter* if you wish to start a new paragraph.
- Symbols, called non-printing characters, can be hidden by clicking the *Show/Hide* button on your toolbar.
- To insert text, move the cursor to the point where you want the insertion to go, click on the mouse once, and type the text.
- To move several lines of text, select the text and click the *Cut* button on your toolbar. Then position your cursor in the location that you want to move the cut text and click *Paste.* If you move to the wrong place, click *Undo.*
- The spell check feature does not catch words that are misspelled to look like other words, like "cold" instead of "gold." Always reread your document to catch all spelling mistakes.
- To learn about other word processing methods, read the user's manual or click on the *Help* button.
- You can integrate databases, graphics, and spreadsheets into documents by copying from another program and pasting it into your document, or by using desktop publishing (DTP). DTP software allows you to put text and graphics together to finish your document with a professional look. This software varies in how it is used and its capabilities.

Use a Database

A collection of facts stored in a computer and sorted into different fields is called a database. A database can be reorganized in any way that suits your needs.

Learn the Skill A computer program that allows you to create your own database is a database management system (DBMS). It allows you to add, delete, or change information. Take time to get to know the features of your database software.

- Determine what facts you would like to include and research to collect your information.
- Determine how you want to organize the information.
- Follow the instructions for your particular DBMS to set up fields. Then enter each item of data in the appropriate field.
- Follow the instructions to sort the information in order of importance.
- Evaluate the information in your database, and add, delete, or change as necessary.

Use the Internet

The Internet is a global network of computers where information is stored and shared. To use the Internet, like the students in **Figure 17,** you need a modem to connect your computer to a phone line and an Internet Service Provider account.

Learn the Skill To access internet sites and information, use a "Web browser," which lets you view and explore pages on the World Wide Web. Each page is its own site, and each site has its own address, called a URL. Once you have found a Web browser, follow these steps for a search (this also is how you search a database).

Figure 17 The Internet allows you to search a global network for a variety of information.

- Be as specific as possible. If you know you want to research "gold," don't type in "elements." Keep narrowing your search until you find what you want.
- Web sites that end in *.com* are commercial Web sites; *.org, .edu,* and *.gov* are non-profit, educational, or government Web sites.
- Electronic encyclopedias, almanacs, indexes, and catalogs will help locate and select relevant information.
- Develop a "home page" with relative ease. When developing a Web site, NEVER post pictures or disclose personal information such as location, names, or phone numbers. Your school or community usually can host your Web site. A basic understanding of HTML (hypertext mark-up language), the language of Web sites, is necessary. Software that creates HTML code is called authoring software, and can be downloaded free from many Web sites. This software allows text and pictures to be arranged as the software is writing the HTML code.

Use a Spreadsheet

A spreadsheet, shown in **Figure 18,** can perform mathematical functions with any data arranged in columns and rows. By entering a simple equation into a cell, the program can perform operations in specific cells, rows, or columns.

Learn the Skill Each column (vertical) is assigned a letter, and each row (horizontal) is assigned a number. Each point where a row and column intersect is called a cell, and is labeled according to where it is located—Column A, Row 1 (A1).

- Decide how to organize the data, and enter it in the correct row or column.
- Spreadsheets can use standard formulas or formulas can be customized to calculate cells.
- To make a change, click on a cell to make it activate, and enter the edited data or formula.
- Spreadsheets also can display your results in graphs. Choose the style of graph that best represents the data.

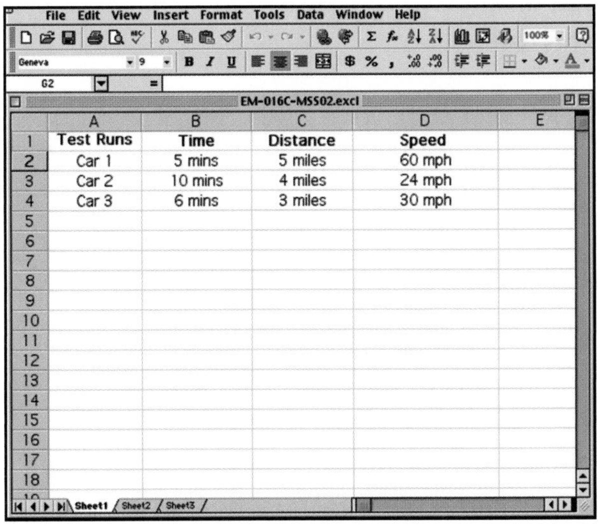

	A	B	C	D	E
1	Test Runs	Time	Distance	Speed	
2	Car 1	5 mins	5 miles	60 mph	
3	Car 2	10 mins	4 miles	24 mph	
4	Car 3	6 mins	3 miles	30 mph	

Figure 18 A spreadsheet allows you to perform mathematical operations on your data.

Use Graphics Software

Adding pictures, called graphics, to your documents is one way to make your documents more meaningful and exciting. This software adds, edits, and even constructs graphics. There is a variety of graphics software programs. The tools used for drawing can be a mouse, keyboard, or other specialized devices. Some graphics programs are simple. Others are complicated, called computer-aided design (CAD) software.

Learn the Skill It is important to have an understanding of the graphics software being used before starting. The better the software is understood, the better the results. The graphics can be placed in a word-processing document.

- Clip art can be found on a variety of internet sites, and on CDs. These images can be copied and pasted into your document.
- When beginning, try editing existing drawings, then work up to creating drawings.
- The images are made of tiny rectangles of color called pixels. Each pixel can be altered.
- Digital photography is another way to add images. The photographs in the memory of a digital camera can be downloaded into a computer, then edited and added to the document.
- Graphics software also can allow animation. The software allows drawings to have the appearance of movement by connecting basic drawings automatically. This is called in-betweening, or tweening.
- Remember to save often.

Presentation Skills

Develop Multimedia Presentations

Most presentations are more dynamic if they include diagrams, photographs, videos, or sound recordings, like the one shown in **Figure 19.** A multimedia presentation involves using stereos, overhead projectors, televisions, computers, and more.

Learn the Skill Decide the main points of your presentation, and what types of media would best illustrate those points.

- Make sure you know how to use the equipment you are working with.
- Practice the presentation using the equipment several times.
- Enlist the help of a classmate to push play or turn lights out for you. Be sure to practice your presentation with him or her.
- If possible, set up all of the equipment ahead of time, and make sure everything is working properly.

Figure 19 These students are engaging the audience using a variety of tools.

Computer Presentations

There are many different interactive computer programs that you can use to enhance your presentation. Most computers have a compact disc (CD) drive that can play both CDs and digital video discs (DVDs). Also, there is hardware to connect a regular CD, DVD, or VCR. These tools will enhance your presentation.

Another method of using the computer to aid in your presentation is to develop a slide show using a computer program. This can allow movement of visuals at the presenter's pace, and can allow for visuals to build on one another.

Learn the Skill In order to create multimedia presentations on a computer, you need to have certain tools. These may include traditional graphic tools and drawing programs, animation programs, and authoring systems that tie everything together. Your computer will tell you which tools it supports. The most important step is to learn about the tools that you will be using.

- Often, color and strong images will convey a point better than words alone. Use the best methods available to convey your point.
- As with other presentations, practice many times.
- Practice your presentation with the tools you and any assistants will be using.
- Maintain eye contact with the audience. The purpose of using the computer is not to prompt the presenter, but to help the audience understand the points of the presentation.

Math Review

Use Fractions

A fraction compares a part to a whole. In the fraction $\frac{2}{3}$, the 2 represents the part and is the numerator. The 3 represents the whole and is the denominator.

Reduce Fractions To reduce a fraction, you must find the largest factor that is common to both the numerator and the denominator, the greatest common factor (GCF). Divide both numbers by the GCF. The fraction has then been reduced, or it is in its simplest form.

Example Twelve of the 20 chemicals in the science lab are in powder form. What fraction of the chemicals used in the lab are in powder form?

Step 1 Write the fraction.

$$\frac{part}{whole} = \frac{12}{20}$$

Step 2 To find the GCF of the numerator and denominator, list all of the factors of each number.

Factors of 12: 1, 2, 3, 4, 6, 12 (the numbers that divide evenly into 12)

Factors of 20: 1, 2, 4, 5, 10, 20 (the numbers that divide evenly into 20)

Step 3 List the common factors.

1, 2, 4.

Step 4 Choose the greatest factor in the list.

The GCF of 12 and 20 is 4.

Step 5 Divide the numerator and denominator by the GCF.

$$\frac{12 \div 4}{20 \div 4} = \frac{3}{5}$$

In the lab, $\frac{3}{5}$ of the chemicals are in powder form.

Practice Problem At an amusement park, 66 of 90 rides have a height restriction. What fraction of the rides, in its simplest form, has a height restriction?

Add and Subtract Fractions To add or subtract fractions with the same denominator, add or subtract the numerators and write the sum or difference over the denominator. After finding the sum or difference, find the simplest form for your fraction.

Example 1 In the forest outside your house, $\frac{1}{8}$ of the animals are rabbits, $\frac{3}{8}$ are squirrels, and the remainder are birds and insects. How many are mammals?

Step 1 Add the numerators.

$$\frac{1}{8} + \frac{3}{8} = \frac{(1+3)}{8} = \frac{4}{8}$$

Step 2 Find the GCF.

$$\frac{4}{8} \ (GCF, 4)$$

Step 3 Divide the numerator and denominator by the GCF.

$$\frac{4}{4} = 1, \ \frac{8}{4} = 2$$

$\frac{1}{2}$ of the animals are mammals.

Example 2 If $\frac{7}{16}$ of the Earth is covered by freshwater, and $\frac{1}{16}$ of that is in glaciers, how much freshwater is not frozen?

Step 1 Subtract the numerators.

$$\frac{7}{16} - \frac{1}{16} = \frac{(7-1)}{16} = \frac{6}{16}$$

Step 2 Find the GCF.

$$\frac{6}{16} \ (GCF, 2)$$

Step 3 Divide the numerator and denominator by the GCF.

$$\frac{6}{2} = 3, \ \frac{16}{2} = 8$$

$\frac{3}{8}$ of the freshwater is not frozen.

Practice Problem A bicycle rider is going 15 km/h for $\frac{4}{9}$ of his ride, 10 km/h for $\frac{2}{9}$ of his ride, and 8 km/h for the remainder of the ride. How much of his ride is he going over 8 km/h?

Reduce Fractions

$$\frac{66 \div 6}{90 \div 6} = \frac{11}{15}$$

Add and Subtract Fractions

$$\frac{4}{9} + \frac{2}{9} = \frac{6}{9}$$

$$\frac{6 \div 3}{9 \div 3} = \frac{2}{3}$$

Math Skill Handbook

Unlike Denominators

Problem 1

$1 \times 5 = 5, 8 \times 5 = 40$

$1 \times 4 = 4, 10 \times 4 = 40$

$\frac{5}{40} + \frac{4}{40} = \frac{9}{40}$

Problem 2

If $\frac{7}{10}$ are involuntary, the remainder are voluntary.

$\frac{10}{10} - \frac{7}{10} = \frac{3}{10}$

Unlike Denominators To add or subtract fractions with unlike denominators, first find the least common denominator (LCD). This is the smallest number that is a common multiple of both denominators. Rename each fraction with the LCD, and then add or subtract. Find the simplest form if necessary.

Example 1 A chemist makes a paste that is $\frac{1}{2}$ table salt (NaCl), $\frac{1}{3}$ sugar ($C_6H_{12}O_6$), and the rest water (H_2O). How much of the paste is a solid?

Step 1 Find the LCD of the fractions.

$\frac{1}{2} + \frac{1}{3}$ (LCD, 6)

Step 2 Rename each numerator and each denominator with the LCD.

$1 \times 3 = 3, \; 2 \times 3 = 6$

$1 \times 2 = 2, \; 3 \times 2 = 6$

Step 3 Add the numerators.

$\frac{3}{6} + \frac{2}{6} = \frac{(3 + 2)}{6} = \frac{5}{6}$

$\frac{5}{6}$ of the paste is a solid.

Example 2 The average precipitation in Grand Junction, CO, is $\frac{7}{10}$ inch in November, and $\frac{3}{5}$ inch in December. What is the total average precipitation?

Step 1 Find the LCD of the fractions.

$\frac{7}{10} + \frac{3}{5}$ (LCD, 10)

Step 2 Rename each numerator and each denominator with the LCD.

$7 \times 1 = 7, \; 10 \times 1 = 10$

$3 \times 2 = 6, \; 5 \times 2 = 10$

Step 3 Add the numerators.

$\frac{7}{10} + \frac{6}{10} = \frac{(7 + 6)}{10} = \frac{13}{10}$

$\frac{13}{10}$ inches total precipitation, or $1\frac{3}{10}$ inches.

Practice Problem On an electric bill, about $\frac{1}{8}$ of the energy is from solar energy and about $\frac{1}{10}$ is from wind power. How much of the total bill is from solar energy and wind power combined?

Example 3 In your body, $\frac{7}{10}$ of your muscle contractions are involuntary (cardiac and smooth muscle tissue). Smooth muscle makes $\frac{3}{15}$ of your muscle contractions. How many of your muscle contractions are made by cardiac muscle?

Step 1 Find the LCD of the fractions.

$\frac{7}{10} - \frac{3}{15}$ (LCD, 30)

Step 2 Rename each numerator and each denominator with the LCD.

$7 \times 3 = 21, \; 10 \times 3 = 30$

$3 \times 2 = 6, \; 15 \times 2 = 30$

Step 3 Subtract the numerators.

$\frac{21}{30} - \frac{6}{30} = \frac{(21 - 6)}{30} = \frac{15}{30}$

Step 4 Find the GCF.

$\frac{15}{30}$ (GCF, 15)

$\frac{1}{2}$

$\frac{1}{2}$ of all muscle contractions are cardiac muscle.

Example 4 Tony wants to make cookies that call for $\frac{3}{4}$ of a cup of flour, but he only has $\frac{1}{3}$ of a cup. How much more flour does he need?

Step 1 Find the LCD of the fractions.

$\frac{3}{4} - \frac{1}{3}$ (LCD, 12)

Step 2 Rename each numerator and each denominator with the LCD.

$3 \times 3 = 9, \; 4 \times 3 = 12$

$1 \times 4 = 4, \; 3 \times 4 = 12$

Step 3 Subtract the numerators.

$\frac{9}{12} - \frac{4}{12} = \frac{(9 - 4)}{12} = \frac{5}{12}$

$\frac{5}{12}$ of a cup of flour.

Practice Problem Using the information provided to you in Example 3 above, determine how many muscle contractions are voluntary (skeletal muscle).

Math Skill Handbook

Multiply Fractions To multiply with fractions, multiply the numerators and multiply the denominators. Find the simplest form if necessary.

Example Multiply $\frac{3}{5}$ by $\frac{1}{3}$.

Step 1 Multiply the numerators and denominators.

$$\frac{3}{5} \times \frac{1}{3} = \frac{(3 \times 1)}{(5 \times 3)} = \frac{3}{15}$$

Step 2 Find the GCF.

$$\frac{3}{15} \quad (\text{GCF, 3})$$

Step 3 Divide the numerator and denominator by the GCF.

$$\frac{3}{3} = 1, \quad \frac{15}{3} = 5$$

$$\frac{1}{5}$$

$\frac{3}{5}$ multiplied by $\frac{1}{3}$ is $\frac{1}{5}$.

Practice Problem Multiply $\frac{3}{14}$ by $\frac{5}{16}$.

Find a Reciprocal Two numbers whose product is 1 are called multiplicative inverses, or reciprocals.

Example Find the reciprocal of $\frac{3}{8}$.

Step 1 Inverse the fraction by putting the denominator on top and the numerator on the bottom.

$$\frac{8}{3}$$

The reciprocal of $\frac{3}{8}$ is $\frac{8}{3}$.

Practice Problem Find the reciprocal of $\frac{4}{9}$.

Divide Fractions To divide one fraction by another fraction, multiply the dividend by the reciprocal of the divisor. Find the simplest form if necessary.

Example 1 Divide $\frac{1}{9}$ by $\frac{1}{3}$.

Step 1 Find the reciprocal of the divisor.

The reciprocal of $\frac{1}{3}$ is $\frac{3}{1}$.

Step 2 Multiply the dividend by the reciprocal of the divisor.

$$\frac{\frac{1}{9}}{\frac{1}{3}} = \frac{1}{9} \times \frac{3}{1} = \frac{(1 \times 3)}{(9 \times 1)} = \frac{3}{9}$$

Step 3 Find the GCF.

$$\frac{3}{9} \quad (\text{GCF, 3})$$

Step 4 Divide the numerator and denominator by the GCF.

$$\frac{3}{3} = 1, \quad \frac{9}{3} = 3$$

$$\frac{1}{3}$$

$\frac{1}{9}$ divided by $\frac{1}{3}$ is $\frac{1}{3}$.

Example 2 Divide $\frac{3}{5}$ by $\frac{1}{4}$.

Step 1 Find the reciprocal of the divisor.

The reciprocal of $\frac{1}{4}$ is $\frac{4}{1}$.

Step 2 Multiply the dividend by the reciprocal of the divisor.

$$\frac{\frac{3}{5}}{\frac{1}{4}} = \frac{3}{5} \times \frac{4}{1} = \frac{(3 \times 4)}{(5 \times 1)} = \frac{12}{5}$$

$\frac{3}{5}$ divided by $\frac{1}{4}$ is $\frac{12}{5}$ or $2\frac{2}{5}$.

Practice Problem Divide $\frac{3}{11}$ by $\frac{7}{10}$.

Multiply Fractions
$$\frac{3}{14} \times \frac{5}{16} = \frac{(3 \times 5)}{(14 \times 16)} = \frac{15}{224}$$

Find a Reciprocal
$$\frac{9}{4}$$

Divide Fractions
The reciprocal of $\frac{7}{10}$ is $\frac{10}{7}$.
$$\frac{3}{11} \times \frac{10}{7} = \frac{(3 \times 10)}{(11 \times 7)} = \frac{30}{77}$$

Use Ratios

When you compare two numbers by division, you are using a ratio. Ratios can be written 3 to 5, 3:5, or $\dfrac{3}{5}$. Ratios, like fractions, also can be written in simplest form.

Ratios can represent probabilities, also called odds. This is a ratio that compares the number of ways a certain outcome occurs to the number of outcomes. For example, if you flip a coin 100 times, what are the odds that it will come up heads? There are two possible outcomes, heads or tails, so the odds of coming up heads are 50:100. Another way to say this is that 50 out of 100 times the coin will come up heads. In its simplest form, the ratio is 1:2.

Example 1 A chemical solution contains 40 g of salt and 64 g of baking soda. What is the ratio of salt to baking soda as a fraction in simplest form?

Step 1 Write the ratio as a fraction.
$$\dfrac{\text{salt}}{\text{baking soda}} = \dfrac{40}{64}$$

Step 2 Express the fraction in simplest form.
The GCF of 40 and 64 is 8.
$$\dfrac{40}{64} = \dfrac{40 \div 8}{64 \div 8} = \dfrac{5}{8}$$

The ratio of salt to baking soda in the sample is 5:8.

Example 2 Sean rolls a 6-sided die 6 times. What are the odds that the side with a 3 will show?

Step 1 Write the ratio as a fraction.
$$\dfrac{\text{number of sides with a 3}}{\text{number of sides}} = \dfrac{1}{6}$$

Step 2 Multiply by the number of attempts.
$$\dfrac{1}{6} \times 6 \text{ attempts} = \dfrac{6}{6} \text{ attempts} = 1 \text{ attempt}$$

1 attempt out of 6 will show a 3.

Practice Problem Two metal rods measure 100 cm and 144 cm in length. What is the ratio of their lengths in simplest form?

Use Decimals

A fraction with a denominator that is a power of ten can be written as a decimal. For example, 0.27 means $\dfrac{27}{100}$. The decimal point separates the ones place from the tenths place.

Any fraction can be written as a decimal using division. For example, the fraction $\dfrac{5}{8}$ can be written as a decimal by dividing 5 by 8. Written as a decimal, it is 0.625.

Add or Subtract Decimals When adding and subtracting decimals, line up the decimal points before carrying out the operation.

Example 1 Find the sum of 47.68 and 7.80.

Step 1 Line up the decimal places when you write the numbers.
$$\begin{array}{r} 47.68 \\ +\ 7.80 \\ \hline \end{array}$$

Step 2 Add the decimals.
$$\begin{array}{r} 47.68 \\ +\ 7.80 \\ \hline 55.48 \end{array}$$

The sum of 47.68 and 7.80 is 55.48.

Example 2 Find the difference of 42.17 and 15.85.

Step 1 Line up the decimal places when you write the number.
$$\begin{array}{r} 42.17 \\ -15.85 \\ \hline \end{array}$$

Step 2 Subtract the decimals.
$$\begin{array}{r} 42.17 \\ -15.85 \\ \hline 26.32 \end{array}$$

The difference of 42.17 and 15.85 is 26.32.

Practice Problem Find the sum of 1.245 and 3.842.

Multiply Decimals To multiply decimals, multiply the numbers like any other number, ignoring the decimal point. Count the decimal places in each factor. The product will have the same number of decimal places as the sum of the decimal places in the factors.

Example Multiply 2.4 by 5.9.

Step 1 Multiply the factors like two whole numbers.
$24 \times 59 = 1416$

Step 2 Find the sum of the number of decimal places in the factors. Each factor has one decimal place, for a sum of two decimal places.

Step 3 The product will have two decimal places.
14.16

The product of 2.4 and 5.9 is 14.16.

Practice Problem Multiply 4.6 by 2.2.

Divide Decimals When dividing decimals, change the divisor to a whole number. To do this, multiply both the divisor and the dividend by the same power of ten. Then place the decimal point in the quotient directly above the decimal point in the dividend. Then divide as you do with whole numbers.

Example Divide 8.84 by 3.4.

Step 1 Multiply both factors by 10.
$3.4 \times 10 = 34$, $8.84 \times 10 = 88.4$

Step 2 Divide 88.4 by 34.

$$\begin{array}{r} 2.6 \\ 34\overline{)88.4} \\ -68 \\ \hline 204 \\ -204 \\ \hline 0 \end{array}$$

8.84 divided by 3.4 is 2.6.

Practice Problem Divide 75.6 by 3.6.

Use Proportions

An equation that shows that two ratios are equivalent is a proportion. The ratios $\frac{2}{4}$ and $\frac{5}{10}$ are equivalent, so they can be written as $\frac{2}{4} = \frac{5}{10}$. This equation is a proportion.

When two ratios form a proportion, the cross products are equal. To find the cross products in the proportion $\frac{2}{4} = \frac{5}{10}$, multiply the 2 and the 10, and the 4 and the 5. Therefore $2 \times 10 = 4 \times 5$, or $20 = 20$.

Because you know that both proportions are equal, you can use cross products to find a missing term in a proportion. This is known as solving the proportion.

Example The heights of a tree and a pole are proportional to the lengths of their shadows. The tree casts a shadow of 24 m when a 6-m pole casts a shadow of 4 m. What is the height of the tree?

Step 1 Write a proportion.
$$\frac{\text{height of tree}}{\text{height of pole}} = \frac{\text{length of tree's shadow}}{\text{length of pole's shadow}}$$

Step 2 Substitute the known values into the proportion. Let h represent the unknown value, the height of the tree.
$$\frac{h}{6} = \frac{24}{4}$$

Step 3 Find the cross products.
$h \times 4 = 6 \times 24$

Step 4 Simplify the equation.
$4h = 144$

Step 5 Divide each side by 4.
$$\frac{4h}{4} = \frac{144}{4}$$
$h = 36$

The height of the tree is 36 m.

Practice Problem The ratios of the weights of two objects on the Moon and on Earth are in proportion. A rock weighing 3 N on the Moon weighs 18 N on Earth. How much would a rock that weighs 5 N on the Moon weigh on Earth?

Multiply Decimals

Multiply 4.6 and 2.2 by 10.
$46 \times 22 = 1012$
Each factor had one decimal place.
10.12

Divide Decimals

Multiply both factors by 10.
Divide 756 by 36.

$$\begin{array}{r} 21 \\ 36\overline{)756} \\ 72 \\ \hline 36 \\ 36 \\ \hline 0 \end{array}$$

Use Proportions

$$\frac{3}{18} = \frac{5}{w}$$

$w \times 3 = 5 \times 18$

$$\frac{3w}{3} = \frac{90}{3}$$

$w = 30$

Use Percentages

$$\frac{73}{365} = \frac{x}{100}$$

$$\frac{7300}{365} = \frac{365x}{365}$$

$$20\% = x$$

Solve One-Step Equations

$$h = gd$$

$$\frac{17.4}{12.3} = \frac{12.3d}{12.3}$$

$$1.41 = d$$

Use Percentages

The word *percent* means "out of one hundred." It is a ratio that compares a number to 100. Suppose you read that 77 percent of the Earth's surface is covered by water. That is the same as reading that the fraction of the Earth's surface covered by water is $\frac{77}{100}$. To express a fraction as a percent, first find the equivalent decimal for the fraction. Then, multiply the decimal by 100 and add the percent symbol.

Example Express $\frac{13}{20}$ as a percent.

Step 1 Find the equivalent decimal for the fraction.

$$\begin{array}{r} 0.65 \\ 20\overline{)13.00} \\ \underline{12\ 0} \\ 1\ 00 \\ \underline{1\ 00} \\ 0 \end{array}$$

Step 2 Rewrite the fraction $\frac{13}{20}$ as 0.65.

Step 3 Multiply 0.65 by 100 and add the % sign.
$$0.65 \times 100 = 65 = 65\%$$

So, $\frac{13}{20} = 65\%$.

This also can be solved as a proportion.

Example Express $\frac{13}{20}$ as a percent.

Step 1 Write a proportion.
$$\frac{13}{20} = \frac{x}{100}$$

Step 2 Find the cross products.
$$1300 = 20x$$

Step 3 Divide each side by 20.
$$\frac{1300}{20} = \frac{20x}{20}$$
$$65\% = x$$

Practice Problem In one year, 73 of 365 days were rainy in one city. What percent of the days in that city were rainy?

Solve One-Step Equations

A statement that two things are equal is an equation. For example, $A = B$ is an equation that states that A is equal to B.

An equation is solved when a variable is replaced with a value that makes both sides of the equation equal. To make both sides equal the inverse operation is used. Addition and subtraction are inverses, and multiplication and division are inverses.

Example 1 Solve the equation $x - 10 = 35$.

Step 1 Find the solution by adding 10 to each side of the equation.
$$x - 10 = 35$$
$$x - 10 + 10 = 35 + 10$$
$$x = 45$$

Step 2 Check the solution.
$$x - 10 = 35$$
$$45 - 10 = 35$$
$$35 = 35$$

Both sides of the equation are equal, so $x = 45$.

Example 2 In the formula $a = bc$, find the value of c if $a = 20$ and $b = 2$.

Step 1 Rearrange the formula so the unknown value is by itself on one side of the equation by dividing both sides by b.

$$a = bc$$
$$\frac{a}{b} = \frac{bc}{b}$$
$$\frac{a}{b} = c$$

Step 2 Replace the variables a and b with the values that are given.

$$\frac{a}{b} = c$$
$$\frac{20}{2} = c$$
$$10 = c$$

Step 3 Check the solution.

$$a = bc$$
$$20 = 2 \times 10$$
$$20 = 20$$

Both sides of the equation are equal, so $c = 10$ is the solution when $a = 20$ and $b = 2$.

Practice Problem In the formula $h = gd$, find the value of d if $g = 12.3$ and $h = 17.4$.

Math Skill Handbook

Use Statistics

The branch of mathematics that deals with collecting, analyzing, and presenting data is statistics. In statistics, there are three common ways to summarize data with a single number—the mean, the median, and the mode.

The **mean** of a set of data is the arithmetic average. It is found by adding the numbers in the data set and dividing by the number of items in the set.

The **median** is the middle number in a set of data when the data are arranged in numerical order. If there were an even number of data points, the median would be the mean of the two middle numbers.

The **mode** of a set of data is the number or item that appears most often.

Another number that often is used to describe a set of data is the range. The **range** is the difference between the largest number and the smallest number in a set of data.

A **frequency table** shows how many times each piece of data occurs, usually in a survey. **Table 2** below shows the results of a student survey on favorite color.

Table 2 Student Color Choice		
Color	**Tally**	**Frequency**
red	IIII	4
blue	ⷭ	5
black	II	2
green	III	3
purple	ⷭ II	7
yellow	ⷭ I	6

Based on the frequency table data, which color is the favorite?

Example The speeds (in m/s) for a race car during five different time trials are 39, 37, 44, 36, and 44.

To find the mean:

Step 1 Find the sum of the numbers.
$$39 + 37 + 44 + 36 + 44 = 200$$

Step 2 Divide the sum by the number of items, which is 5.
$$200 \div 5 = 40$$

The mean is 40 m/s.

To find the median:

Step 1 Arrange the measures from least to greatest.
36, 37, 39, 44, 44

Step 2 Determine the middle measure.
36, 37, <u>39</u>, 44, 44

The median is 39 m/s.

To find the mode:

Step 1 Group the numbers that are the same together.
44, 44, 36, 37, 39

Step 2 Determine the number that occurs most in the set.
<u>44, 44</u>, 36, 37, 39

The mode is 44 m/s.

To find the range:

Step 1 Arrange the measures from largest to smallest.
44, 44, 39, 37, 36

Step 2 Determine the largest and smallest measures in the set.
<u>44</u>, 44, 39, 37, <u>36</u>

Step 3 Find the difference between the largest and smallest measures.
$$44 - 36 = 8$$

The range is 8 m/s.

Practice Problem Find the mean, median, mode, and range for the data set 8, 4, 12, 8, 11, 14, 16.

Use Statistics

mean
$$8 + 4 + 12 + 8 + 11 + 14 + 16 = 73$$
$$73 \div 7 = 10.4$$

median
4, 8, 8, <u>11</u>, 12, 14, 16

mode
4, <u>8, 8</u>, 11, 12, 14, 16

range
<u>4</u>, 8, 8, 11, 12, 14, <u>16</u>
$$16 - 4 = 12$$

Math Skill Handbook

Perimeter

Problem 1

$P = 2(18 \text{ m} + 7 \text{ m})$

$P = 2(25 \text{ m})$

$P = 50 \text{ m}$

Problem 2

$P = 1.6 \text{ cm} + 2.4 \text{ cm} + 2.4 \text{ cm}$

$P = 6.4 \text{ cm}$

Area of a Rectangle

$A = (4 \text{ m} \times 4 \text{ m})$

$A = 16 \text{ m}^2$

Area of a Triangle

$A = \frac{1}{2}(27 \text{ cm} \times 17 \text{ cm})$

$A = \frac{1}{2}(459 \text{ cm}^2)$

$A = 229.5 \text{ cm}^2$

Use Geometry

The branch of mathematics that deals with the measurement, properties, and relationships of points, lines, angles, surfaces, and solids is called geometry.

Perimeter The **perimeter** (P) is the distance around a geometric figure. To find the perimeter of a rectangle, add the length and width and multiply that sum by two, or $2(l + w)$. To find perimeters of irregular figures, add the length of the sides.

Example 1 Find the perimeter of a rectangle that is 3 m long and 5 m wide.

Step 1 You know that the perimeter is 2 times the sum of the width and length.

$P = 2(3 \text{ m} + 5 \text{ m})$

Step 2 Find the sum of the width and length.

$P = 2(8 \text{ m})$

Step 3 Multiply by 2.

$P = 16 \text{ m}$

The perimeter is 16 m.

Example 2 Find the perimeter of a shape with sides measuring 2 cm, 5 cm, 6 cm, 3 cm.

Step 1 You know that the perimeter is the sum of all the sides.

$P = 2 + 5 + 6 + 3$

Step 2 Find the sum of the sides.

$P = 2 + 5 + 6 + 3$

$P = 16$

The perimeter is 16 cm.

Practice Problem Find the perimeter of a rectangle with a length of 18 m and a width of 7 m.

Practice Problem Find the perimeter of a triangle measuring 1.6 cm by 2.4 cm by 2.4 cm.

Area of a Rectangle The **area** (A) is the number of square units needed to cover a surface. To find the area of a rectangle, multiply the length times the width, or $l \times w$. When finding area, the units also are multiplied. Area is given in square units.

Example Find the area of a rectangle with a length of 1 cm and a width of 10 cm.

Step 1 You know that the area is the length multiplied by the width.

$A = (1 \text{ cm} \times 10 \text{ cm})$

Step 2 Multiply the length by the width. Also multiply the units.

$A = 10 \text{ cm}^2$

The area is 10 cm².

Practice Problem Find the area of a square whose sides measure 4 m.

Area of a Triangle To find the area of a triangle, use the formula:

$$A = \frac{1}{2}(\text{base} \times \text{height})$$

The base of a triangle can be any of its sides. The height is the perpendicular distance from a base to the opposite endpoint, or vertex.

Example Find the area of a triangle with a base of 18 m and a height of 7 m.

Step 1 You know that the area is $\frac{1}{2}$ the base times the height.

$A = \frac{1}{2}(18 \text{ m} \times 7 \text{ m})$

Step 2 Multiply $\frac{1}{2}$ by the product of 18×7. Multiply the units.

$A = \frac{1}{2}(126 \text{ m}^2)$

$A = 63 \text{ m}^2$

The area is 63 m².

Practice Problem Find the area of a triangle with a base of 27 cm and a height of 17 cm.

Circumference of a Circle The **diameter** (*d*) of a circle is the distance across the circle through its center, and the **radius** (*r*) is the distance from the center to any point on the circle. The radius is half of the diameter. The distance around the circle is called the **circumference** (C). The formula for finding the circumference is:

$$C = 2\pi r \ or \ C = \pi d$$

The circumference divided by the diameter is always equal to 3.1415926... This nonterminating and nonrepeating number is represented by the Greek letter π (pi). An approximation often used for π is 3.14.

Example 1 Find the circumference of a circle with a radius of 3 m.

Step 1 You know the formula for the circumference is 2 times the radius times π.
$C = 2\pi(3)$

Step 2 Multiply 2 times the radius.
$C = 6\pi$

Step 3 Multiply by π.
$C = 19$ m

The circumference is 19 m.

Example 2 Find the circumference of a circle with a diameter of 24.0 cm.

Step 1 You know the formula for the circumference is the diameter times π.
$C = \pi(24.0)$

Step 2 Multiply the diameter by π.
$C = 75.4$ cm

The circumference is 75.4 cm.

Practice Problem Find the circumference of a circle with a radius of 19 cm.

Area of a Circle The formula for the area of a circle is:
$$A = \pi r^2$$

Example 1 Find the area of a circle with a radius of 4.0 cm.

Step 1 $A = \pi(4.0)^2$

Step 2 Find the square of the radius.
$A = 16\pi$

Step 3 Multiply the square of the radius by π.
$A = 50$ cm^2

The area of the circle is 50 cm^2.

Example 2 Find the area of a circle with a radius of 225 m.

Step 1 $A = \pi(225)^2$

Step 2 Find the square of the radius.
$A = 50625\pi$

Step 3 Multiply the square of the radius by π.
$A = 158962.5$

The area of the circle is 158,962 m^2.

Example 3 Find the area of a circle whose diameter is 20.0 mm.

Step 1 You know the formula for the area of a circle is the square of the radius times π, and that the radius is half of the diameter.
$A = \pi\left(\dfrac{20.0}{2}\right)^2$

Step 2 Find the radius.
$A = \pi(10.0)^2$

Step 3 Find the square of the radius.
$A = 100\pi$

Step 4 Multiply the square of the radius by π.
$A = 314$ mm^2

The area is 314 mm^2.

Practice Problem Find the area of a circle with a radius of 16 m.

$C = 2\pi r$
$C = 2\pi(19)$
$C = 38\pi$
$C = 119.3$

Area of a Circle

$A = \pi r^2$
$A = \pi(16 \text{ m})^2$
$A = \pi \, 256 \text{ m}^2$
$A = 803.8 \text{ m}^2$

Volume

Problem 1

$V = 8\,m \times 4\,m \times 4\,m$

$V = 128\,m^3$

Problem 2

$V = \pi r^2 \times \text{height}$

$V = \left[\pi\left(\frac{1}{2} \times 7\right)^2\right] \times 16$

$V = [\pi(3.5)^2] \times 16$

$V = [\pi(12.25)] \times 16$

$V = 38.46 \times 16$

$V = 615.36$

Volume The measure of space occupied by a solid is the **volume** (V). To find the volume of a rectangular solid multiply the length times width times height, or $V = l \times w \times h$. It is measured in cubic units, such as cubic centimeters (cm^3).

Example Find the volume of a rectangular solid with a length of 2.0 m, a width of 4.0 m, and a height of 3.0 m.

Step 1 You know the formula for volume is the length times the width times the height.

$V = 2.0\,m \times 4.0\,m \times 3.0\,m$

Step 2 Multiply the length times the width times the height.

$V = 24\,m^3$

The volume is 24 m³.

Practice Problem Find the volume of a rectangular solid that is 8 m long, 4 m wide, and 4 m high.

To find the volume of other solids, multiply the area of the base times the height.

Example 1 Find the volume of a solid that has a triangular base with a length of 8.0 m and a height of 7.0 m. The height of the entire solid is 15.0 m.

Step 1 You know that the base is a triangle, and the area of a triangle is $\frac{1}{2}$ the base times the height, and the volume is the area of the base times the height.

$V = \left[\frac{1}{2}(b \times h)\right] \times 15$

Step 2 Find the area of the base.

$V = \left[\frac{1}{2}(8 \times 7)\right] \times 15$

$V = \left(\frac{1}{2} \times 56\right) \times 15$

Step 3 Multiply the area of the base by the height of the solid.

$V = 28 \times 15$

$V = 420\,m^3$

The volume is 420 m³.

Example 2 Find the volume of a cylinder that has a base with a radius of 12.0 cm, and a height of 21.0 cm.

Step 1 You know that the base is a circle, and the area of a circle is the square of the radius times π, and the volume is the area of the base times the height.

$V = (\pi r^2) \times 21$

$V = (\pi 12^2) \times 21$

Step 2 Find the area of the base.

$V = 144\pi \times 21$

$V = 452 \times 21$

Step 3 Multiply the area of the base by the height of the solid.

$V = 9490\,cm^3$

The volume is 9490 cm³.

Example 3 Find the volume of a cylinder that has a diameter of 15 mm and a height of 4.8 mm.

Step 1 You know that the base is a circle with an area equal to the square of the radius times π. The radius is one-half the diameter. The volume is the area of the base times the height.

$V = (\pi r^2) \times 4.8$

$V = \left[\pi\left(\frac{1}{2} \times 15\right)^2\right] \times 4.8$

$V = (\pi 7.5^2) \times 4.8$

Step 2 Find the area of the base.

$V = 56.25\pi \times 4.8$

$V = 176.63 \times 4.8$

Step 3 Multiply the area of the base by the height of the solid.

$V = 847.8$

The volume is 847.8 mm³.

Practice Problem Find the volume of a cylinder with a diameter of 7 cm in the base and a height of 16 cm.

Science Applications

Measure in SI

The metric system of measurement was developed in 1795. A modern form of the metric system, called the International System (SI), was adopted in 1960 and provides the standard measurements that all scientists around the world can understand.

The SI system is convenient because unit sizes vary by powers of 10. Prefixes are used to name units. Look at **Table 3** for some common SI prefixes and their meanings.

Table 3 Some SI Prefixes			
Prefix	**Symbol**	**Meaning**	
kilo-	k	1,000	thousand
hecto-	h	100	hundred
deka-	da	10	ten
deci-	d	0.1	tenth
centi-	c	0.01	hundredth
milli-	m	0.001	thousandth

Example How many grams equal one kilogram?

Step 1 Find the prefix *kilo* in **Table 3.**

Step 2 Using **Table 3,** determine the meaning of *kilo*. According to the table, it means 1,000. When the prefix *kilo* is added to a unit, it means that there are 1,000 of the units in a "*kilo*unit."

Step 3 Apply the prefix to the units in the question. The units in the question are grams. There are 1,000 grams in a kilogram.

Practice Problem Is a milligram larger or smaller than a gram? How many of the smaller units equal one larger unit? What fraction of the larger unit does one smaller unit represent?

Dimensional Analysis

Convert SI Units In science, quantities such as length, mass, and time sometimes are measured using different units. A process called dimensional analysis can be used to change one unit of measure to another. This process involves multiplying your starting quantity and units by one or more conversion factors. A conversion factor is a ratio equal to one and can be made from any two equal quantities with different units. If 1,000 mL equal 1 L then two ratios can be made.

$$\frac{1,000 \text{ mL}}{1 \text{ L}} = \frac{1 \text{ L}}{1,000 \text{ mL}} = 1$$

One can covert between units in the SI system by using the equivalents in **Table 3** to make conversion factors.

Example 1 How many cm are in 4 m?

Step 1 Write conversion factors for the units given. From **Table 3,** you know that 100 cm = 1 m. The conversion factors are

$$\frac{100 \text{ cm}}{1 \text{ m}} \quad and \quad \frac{1 \text{ m}}{100 \text{ cm}}$$

Step 2 Decide which conversion factor to use. Select the factor that has the units you are converting from (m) in the denominator and the units you are converting to (cm) in the numerator.

$$\frac{100 \text{ cm}}{1 \text{ m}}$$

Step 3 Multiply the starting quantity and units by the conversion factor. Cancel the starting units with the units in the denominator. There are 400 cm in 4 m.

$$4 \text{ m} \times \frac{100 \text{ cm}}{1 \text{ m}} = 400 \text{ cm}$$

Practice Problem How many milligrams are in one kilogram? (Hint: You will need to use two conversion factors from **Table 3**.)

Measure in SI

smaller; 1000; one thousandth

Dimensional Analysis

$$x \text{ mg} = 1 \text{ kg} \times \frac{1000 \text{ g}}{1 \text{ kg}} \times \frac{1000 \text{ mg}}{1 \text{ g}} =$$
1,000,000 mg
1,000,000 mg = 1 kg

Convert Between Unit Systems

$$\frac{(1 \text{ in})^3}{(2.54 \text{ cm})^3}$$

$$= \frac{1 \text{ in} \times 1 \text{ in} \times 1 \text{ in}}{2.54 \text{ cm} \times 2.54 \text{ cm} \times 2.54 \text{ cm}}$$

$$= \frac{1 \text{ in}^3}{16.39 \text{ cm}^3}$$

Table 4 Unit System Equivalents

Type of Measurement	Equivalent
Length	1 in = 2.54 cm
	1 yd = 0.91 m
	1 mi = 1.61 km
Mass and Weight*	1 oz = 28.35 g
	1 lb = 0.45 kg
	1 ton (short) = 0.91 tonnes (metric tons)
	1 lb = 4.45 N
Volume	$1 \text{ in}^3 = 16.39 \text{ cm}^3$
	1 qt = 0.95 L
	1 gal = 3.78 L
Area	$1 \text{ in}^2 = 6.45 \text{ cm}^2$
	$1 \text{ yd}^2 = 0.83 \text{ m}^2$
	$1 \text{ mi}^2 = 2.59 \text{ km}^2$
	1 acre = 0.40 hectares
Temperature	$°C = \frac{(°F - 32)}{1.8}$
	K = °C + 273

*Weight is measured in standard Earth gravity.

Convert Between Unit Systems **Table 4** gives a list of equivalents that can be used to convert between English and SI units.

Example If a meterstick has a length of 100 cm, how long is the meterstick in inches?

Step 1 Write the conversion factors for the units given. From **Table 4,** 1 in = 2.54 cm.

$$\frac{1 \text{ in}}{2.54 \text{ cm}} \quad and \quad \frac{2.54 \text{ cm}}{1 \text{ in}}$$

Step 2 Determine which conversion factor to use. You are converting from cm to in. Use the conversion factor with cm on the bottom.

$$\frac{1 \text{ in}}{2.54 \text{ cm}}$$

Step 3 Multiply the starting quantity and units by the conversion factor. Cancel the starting units with the units in the denominator. Round your answer based on the number of significant figures in the conversion factor.

$$100 \text{ cm} \times \frac{1 \text{ in}}{2.54 \text{ cm}} = 39.37 \text{ in}$$

The meterstick is 39.4 in long.

Practice Problem A book has a mass of 5 lbs. What is the mass of the book in kg?

Practice Problem Use the equivalent for in and cm (1 in = 2.54 cm) to show how $1 \text{ in}^3 = 16.39 \text{ cm}^3$.

Precision and Significant Digits

When you make a measurement, the value you record depends on the precision of the measuring instrument. This precision is represented by the number of significant digits recorded in the measurement. When counting the number of significant digits, all digits are counted except zeros at the end of a number with no decimal point such as 2,050, and zeros at the beginning of a decimal such as 0.03020. When adding or subtracting numbers with different precision, round the answer to the smallest number of decimal places of any number in the sum or difference. When multiplying or dividing, the answer is rounded to the smallest number of significant digits of any number being multiplied or divided.

Example The lengths 5.28 and 5.2 are measured in meters. Find the sum of these lengths and record your answer using the correct number of significant digits.

Step 1 Find the sum.

5.28 m	2 digits after the decimal
+ 5.2 m	1 digit after the decimal
10.48 m	

Step 2 Round to one digit after the decimal because the least number of digits after the decimal of the numbers being added is 1.

The sum is 10.5 m.

Practice Problem How many significant digits are in the measurement 7,071,301 m? How many significant digits are in the measurement 0.003010 g?

Practice Problem Multiply 5.28 and 5.2 using the rule for multiplying and dividing. Record the answer using the correct number of significant digits.

Scientific Notation

Many times numbers used in science are very small or very large. Because these numbers are difficult to work with scientists use scientific notation. To write numbers in scientific notation, move the decimal point until only one non-zero digit remains on the left. Then count the number of places you moved the decimal point and use that number as a power of ten. For example, the average distance from the Sun to Mars is 227,800,000,000 m. In scientific notation, this distance is 2.278×10^{11} m. Because you moved the decimal point to the left, the number is a positive power of ten.

The mass of an electron is about 0.000 000 000 000 000 000 000 000 000 000 911 kg. Expressed in scientific notation, this mass is 9.11×10^{-31} kg. Because the decimal point was moved to the right, the number is a negative power of ten.

Example Earth is 149,600,000 km from the Sun. Express this in scientific notation.

Step 1 Move the decimal point until one non-zero digit remains on the left.
1.496 000 00

Step 2 Count the number of decimal places you have moved. In this case, eight.

Step 3 Show that number as a power of ten, 10^8.

The Earth is 1.496×10^8 km from the Sun.

Practice Problem How many significant digits are in 149,600,000 km? How many significant digits are in 1.496×10^8 km?

Practice Problem Parts used in a high performance car must be measured to 7×10^{-6} m. Express this number as a decimal.

Practice Problem A CD is spinning at 539 revolutions per minute. Express this number in scientific notation.

Precision and Significant Digits

Problem 1
7; 4

Problem 2
$5.28 \times 5.2 = 27.456$

5.28 has 3 significant digits.

5.2 has 2 significant digits.

When multiplying and dividing, the answer is rounded to the smallest number of significant digits of the numbers being multiplied or divided—in this case, 2.

27.456 is rounded to 27.

Scientific Notation

Problem 1
4; 4

Problem 2
0.000007

Problem 3
5.39×10^2

Line Graph

x	y
3	52
6	72
9	83
12	86

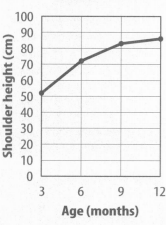

Puppy Growth

Make and Use Graphs

Data in tables can be displayed in a graph—a visual representation of data. Common graph types include line graphs, bar graphs, and circle graphs.

Line Graph A line graph shows a relationship between two variables that change continuously. The independent variable is changed and is plotted on the *x*-axis. The dependent variable is observed, and is plotted on the *y*-axis.

Example Draw a line graph of the data below from a cyclist in a long-distance race.

Table 5 Bicycle Race Data	
Time (h)	**Distance (km)**
0	0
1	8
2	16
3	24
4	32
5	40

Step 1 Determine the *x*-axis and *y*-axis variables. Time varies independently of distance and is plotted on the *x*-axis. Distance is dependent on time and is plotted on the *y*-axis.

Step 2 Determine the scale of each axis. The *x*-axis data ranges from 0 to 5. The *y*-axis data ranges from 0 to 40.

Step 3 Using graph paper, draw and label the axes. Include units in the labels.

Step 4 Draw a point at the intersection of the time value on the *x*-axis and corresponding distance value on the *y*-axis. Connect the points and label the graph with a title, as shown in **Figure 20.**

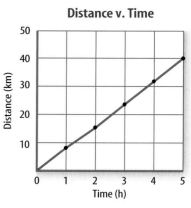

Distance v. Time

Figure 20 This line graph shows the relationship between distance and time during a bicycle ride.

Practice Problem A puppy's shoulder height is measured during the first year of her life. The following measurements were collected: (3 mo, 52 cm), (6 mo, 72 cm), (9 mo, 83 cm), (12 mo, 86 cm). Graph this data.

Find a Slope The slope of a straight line is the ratio of the vertical change, rise, to the horizontal change, run.

$$\text{Slope} = \frac{\text{vertical change (rise)}}{\text{horizontal change (run)}} = \frac{\text{change in } y}{\text{change in } x}$$

Example Find the slope of the graph in **Figure 20.**

Step 1 You know that the slope is the change in *y* divided by the change in *x*.

$$\text{Slope} = \frac{\text{change in } y}{\text{change in } x}$$

Step 2 Determine the data points you will be using. For a straight line, choose the two sets of points that are the farthest apart.

$$\text{Slope} = \frac{(40-0) \text{ km}}{(5-0) \text{ hr}}$$

Step 3 Find the change in *y* and *x*.

$$\text{Slope} = \frac{40 \text{ km}}{5 \text{ h}}$$

Step 4 Divide the change in *y* by the change in *x*.

$$\text{Slope} = \frac{8 \text{ km}}{\text{h}}$$

The slope of the graph is 8 km/h.

Math Skill Handbook

Bar Graph To compare data that does not change continuously you might choose a bar graph. A bar graph uses bars to show the relationships between variables. The *x*-axis variable is divided into parts. The parts can be numbers such as years, or a category such as a type of animal. The *y*-axis is a number and increases continuously along the axis.

Example A recycling center collects 4.0 kg of aluminum on Monday, 1.0 kg on Wednesday, and 2.0 kg on Friday. Create a bar graph of this data.

Step 1 Select the *x*-axis and *y*-axis variables. The measured numbers (the masses of aluminum) should be placed on the *y*-axis. The variable divided into parts (collection days) is placed on the *x*-axis.

Step 2 Create a graph grid like you would for a line graph. Include labels and units.

Step 3 For each measured number, draw a vertical bar above the *x*-axis value up to the *y*-axis value. For the first data point, draw a vertical bar above Monday up to 4.0 kg.

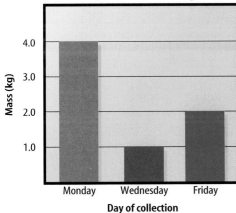

Aluminum Collected During Week

Practice Problem Draw a bar graph of the gases in air: 78% nitrogen, 21% oxygen, 1% other gases.

Circle Graph To display data as parts of a whole, you might use a circle graph. A circle graph is a circle divided into sections that represent the relative size of each piece of data. The entire circle represents 100%, half represents 50%, and so on.

Example Air is made up of 78% nitrogen, 21% oxygen, and 1% other gases. Display the composition of air in a circle graph.

Step 1 Multiply each percent by 360° and divide by 100 to find the angle of each section in the circle.

$$78\% \times \frac{360°}{100} = 280.8°$$
$$21\% \times \frac{360°}{100} = 75.6°$$
$$1\% \times \frac{360°}{100} = 3.6°$$

Step 2 Use a compass to draw a circle and to mark the center of the circle. Draw a straight line from the center to the edge of the circle.

Step 3 Use a protractor and the angles you calculated to divide the circle into parts. Place the center of the protractor over the center of the circle and line the base of the protractor over the straight line.

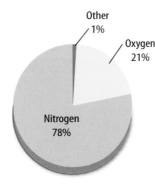

Practice Problem Draw a circle graph to represent the amount of aluminum collected during the week shown in the bar graph to the left.

Bar Graph

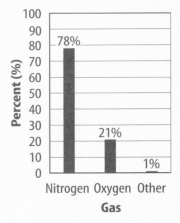

Composition of Air

Circle Graph

The total amount of aluminum collected is:

4.0 kg + 1.0 kg + 2.0 kg = 7.0 kg

$$\frac{4.0\ kg}{7.0\ kg} = \frac{x}{360°}; \ x = 206°$$
$$\frac{1.0\ kg}{7.0\ kg} = \frac{x}{360°}; \ x = 51°$$
$$\frac{2.0\ kg}{7.0\ kg} = \frac{x}{360°}; \ x = 103°$$

Math Skill Handbook

PERIODIC TABLE OF THE ELEMENTS

Columns of elements are called groups. Elements in the same group have similar chemical properties.

Element — Hydrogen
Atomic number — 1
Symbol — H
Atomic mass — 1.008

State of matter

Gas
Liquid
Solid
Synthetic

The first three symbols tell you the state of matter of the element at room temperature. The fourth symbol identifies elements that are not present in significant amounts on Earth. Useful amounts are made synthetically.

	1		2
1	Hydrogen 1 **H** 1.008		
2	Lithium 3 **Li** 6.941		Beryllium 4 **Be** 9.012
3	Sodium 11 **Na** 22.990		Magnesium 12 **Mg** 24.305

	3	4	5	6	7	8	9
4	Scandium 21 **Sc** 44.956	Titanium 22 **Ti** 47.867	Vanadium 23 **V** 50.942	Chromium 24 **Cr** 51.996	Manganese 25 **Mn** 54.938	Iron 26 **Fe** 55.845	Cobalt 27 **Co** 58.933
5	Yttrium 39 **Y** 88.906	Zirconium 40 **Zr** 91.224	Niobium 41 **Nb** 92.906	Molybdenum 42 **Mo** 95.94	Technetium 43 **Tc** (98)	Ruthenium 44 **Ru** 101.07	Rhodium 45 **Rh** 102.906
6	Lanthanum 57 **La** 138.906	Hafnium 72 **Hf** 178.49	Tantalum 73 **Ta** 180.948	Tungsten 74 **W** 183.84	Rhenium 75 **Re** 186.207	Osmium 76 **Os** 190.23	Iridium 77 **Ir** 192.217
7	Actinium 89 **Ac** (227)	Rutherfordium 104 **Rf** (261)	Dubnium 105 **Db** (262)	Seaborgium 106 **Sg** (266)	Bohrium 107 **Bh** (264)	Hassium 108 **Hs** (277)	Meitnerium 109 **Mt** (268)

*(Row 4 also: Potassium 19 **K** 39.098, Calcium 20 **Ca** 40.078; Row 5: Rubidium 37 **Rb** 85.468, Strontium 38 **Sr** 87.62; Row 6: Cesium 55 **Cs** 132.905, Barium 56 **Ba** 137.327; Row 7: Francium 87 **Fr** (223), Radium 88 **Ra** (226))*

The number in parentheses is the mass number of the longest-lived isotope for that element.

Rows of elements are called periods. Atomic number increases across a period.

The arrow shows where these elements would fit into the periodic table. They are moved to the bottom of the table to save space.

Lanthanide series	Cerium 58 **Ce** 140.116	Praseodymium 59 **Pr** 140.908	Neodymium 60 **Nd** 144.24	Promethium 61 **Pm** (145)	Samarium 62 **Sm** 150.36
Actinide series	Thorium 90 **Th** 232.038	Protactinium 91 **Pa** 231.036	Uranium 92 **U** 238.029	Neptunium 93 **Np** (237)	Plutonium 94 **Pu** (244)

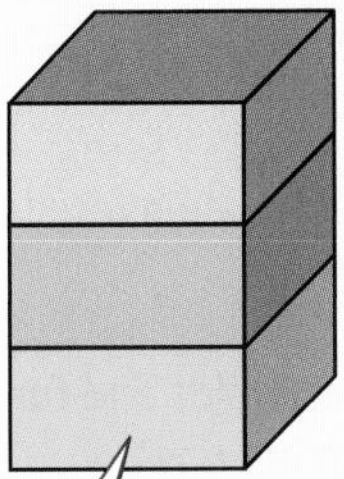

Metal

Metalloid

Nonmetal

The color of an element's block tells you if the element is a metal, nonmetal, or metalloid.

Scienceonline

Visit bookc.msscience.com for updates to the periodic table.

			13	14	15	16	17	18
								Helium 2 He 4.003
			Boron 5 B 10.811	Carbon 6 C 12.011	Nitrogen 7 N 14.007	Oxygen 8 O 15.999	Fluorine 9 F 18.998	Neon 10 Ne 20.180
10	11	12	Aluminum 13 Al 26.982	Silicon 14 Si 28.086	Phosphorus 15 P 30.974	Sulfur 16 S 32.065	Chlorine 17 Cl 35.453	Argon 18 Ar 39.948
Nickel 28 Ni 58.693	Copper 29 Cu 63.546	Zinc 30 Zn 65.409	Gallium 31 Ga 69.723	Germanium 32 Ge 72.64	Arsenic 33 As 74.922	Selenium 34 Se 78.96	Bromine 35 Br 79.904	Krypton 36 Kr 83.798
Palladium 46 Pd 106.42	Silver 47 Ag 107.868	Cadmium 48 Cd 112.411	Indium 49 In 114.818	Tin 50 Sn 118.710	Antimony 51 Sb 121.760	Tellurium 52 Te 127.60	Iodine 53 I 126.904	Xenon 54 Xe 131.293
Platinum 78 Pt 195.078	Gold 79 Au 196.967	Mercury 80 Hg 200.59	Thallium 81 Tl 204.383	Lead 82 Pb 207.2	Bismuth 83 Bi 208.980	Polonium 84 Po (209)	Astatine 85 At (210)	Radon 86 Rn (222)
Darmstadtium 110 Ds (281)	Roentgenium 111 Rg (272)	Ununbium * 112 Uub (285)		Ununquadium * 114 Uuq (289)				

∗ The names and symbols for elements 112 and 114 are temporary. Final names will be selected when the elements' discoveries are verified.

Europium 63 Eu 151.964	Gadolinium 64 Gd 157.25	Terbium 65 Tb 158.925	Dysprosium 66 Dy 162.500	Holmium 67 Ho 164.930	Erbium 68 Er 167.259	Thulium 69 Tm 168.934	Ytterbium 70 Yb 173.04	Lutetium 71 Lu 174.967
Americium 95 Am (243)	Curium 96 Cm (247)	Berkelium 97 Bk (247)	Californium 98 Cf (251)	Einsteinium 99 Es (252)	Fermium 100 Fm (257)	Mendelevium 101 Md (258)	Nobelium 102 No (259)	Lawrencium 103 Lr (262)

Use and Care of a Microscope

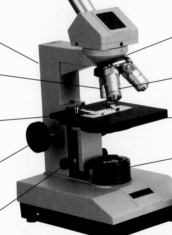

Eyepiece Contains magnifying lenses you look through.

Arm Supports the body tube.

Low-power objective Contains the lens with the lowest power magnification.

Stage clips Hold the microscope slide in place.

Coarse adjustment Focuses the image under low power.

Fine adjustment Sharpens the image under high magnification.

Body tube Connects the eyepiece to the revolving nosepiece.

Revolving nosepiece Holds and turns the objectives into viewing position.

High-power objective Contains the lens with the highest magnification.

Stage Supports the microscope slide.

Light source Provides light that passes upward through the diaphragm, the specimen, and the lenses.

Base Provides support for the microscope.

Caring for a Microscope

1. Always carry the microscope holding the arm with one hand and supporting the base with the other hand.

2. Don't touch the lenses with your fingers.

3. The coarse adjustment knob is used only when looking through the lowest-power objective lens. The fine adjustment knob is used when the high-power objective is in place.

4. Cover the microscope when you store it.

Using a Microscope

1. Place the microscope on a flat surface that is clear of objects. The arm should be toward you.

2. Look through the eyepiece. Adjust the diaphragm so light comes through the opening in the stage.

3. Place a slide on the stage so the specimen is in the field of view. Hold it firmly in place by using the stage clips.

4. Always focus with the coarse adjustment and the low-power objective lens first. After the object is in focus on low power, turn the nosepiece until the high-power objective is in place. Use ONLY the fine adjustment to focus with the high-power objective lens.

Making a Wet-Mount Slide

1. Carefully place the item you want to look at in the center of a clean, glass slide. Make sure the sample is thin enough for light to pass through.

2. Use a dropper to place one or two drops of water on the sample.

3. Hold a clean coverslip by the edges and place it at one edge of the water. Slowly lower the coverslip onto the water until it lies flat.

4. If you have too much water or a lot of air bubbles, touch the edge of a paper towel to the edge of the coverslip to draw off extra water and draw out unwanted air.

Diversity of Life: Classification of Living Organisms

A six-kingdom system of classification of organisms is used today. Two kingdoms—Kingdom Archaebacteria and Kingdom Eubacteria—contain organisms that do not have a nucleus and that lack membrane-bound structures in the cytoplasm of their cells. The members of the other four kingdoms have a cell or cells that contain a nucleus and structures in the cytoplasm, some of which are surrounded by membranes. These kingdoms are Kingdom Protista, Kingdom Fungi, Kingdom Plantae, and Kingdom Animalia.

Kingdom Archaebacteria

one-celled; some absorb food from their surroundings; some are photosynthetic; some are chemosynthetic; many are found in extremely harsh environments including salt ponds, hot springs, swamps, and deep-sea hydrothermal vents

Kingdom Eubacteria

one-celled; most absorb food from their surroundings; some are photosynthetic; some are chemosynthetic; many are parasites; many are round, spiral, or rod-shaped; some form colonies

Kingdom Protista

Phylum Euglenophyta one-celled; photosynthetic or take in food; most have one flagellum; euglenoids

Phylum Bacillariophyta one-celled; photosynthetic; have unique double shells made of silica; diatoms

Phylum Dinoflagellata one-celled; photosynthetic; contain red pigments; have two flagella; dinoflagellates

Phylum Chlorophyta one-celled, many-celled, or colonies; photosynthetic; contain chlorophyll; live on land, in freshwater, or salt water; green algae

Phylum Rhodophyta most are many-celled; photosynthetic; contain red pigments; most live in deep, saltwater environments; red algae

Phylum Phaeophyta most are many-celled; photosynthetic; contain brown pigments; most live in saltwater environments; brown algae

Phylum Rhizopoda one-celled; take in food; are free-living or parasitic; move by means of pseudopods; amoebas

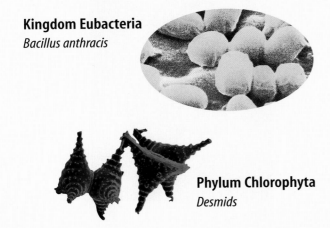

Kingdom Eubacteria
Bacillus anthracis

Phylum Chlorophyta
Desmids

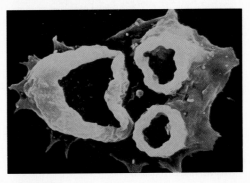

Amoeba

Phylum Zoomastigina one-celled; take in food; free-living or parasitic; have one or more flagella; zoomastigotes

Phylum Ciliophora one-celled; take in food; have large numbers of cilia; ciliates

Phylum Sporozoa one-celled; take in food; have no means of movement; are parasites in animals; sporozoans

Phylum Myxomycota
Slime mold

Phylum Oomycota
Phytophthora infestans

Phyla Myxomycota and Acrasiomycota one- or many-celled; absorb food; change form during life cycle; cellular and plasmodial slime molds

Phylum Oomycota many-celled; are either parasites or decomposers; live in freshwater or salt water; water molds, rusts and downy mildews

Kingdom Fungi

Phylum Zygomycota many-celled; absorb food; spores are produced in sporangia; zygote fungi; bread mold

Phylum Ascomycota one- and many-celled; absorb food; spores produced in asci; sac fungi; yeast

Phylum Basidiomycota many-celled; absorb food; spores produced in basidia; club fungi; mushrooms

Phylum Deuteromycota members with unknown reproductive structures; imperfect fungi; *Penicillium*

Phylum Mycophycota organisms formed by symbiotic relationship between an ascomycote or a basidiomycote and green alga or cyanobacterium; lichens

Lichens

Kingdom Plantae

Divisions Bryophyta (mosses), **Anthocerophyta** (hornworts), **Hepaticophyta** (liverworts), **Psilophyta** (whisk ferns) many-celled nonvascular plants; reproduce by spores produced in capsules; green; grow in moist, land environments

Division Lycophyta many-celled vascular plants; spores are produced in conelike structures; live on land; are photosynthetic; club mosses

Division Arthrophyta vascular plants; ribbed and jointed stems; scalelike leaves; spores produced in conelike structures; horsetails

Division Pterophyta vascular plants; leaves called fronds; spores produced in clusters of sporangia called sori; live on land or in water; ferns

Division Ginkgophyta deciduous trees; only one living species; have fan-shaped leaves with branching veins and fleshy cones with seeds; ginkgoes

Division Cycadophyta palmlike plants; have large, featherlike leaves; produces seeds in cones; cycads

Division Coniferophyta deciduous or evergreen; trees or shrubs; have needlelike or scalelike leaves; seeds produced in cones; conifers

Division Anthophyta
Tomato plant

Division Gnetophyta shrubs or woody vines; seeds are produced in cones; division contains only three genera; gnetum

Division Anthophyta dominant group of plants; flowering plants; have fruits with seeds

Kingdom Animalia

Phylum Porifera aquatic organisms that lack true tissues and organs; are asymmetrical and sessile; sponges

Phylum Cnidaria radially symmetrical organisms; have a digestive cavity with one opening; most have tentacles armed with stinging cells; live in aquatic environments singly or in colonies; includes jellyfish, corals, hydra, and sea anemones

Phylum Platyhelminthes bilaterally symmetrical worms; have flattened bodies; digestive system has one opening; parasitic and free-living species; flatworms

Division Bryophyta
Liverwort

Phylum Platyhelminthes
Flatworm

Phylum Chordata

Phylum Nematoda round, bilaterally symmetrical body; have digestive system with two openings; free-living forms and parasitic forms; roundworms

Phylum Mollusca soft-bodied animals, many with a hard shell and soft foot or footlike appendage; a mantle covers the soft body; aquatic and terrestrial species; includes clams, snails, squid, and octopuses

Phylum Annelida bilaterally symmetrical worms; have round, segmented bodies; terrestrial and aquatic species; includes earthworms, leeches, and marine polychaetes

Phylum Arthropoda largest animal group; have hard exoskeletons, segmented bodies, and pairs of jointed appendages; land and aquatic species; includes insects, crustaceans, and spiders

Phylum Echinodermata marine organisms; have spiny or leathery skin and a water-vascular system with tube feet; are radially symmetrical; includes sea stars, sand dollars, and sea urchins

Phylum Chordata organisms with internal skeletons and specialized body systems; most have paired appendages; all at some time have a notochord, nerve cord, gill slits, and a post-anal tail; include fish, amphibians, reptiles, birds, and mammals

Glossary/Glosario

Cómo usar el glosario en español:
1. Busca el término en inglés que desees encontrar.
2. El término en español, junto con la definición, se encuentran en la columna de la derecha.

Pronunciation Key

Use the following key to help you sound out words in the glossary.

a	back (BAK)	ew	food (FEWD)
ay	day (DAY)	yoo	pure (PYOOR)
ah	father (FAH thur)	yew	few (FYEW)
ow	flower (FLOW ur)	uh	comma (CAH muh)
ar	car (CAR)	u (+ con)	rub (RUB)
e	less (LES)	sh	shelf (SHELF)
ee	leaf (LEEF)	ch	nature (NAY chur)
ih	trip (TRIHP)	g	gift (GIHFT)
i (i + con + e)	idea (i DEE uh)	j	gem (JEM)
oh	go (GOH)	ing	sing (SING)
aw	soft (SAWFT)	zh	vision (VIH zhun)
or	orbit (OR buht)	k	cake (KAYK)
oy	coin (COYN)	s	seed, cent (SEED, SENT)
oo	foot (FOOT)	z	zone, raise (ZOHN, RAYZ)

English **A** **Español**

aggression: forceful behavior, such as fighting, used by an animal to control or dominate another animal in order to protect their young, defend territory, or get food. (p. 142)

amniotic egg: egg covered with a shell that provides a complete environment for the embryo's development; for reptiles, a major adaptation for living on land. (p. 91)

anus: opening at the end of the digestive tract through which wastes leave the body. (p. 25)

appendages: jointed structures of arthropods, such as legs, wings, or antennae. (p. 48)

agresión: comportamiento violento, como la lucha, manifestado por un animal para controlar o dominar a otro animal con el fin de proteger a sus crías, defender su territorio o conseguir alimento. (p. 142)

huevo amniótico: huevo cubierto por un cascarón coriáceo que proporciona un ambiente completo para el desarrollo del embrión; para los reptiles, una gran adaptación para vivir en la tierra. (p. 91)

ano: apertura al final del tracto digestivo a través de la cual los desechos salen del cuerpo. (p. 25)

apéndices: estructuras articuladas de los artrópodos, como las patas, alas o antenas. (p. 48)

B

behavior: the way in which an organism interacts with other organisms and its environment; can be innate or learned. (p. 134)

bilateral symmetry: body parts arranged in a similar way on both sides of the body, with each half being nearly a mirror image of the other half. (p. 13)

comportamiento: forma en la que un organismo interactúa con otros organismos y su entorno; puede ser innato o aprendido. (p. 134)

simetría bilateral: disposición de las partes del cuerpo de manera similar a ambos lados de éste, de tal forma que cada mitad es una imagen especular de la otra. (p. 13)

C

carnivore: animal that eats only other animals or the remains of other animals; mammal having large, sharp canine teeth and strong jaw muscles for eating flesh. (pp. 9, 115)

cartilage: tough, flexible tissue that joins vertebrae and makes up all or part of the vertebrate endoskeleton. (p. 73)

chordate: animal that has a notochord, a nerve cord, pharyngeal pouches, and a postanal tail present at some stage in its development. (p. 72)

closed circulatory system: blood circulation system in which blood moves through the body in closed vessels. (p. 40)

conditioning: occurs when the response to a stimulus becomes associated with another stimulus. (p. 138)

contour feathers: strong, lightweight feathers that give birds their coloring and shape and that are used for flight. (p. 108)

courtship behavior: behavior that allows males and females of the same species to recognize each other and prepare to mate. (p. 143)

crop: digestive system sac in which earthworms store ingested soil. (p. 44)

cyclic behavior: behavior that occurs in repeated patterns. (p. 146)

carnívoro: animal que se alimenta exclusivamente de otros animales o de los restos de otros animales; mamífero con caninos largos y afilados y músculos fuertes en la mandíbula que le sirven para alimentarse de carne. (pp. 9, 115)

cartílago: tejido resistente y flexible que conecta a las vértebras y constituye todo o parte del endoesqueleto de los vertebrados. (p. 73)

cordado: animal que posee notocordio, un cordón nervioso, bolsas faríngeas y que presenta cola postnatal en alguna etapa de su desarrollo. (p. 72)

sistema circulatorio cerrado: sistema circulatorio sanguíneo en el cual la sangre se mueve a través del cuerpo en vasos cerrados. (p. 40)

condicionamiento: ocurre cuando la respuesta a un estímulo llega a estar asociada con otro estímulo. (p. 138)

plumas de contorno: plumas fuertes y ligeras que dan a las aves su colorido y forma y que son usadas para volar. (p. 108)

comportamiento de cortejo: comportamiento que permite que los machos y hembras de la misma especie se reconozcan entre sí y se preparen para el apareamiento. (p. 143)

buche: saco del sistema digestivo en el que los gusanos de tierra almacenan el suelo ingerido. (p. 44)

comportamiento cíclico: comportamiento que ocurre en patrones repetidos. (p. 146)

D

down feathers: soft, fluffy feathers that provide an insulating layer next to the skin of adult birds and that cover the bodies of young birds. (p. 108)

plumón: plumas suaves y esponjadas que proporcionan una capa aislante junto a la piel de las aves adultas y que cubren los cuerpos de las aves jóvenes. (p. 108)

E

ectotherm: vertebrate animal whose internal temperature changes when the temperature of its environment changes. (p. 75)

endoskeleton: supportive framework of bone and/or cartilage that provides an internal place for muscle attachment and protects a vertebrate's internal organs. (p. 73)

ectotérmico: animal vertebrado cuya temperatura interna cambia cuando cambia la temperatura de su ambiente. (p. 75)

endoesqueleto: estructura ósea y/o cartilaginosa de soporte que proporciona un medio interno para la fijación de los músculos y que protege a los órganos internos de los vertebrados. (p. 73)

endotherm: vertebrate animal with a nearly constant internal temperature. (pp. 75, 108)

estivation: inactivity in hot, dry months. (p. 85)

exoskeleton: thick, hard, outer covering that protects and supports arthropod bodies and provides places for muscles to attach. (p. 48)

endotérmico: animal vertebrado con una temperatura interna casi constante. (pp. 75, 108)

estivación: inactividad durante los meses cálidos y secos. (p. 85)

exoesqueleto: cubierta externa, dura y gruesa que protege y soporta el cuerpo de los artrópodos y proporciona lugares para que los músculos se fijen. (p. 48)

F

fin: structure used by fish for steering, balancing, and movement. (p. 77)

free-living organism: organism that does not depend on another organism for food or a place to live. (p. 22)

aleta: estructura parecida a un abanico usada por los peces para mantener la dirección, equilibrio y movimiento. (p. 77)

organismo de vida libre: organismo que no depende de otro para alimentarse o para tener un lugar en donde vivir. (p. 22)

G

gestation period: period during which an embryo develops in the uterus; the length of time varies among species. (p. 119)

gills: organs that exchange carbon dioxide for oxygen in the water. (p. 38)

gizzard: muscular digestive system structure in which earthworms grind soil and organic matter. (p. 44)

periodo de gestación: periodo durante el cual un embrión se desarrolla en el útero; este periodo varía de una especie a otra. (p. 119)

agallas: órganos que intercambian dióxido de carbono y oxígeno en el agua. (p. 38)

molleja: estructura muscular del sistema digestivo en la que los gusanos de tierra muelen el suelo y materia orgánica. (p. 44)

H

herbivore: animal that eats only plants or parts of plants; mammals with large premolars and molars for eating only plants. (pp. 9, 115)

hermaphrodite (hur MA fruh dite): animal that produces both sperm and eggs in the same body. (p. 16)

hibernation: cyclic response of inactivity and slowed metabolism that occurs during periods of cold temperatures and limited food supplies. (pp. 85, 147)

herbívoro: animal que se alimenta exclusivamente de plantas o de partes de las plantas; mamífero con premolares y molares grandes que se alimenta exclusivamente de plantas. (pp. 9, 115)

hermafrodita: animal que produce óvulos y espermatozoides en el mismo cuerpo. (p. 16)

hibernación: respuesta cíclica de inactividad y disminución del metabolismo que ocurre durante periodos de bajas temperaturas y suministro limitado de alimento. (pp. 85, 147)

I

imprinting: occurs when an animal forms a social attachment to another organism during a specific period following birth or hatching. (p. 137)

impronta: ocurre cuando un animal forma un vínculo social con otro organismo durante un periodo específico después del nacimiento o eclosión. (p. 137)

innate behavior: behavior that an organism is born with and does not have to be learned, such as a reflex or instinct. (p. 135)

insight: form of reasoning that allows animals to use past experiences to solve new problems. (p. 139)

instinct: complex pattern of innate behavior, such as spinning a web, that can take weeks to complete. (p. 136)

invertebrate: animal without a backbone. (p. 12)

comportamiento innato: comportamiento con el que nace un organismo y que no necesita ser aprendido, tal como los reflejos o los instintos. (p. 135)

comprensión: forma de razonamiento que permite a los animales usar experiencias pasadas para solucionar problemas nuevos. (p. 139)

instinto: patrón complejo de comportamiento innato, como tejer una telaraña, que puede durar semanas para completarse. (p. 136)

invertebrado: animal que no posee columna vertebral. (p. 12)

M

mammals: endothermic vertebrates that have hair, teeth specialized for eating certain foods, and mammary glands; in females, mammary glands produce milk for feeding their young. (p. 114)

mammary glands: milk-producing glands of female mammals used to feed their young. (p. 114)

mantle: thin layer of tissue that covers a mollusk's body organs; secretes the shell or protects the body of mollusks without shells. (p. 38)

marsupial: a mammal with an external pouch for the development of its immature young. (p. 118)

medusa (mih DEW suh): cnidarian body type that is bell-shaped and free-swimming. (p. 17)

metamorphosis: process in which many insect species change their body form to become adults; can be complete (egg, larva, pupa, adult) or incomplete (egg, nymph, adult). (p. 50)

migration: instinctive seasonal movement of animals to find food or to reproduce in better conditions. (p. 148)

molting: shedding and replacing of an arthropod's exoskeleton. (p. 48)

monotreme: a mammal that lays eggs with tough, leathery shells and whose mammary glands do not have nipples. (p. 118)

mamíferos: vertebrados endotérmicos que poseen pelo y dientes especializados para comer cierto tipo de alimentos y cuyas hembras tienen glándulas mamarias que producen leche para alimentar a sus crías. (p. 114)

glándulas mamarias: glándulas productoras de leche que las hembras de los mamíferos usan para alimentar a sus crías. (p. 114)

manto: capa delgada de tejido que recubre los órganos corporales de los moluscos; secreta el caparazón o protege el cuerpo de los moluscos sin caparazón. (p. 38)

marsupial: mamífero con una bolsa externa para el desarrollo de sus crías inmaduras. (p. 118)

medusa: tipo corporal de los cnidarios con forma de campana y nado libre. (p. 17)

metamorfosis: proceso a través del cual muchas especies de insectos cambian su forma corporal para convertirse en adultos; puede ser completa (huevo, larva, pupa, adulto) o incompleta (huevo, ninfa, adulto). (p. 50)

migración: movimiento estacional instintivo de los animales para encontrar alimento o para reproducirse en mejores condiciones. (p. 148)

muda: muda y reemplazo del exoesqueleto de un artrópodo. (p. 48)

monotrema: mamífero que pone huevos con cascarón coriáceo y resistente y cuyas glándulas mamarias carecen de pezones. (p. 118)

N

nerve cord: tubelike structure above the notochord that in most chordates develops into the brain and spinal cord. (p. 73)

cordón nervioso: estructura en forma de tubo sobre el notocordio que en la mayoría de los cordados se desarrolla en el cerebro y en la médula espinal. (p. 73)

notochord: firm but flexible structure that extends along the upper part of a chordate's body. (p. 72)

notocordio: estructura firme pero flexible que se extiende a lo largo de la parte superior del cuerpo de un cordado. (p. 72)

O

omnivore: animal that eats plants and animals or animal flesh; mammals with incisors, canine teeth, and flat molars for eating plants and other animals. (pp. 9, 115)

open circulatory system: blood circulation system in which blood moves through vessels and into open spaces around the body organs. (p. 38)

omnívoro: animal que se alimenta de plantas y animales; mamífero con incisivos, caninos y molares planos que se alimenta de plantas y otros animales. (pp. 9, 115)

sistema circulatorio abierto: sistema circulatorio sanguíneo en el que la sangre se mueve a través de vasos y entra en espacios abiertos alrededor de los órganos corporales. (p. 38)

P

pharyngeal pouches: in developing chordates, the paired openings found in the area between the mouth and digestive tube. (p. 73)

pheromone (FER uh mohn): powerful chemical produced by an animal to influence the behavior of another animal of the same species. (p. 143)

placenta: an organ that develops from tissue of the embryo and tissues that line the inside of the uterus and that absorbs oxygen and food from the mother's blood. (p. 119)

placental: a mammal whose offspring develop inside the female's uterus. (p. 119)

polyp (PAH lup): cnidarian body type that is vaseshaped and is usually sessile. (p. 17)

postanal tail: muscular structure at the end of a developing chordate. (p. 72)

preening: process in which a bird rubs oil from an oil gland over its feathers to condition them. (p. 108)

bolsas faríngeas: en los cordados en desarrollo, las aperturas pareadas que se encuentran en el área entre la boca y el tubo digestivo. (p. 73)

feromona: químico potente producido por un animal para influir en el comportamiento de otro animal de la misma especie. (p. 143)

placenta: órgano que se desarrolla a partir de tejido embrionario y de los tejidos que cubren la pared interna del útero y que absorbe oxígeno y alimentos de la sangre de la madre. (p. 119)

placentario: mamífero cuyas crías se desarrollan en el útero de la hembra. (p. 119)

pólipo: tipo corporal de los cnidarios con forma de jarro y usualmente sésil. (p. 17)

cola postnatal: estructura muscular en el extremo de un cordado en desarrollo. (p. 72)

acicalamiento: proceso mediante el cual las aves acondicionan sus alas frotándoles grasa producida por una glándula sebácea. (p. 108)

R

radial symmetry: body parts arranged in a circle around a central point. (p. 13)

radula (RA juh luh): in gastropods, the tonguelike organ with rows of teeth used to scrape and tear food. (p. 39)

simetría radial: disposición de las partes del cuerpo circularmente alrededor de un punto central. (p. 13)

rádula: órgano de los gasterópodos en forma de lengua con filas de dientecillos usado para raspar y desgarrar alimentos. (p. 39)

Glossary/Glosario

reflex: simple innate behavior, such as yawning or blinking, that is an automatic response and does not involve a message to the brain. (p. 135)

reflejo: comportamiento innato simple, como bostezar o parpadear, que constituye una respuesta automática y no requiere el envío de un mensaje al cerebro. (p. 135)

scales: thin, hard plates that cover a fish's skin and protect its body. (p. 77)

sessile (SE sile): describes an organism that remains attached to one place during most its lifetime. (p. 15)

setae (SEE tee): bristlelike structures on the outside of each body segment that helps segmented worms move. (p. 43)

social behavior: interactions among members of the same species, including courtship and mating, getting food, caring for young, and protecting each other. (p. 140)

society: a group of animals of the same species that live and work together in an organized way, with each member doing a specific job. (p. 141)

spiracles (SPIHR ih kulz): openings in the abdomen and thorax of insects through which air enters and waste gases leave. (p. 49)

stinging cells: capsules with coiled triggerlike structures that help cnidarians capture food. (p. 18)

escamas: placas duras y delgadas que cubren la piel de los peces y protegen su cuerpo. (p. 77)

sésil: organismo que permanece adherido a un lugar durante la mayor parte de su vida. (p. 15)

cerdas: estructuras en forma de cilios presentes en la parte externa de cada segmento corporal y que ayudan a los gusanos segmentados a moverse. (p. 43)

comportamiento social: interacciones entre los miembros de la misma especie, incluyendo el cortejo y el apareamiento, la obtención de alimento, el cuidado de las crías y la protección de unos a otros. (p. 140)

sociedad: grupo de animales de la misma especie que vive y trabaja conjuntamente de forma organizada, con cada miembro realizando una tarea específica. (p. 141)

espiráculos: aperturas del abdomen y tórax de los insectos a través de las cuales entra aire y salen gases de desecho. (p. 49)

cnidocitos: cápsulas con estructuras enrolladas en forma de gatillo y que ayudan a los cnidarios a capturar su alimento. (p. 18)

tentacles (TEN tih kulz): armlike structures that have stinging cells and surround the mouths of most cnidarians. (p. 18)

tube feet: hydraulic, hollow, thin-walled tubes that end in suction cups and enable echinoderms to move. (p. 58)

tentáculos: estructuras en forma de brazo, que poseen cnidocitos y rodean la boca de la mayoría de los cnidarios. (p. 18)

pie tubular: tubos hidráulicos de pared delgada que terminan en copas de succión y que permiten moverse a los equinodermos. (p. 58)

U

umbilical cord: connects the embryo to the placenta; moves food and oxygen from the placenta to the embryo and removes the embryo's waste products. (p. 119)

cordón umbilical: conecta al embrión con la placenta, lleva nutrientes y oxígeno de la placenta al embrión y retira los productos de desecho de éste. (p. 119)

Glossary/Glosario

vertebrae: backbones that are joined by flexible cartilage and protect a vertebrate's spinal nerve cord. (p. 73)

vertebrate: animal with a backbone. (p. 12)

vértebra: huesos de la espalda unidos por cartílago flexible y que protegen la médula espinal de los vertebrados. (p. 73)

vertebrado: animal que posee columna vertebral. (p. 12)

water-vascular system: network of water-filled canals that allows echinoderms to move, capture food, give off wastes, and exchange carbon dioxide and oxygen. (p. 58)

sistema vascular acuoso: red de canales llenos de agua que permiten a los equinodermos moverse, capturar alimento, eliminar sustancias de desecho e intercambiar dióxido de carbono y oxígeno. (p. 58)

Glossary/Glosario

Index

> Italic numbers = illustration/photo   **Bold numbers = vocabulary term**
> lab = indicates a page on which the entry is used in a lab
> act = indicates a page on which the entry is used in an activity

Index

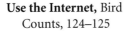

Index

Magnification Key: Magnifications listed are the magnifications at which images were originally photographed.
LM–Light Microscope
SEM–Scanning Electron Microscope
TEM–Transmission Electron Microscope

Acknowledgments: Glencoe would like to acknowledge the artists and agencies who participated in illustrating this program: Absolute Science Illustration; Andrew Evansen; Argosy; Articulate Graphics; Craig Attebery represented by Frank & Jeff Lavaty; CHK America; John Edwards and Associates; Gagliano Graphics; Pedro Julio Gonzalez represented by Melissa Turk & The Artist Network; Robert Hynes represented by Mendola Ltd.; Morgan Cain & Associates; JTH Illustration; Laurie O'Keefe; Matthew Pippin represented by Beranbaum Artist's Representative; Precision Graphics; Publisher's Art; Rolin Graphics, Inc.; Wendy Smith represented by Melissa Turk & The Artist Network; Kevin Torline represented by Berendsen and Associates, Inc.; WILDlife ART; Phil Wilson represented by Cliff Knecht Artist Representative; Zoo Botanica.

Photo Credits

Cover Bill Bachmann/Rainbow; **i ii** Bill Bachmann/Rainbow; **iv** (bkgd)John Evans, (inset)Bill Bachmann/Rainbow; **v** (t)PhotoDisc, (b)John Evans; **vi** (l)John Evans, (r)Geoff Butler; **vii** (l)John Evans, (r)PhotoDisc; **viii** PhotoDisc; **ix** Aaron Haupt Photography; **x** John M. Burnley/Photo Researchers; **xi** Michael Fairchild/Peter Arnold, Inc.; **xii** (t)Andrew J. Martinez/Photo Researchers, (b)Glenn Oliver/Visuals Unlimited; **1** Stephen J. Krasemann/DRK Photo; **2** (t)Fred Habegger/Grant Heilman Photography, Inc., (b)Fritz Polking/Visuals Unlimited; **3** (t)Doug Martin, (b)Richard Megna/Fundamental Photographs; **4** David Woodfall/DRK Photo; **5** (t)Michael Newman/PhotoEdit, (b)James L. Amos/CORBIS; **6–7** N. Sefton/Photo Researchers; **7** Icon Images; **8** Zig Leszczynski/Animals Animals; **9** (l)Jeff Foott/DRK Photo, (c)Leonard Lee Rue III/DRK Photo, (r)Hal Beral/Visuals Unlimited; **10** (t)Ken Lucas/Visuals Unlimited, (bl)Joe McDonald/Visuals Unlimited, (br)Zig Leszczynski/Animals Animals; **11** (tl)Tom J. Ulrich/Visuals Unlimited, (tc)Peter & Beverly Pickford/DRK Photo, (tr)Fred McConnaughey/Photo Researchers, (b)Stuart Westmoreland/Mo Yung Productions/Norbert Wu Productions; **13** (l)Stephen J. Krasemann/DRK Photo, (r)Ford Kristo/DRK Photo; **14** (l)Glenn Oliver/Visuals Unlimited, (r)Andrew J. Martinez/Photo Researchers; **17** (t)Norbert WU/DRK Photo, (bl)Fred Bavendam/Minden Pictures, (br)H. Hall/OSF/Animals Animals; **18** Gerry Ellis/GLOBIO.org; **20** David B. Fleetham/Visuals Unlimited; **21** Larry Stepanowicz/Visuals Unlimited; **23** (tl)T.E. Adams/Visuals Unlimited, (tr)Science VU/Visuals Unlimited, (b)Oliver Meckes/Eye of Science/Photo Researchers; **24** Triarch/Visuals Unlimited; **25** Oliver Meckes/Ottawa/Photo Researchers; **26** (tr)NIBSC/Science Photo Library/Photo Researchers, (cl)Sinclair Stammers/Science Photo Library/Photo Researchers, (cr)Arthur M. Siegelman/Visuals Unlimited, (bl)Oliver Meckes/Photo Researchers, (bcl)Andrew Syred/Science Photo Library/Photo Researchers, (bcr)Eric V. Grave/Photo Researchers, (br)Cabisco/Visuals Unlimited; **27** R. Calentine/Visuals Unlimited; **28** (t)T.E. Adams/Visuals Unlimited, (b)Bob Daemmrich; **29** Matt Meadows; **30** (t)PhotoDisc, (b)Shirley Vanderbilt/Index Stock; **31** James H. Robinson/Animals Animals; **32** R. Calentine/Visuals Unlimited; **33** Donald Specker/Animals Animals; **34** (l)Fred McConnaughey/Photo Researchers, (r)Fred Bavendam/Minden Pictures; **35** (l)Stephen J. Krasemann/DRK Photo, (r)Glenn Oliver/Visuals Unlimited; **36–37** Michael & Patricia Fogden/CORBIS; **38** Wayne Lynch/DRK Photo; **39** (l)Jeff Rotman Photography, (r)James H. Robinson/Animals Animals; **40** (t)David S. Addison/Visuals Unlimited, (b)Joyce & Frank Burek/Animals Animals; **41** Clay Wiseman/Animals Animals; **42** Bates Littlehales/Animals Animals; **43** Beverly Van Pragh/Museum Victoria; **44** Donald Specker/Animals Animals; **45** (t)Charles Fisher, Penn State University, (bl)Mary Beth Angelo/Photo Researchers, (br)Kjell B Sandved/Visuals Unlimited; **46** St. Bartholomew's Hospital/Science Photo Library/Photo Researchers; **48** Tom McHugh/Photo Researchers; **49** (t)Ted Clutter/Photo Researchers, (b)Kjell B. Sandved/Visuals Unlimited; **52** Lynn Stone; **53** (l)Bill Beatty/Animals Animals, (r)Patti Murray/Animals Animals; **54** (tl)Bill Beatty/Wild & Natural, (tc)Robert F. Sisson, (tr)Index Stock, (cl)Brian Gordon Green, (c)Joseph H. Bailey/National Geographic Image Collection, (cr)Jeffrey L. Rotman/CORBIS, (b)Timothy G. Laman/National Geographic Image Collection; **55** (t)James P. Rowan/DRK Photo, (b)Leonard Lee Rue/Photo Researchers; **56** Ken Lucas/Visuals Unlimited; **57** Tom Stack & Assoc.; **58** Scott Smith/Animals Animals; **59** Clay Wiseman/Animals Animals; **60** (tl)Andrew J. Martinez/Photo Researchers, (tr)David Wrobel/Visuals Unlimited, (b)Gerald & Buff Corsi/Visuals Unlimited; **61** Ken Lucas/Visuals Unlimited; **62 63** Matt Meadows; **64** (t)David M. Dennis, (b)Harry Rogers/Photo Researchers; **65** (l)Charles McRae/Visuals Unlimited, (r)Mark Moffet/Minden Pictures; **66** Leroy Simon/Visuals Unlimited; **67** William Leonard/DRK Photo; **68** Joyce & Frank Burek/Animals Animals; **69** (l)Clay Wiseman/Animals Animals, (r)Scott Smith/Animals Animals; **70–71** Robert Lubeck/Animals Animals; **72** Fred Bavendam/Minden Pictures; **73** Omni-Photo Communications; **74** (t to b)H. W. Robison/Visuals Unlimited, Flip Nicklin/Minden Pictures, Flip Nicklin/Minden Pictures, John M. Burnley/Photo Researchers, George Grall/National Geographic Image Collection, M. P. Kahl/DRK Photo, Grace Davies/Omni-Photo Communications; **75** T. A. Wiewandt/DRK Photo; **76** Icon Images; **77** (l to r)Meckes/Ottawa/Photo Researchers, Rick Gillis/University of Wisconsin-La Crosse, Runk/Schoenberger from Grant Heilman, Runk/Schoenberger from Grant Heilman; **78** Ken Lucas/Visuals Unlimited; **79** (tl)James Watt/Animals Animals, (tc)Norbert Wu/DRK Photo, (tr)Fred Bavendam/Minden Pictures, (br)Richard T. Nowitz/Photo Researchers; **80 82** Tom McHugh/Photo Researchers; **83** (t)Tom McHugh/Steinhart Aquarium/Photo Researchers, (bl)Bill Kamin/Visuals Unlimited, (bc)Norbert Wu/DRK Photo, (br)Michael Durham/GLOBIO.org; **84** Runk/Schoenberger from Grant Heilman; **85** Fred Habegger/Grant Heilman; **86** (t)David Northcott/DRK Photo, (bl br)Runk/Schoenberger from Grant Heilman; **87** (l)Runk/Schoenberger from Grant Heilman, (r)George H. Harrison from Grant Heilman; **88** (l)Mark Moffett/Minden Pictures, (r)Michael Fogden/DRK Photo; **89** Rob and Ann Simpson/Visuals Unlimited; **90** Joe McDonald/Visuals Unlimited; **92** (tl)Klaus Uhlenhut/Animals Animals, (tr)Rob & Ann Simpson/Visuals Unlimited, (b)G and C Merker/Visuals Unlimited; **93** (t)Mitsuaki Iwago/Minden Pictures, (b)Belinda Wright/

DRK Photo; **94** (tl)John Sibbick, (tr)Karen Carr, (c)Chris Butler/Science Photo Library/Photo Researchers, (bl)Jerome Connolly, courtesy The Science Museum of Minnesota, (br)Chris Butler; **96** (t)Steve Maslowski/Visuals Unlimited, (b)Michael Newman/PhotoEdit, Inc.; **97** KS Studios; **98** (tl)Hemera Technologies, Inc., (tc)Michael Fogden/Animals Animals, (tr)Tim Flach/Stone/Getty Images, (b)R. Rotolo/Liaison Agency; **100** John Cancalosi/DRK Photo; **102** (tl tr)Runk/Schoenberger from Grant Heilman, (b)Tom McHugh/Photo Researchers; **104–105** Theo Allofs/CORBIS; **106** Michael Habicht/Animals Animals; **108** (l)Crown Studios, (r)KS Studios; **109** (l)Lynn Stone/Animals Animals, (r)Arthur R. Hill/Visuals Unlimited; **111** (l)Zefa Germany/The Stock Market/CORBIS, (r)Sid & Shirley Rucker/DRK Photo; **112** (bkgd)Steve Maslowski, (l)Kennan Ward/CORBIS, (t to b)Wayne Lankinen/DRK Photo, Ron Spomer/Visuals Unlimited, M. Philip Kahl/Gallo Images/CORBIS, Rod Planck/Photo Researchers; **114** Stephen J. Krasemann/DRK Photo; **115** (t)Gerard Lacz/Animals Animals, (bl)Tom Brakefield/DRK Photo, (br)John David Fleck/Liaison Agency/Getty Images; **116** Bob Gurr/DRK Photo; **117** Amos Nachoum/The Stock Market/CORBIS; **118** (t)Jean-Paul Ferrero/AUSCAPE, (bl)Phyllis Greenberg/Animals Animals, (br)John Cancalosi/DRK Photo; **119** (t)Carolina Biological Supply/PhotoTake, NYC, (b)Doug Perine/DRK Photo; **120** (t to b)Stephen J. Krasemann/DRK Photo, David Northcott/DRK Photo, Zig Leszczynski/Animals Animals, Ralph Reinhold/Animals Animals, Anup Shah/Animals Animals, Mickey Gibson/Animals Animals; **121** (t to b)Fred Felleman/Stone/Getty Images, Robert Maier/Animals Animals, Tom Bledsoe/DRK Photo, Wayne Lynch/DRK Photo, Joe McDonald/Animals Animals, Kim Heacox/DRK Photo; **124** (t)David Welling/Animals Animals, (b)Wayne Lankinen/DRK Photo; **125** (t)Richard Day/Animals Animals, (b)Maslowski Photo; **126** (tr)Mark Burnett, (bl)Jeff Foott/DRK Photo, (br)Joe McDonald/Animals Animals; **127** (l r)Tom & Pat Leeson/DRK Photo, (b)Tom Brakefield/DRK Photo; **128** Hans & Judy Beste/Animals Animals; **130** Bob Gurr/DRK Photo; **131** (l)Crown Studios, (r)KS Studios; **132–133** D. Robert & Lorri Franz/CORBIS; **134** (l)Michel Denis-Huot/Jacana/Photo Researchers, (r)Zig Lesczynski/Animals Animals; **135** (l)Jack Ballard/Visuals Unlimited, (c)Anthony Mercieca/Photo Researchers, (r)Joe McDonald/Visuals Unlimited; **136** (t)Stephen J. Krasemann/Peter Arnold, Inc., (b)Leonard Lee Rue/Photo Researchers; **137** (t)The Zoological Society of San Diego, (b)Margret Miller/Photo Researchers; **140** Michael Fairchild/Peter Arnold, Inc.; **141** (t)Bill Bachman/Photo Researchers, (b)Fateh Singh Rathore/Peter Arnold, Inc.; **142** Jim Brandenburg/Minden Pictures; **143** Michael Dick/Animals Animals; **144** (l)Richard Thorn/Visuals Unlimited, (c)Arthur Morris/Visuals Unlimited, (r)Jacana/Photo Researchers; **145** (starfish)Peter J. Herring, (krill)T. Frank/Harbor Branch Oceanographic Institution, (others)Edith Widder/Harbor Branch Oceanographic Institution; **146** Stephen Dalton/Animals Animals; **147** Richard Packwood/Animals Animals; **148** Ken Lucas/Visuals Unlimited; **150** (t)The Zoological Society of San Diego, (b)Gary Carter/Visuals Unlimited; **151** Dave B. Fleetham/Tom Stack & Assoc.; **152** (t)Walter Smith/CORBIS, (b)Bios (Klein/Hubert)/Peter Arnold, Inc.; **153** (l)Valerie Giles/Photo Researchers, (r)J & B Photographers/Animals Animals; **154** not available; **156** Jim Brandenburg/Minden Pictures; **157 158** PhotoDisc; **160** Tom Pantages; **164** Michell D. Bridwell/PhotoEdit, Inc.; **165** (t)Mark Burnett, (b)Dominic Oldershaw; **166** StudiOhio; **167** Timothy Fuller; **168** Aaron Haupt; **170** KS Studios; **171** Matt Meadows; **172** Andrew J. Martinez/Photo Researchers; **173** (t)Runk/Schoenberger from Grant Heilman, (b)Rod Joslin; **175** Amanita Pictures; **176** Bob Daemmrich; **178** Davis Barber/PhotoEdit, Inc.; **196** Matt Meadows; **197** (l)Dr. Richard Kessel, (c)NIBSC/Science Photo Library/Photo Researchers, (r)David John/Visuals Unlimited; **198** (t)Runk/Schoenberger from Grant Heilman, (bl)Andrew Syred/Science Photo Library/Photo Researchers, (br)Rich Brommer; **199** (tr)G.R. Roberts, (l)Ralph Reinhold/Earth Scenes, (br)Scott Johnson/Animals Animals; **200** Martin Harvey/DRK Photo.

PERIODIC TABLE OF THE ELEMENTS

Columns of elements are called groups. Elements in the same group have similar chemical properties.

Gas

Liquid

Solid

Synthetic

Element	Hydrogen
Atomic number	1
Symbol	**H**
Atomic mass	1.008

State of matter

The first three symbols tell you the state of matter of the element at room temperature. The fourth symbol identifies elements that are not present in significant amounts on Earth. Useful amounts are made synthetically.

1

1								
Hydrogen 1 **H** 1.008	**2**							
Lithium 3 **Li** 6.941	Beryllium 4 **Be** 9.012							
Sodium 11 **Na** 22.990	Magnesium 12 **Mg** 24.305	**3**	**4**	**5**	**6**	**7**	**8**	**9**
Potassium 19 **K** 39.098	Calcium 20 **Ca** 40.078	Scandium 21 **Sc** 44.956	Titanium 22 **Ti** 47.867	Vanadium 23 **V** 50.942	Chromium 24 **Cr** 51.996	Manganese 25 **Mn** 54.938	Iron 26 **Fe** 55.845	Cobalt 27 **Co** 58.933
Rubidium 37 **Rb** 85.468	Strontium 38 **Sr** 87.62	Yttrium 39 **Y** 88.906	Zirconium 40 **Zr** 91.224	Niobium 41 **Nb** 92.906	Molybdenum 42 **Mo** 95.94	Technetium 43 **Tc** (98)	Ruthenium 44 **Ru** 101.07	Rhodium 45 **Rh** 102.906
Cesium 55 **Cs** 132.905	Barium 56 **Ba** 137.327	Lanthanum 57 **La** 138.906	Hafnium 72 **Hf** 178.49	Tantalum 73 **Ta** 180.948	Tungsten 74 **W** 183.84	Rhenium 75 **Re** 186.207	Osmium 76 **Os** 190.23	Iridium 77 **Ir** 192.217
Francium 87 **Fr** (223)	Radium 88 **Ra** (226)	Actinium 89 **Ac** (227)	Rutherfordium 104 **Rf** (261)	Dubnium 105 **Db** (262)	Seaborgium 106 **Sg** (266)	Bohrium 107 **Bh** (264)	Hassium 108 **Hs** (277)	Meitnerium 109 **Mt** (268)

The number in parentheses is the mass number of the longest-lived isotope for that element.

Rows of elements are called periods. Atomic number increases across a period.

The arrow shows where these elements would fit into the periodic table. They are moved to the bottom of the table to save space.

Lanthanide series	Cerium 58 **Ce** 140.116	Praseodymium 59 **Pr** 140.908	Neodymium 60 **Nd** 144.24	Promethium 61 **Pm** (145)	Samarium 62 **Sm** 150.36
Actinide series	Thorium 90 **Th** 232.038	Protactinium 91 **Pa** 231.036	Uranium 92 **U** 238.029	Neptunium 93 **Np** (237)	Plutonium 94 **Pu** (244)